Dr. WILLIAMS'S LIBRARY
CATALOGUE 1971—1980

Dr. WILLIAMS'S LIBRARY

LONDON

Catalogue of Accessions

Volume 4

being a catalogue of books published in the
twentieth century and added to the Library
1971—1980

Edited for the Trustees by
JOHN EDWARD BARDWELL

Dr. WILLIAMS'S TRUST
14, GORDON SQUARE,
LONDON · WC1H 0AG

1983

Printed in Great Britain at the Works of
LEICESTER PRINTERS LIMITED, THE CHURCH GATE PRESS, LEICESTER

Preface

The following catalogue lists the books in Dr. Williams's Library published since 1900 and added to the Library in the ten years 1971-1980. Books published before 1900, even though added to the Library since 1970, have not been included.

The Catalogue supersedes the accession lists printed in the Library Bulletins from 1972 to 1981 and is a sequel to the *Catalogue of Accessions, Vol. 3, 1961-1970*.

In arrangement the plan of the earlier catalogues has been followed. The first part is an author catalogue. The second part, or "Supplement", is a list of periodicals and serials. Books published in continuous series regularly taken in the Library are listed in this second part, but author references to all entries in it are included in the author catalogue. In the first part the note [Pamph.] at the end of certain entries is used to describe off-prints and articles removed from other publications as well as separately published items. In the case of off-prints and extracted articles the source is generally not given.

The work of editing the Catalogue has been undertaken by Mr. John E. Bardwell.

The Catalogue is an essential tool for the Library's regular readers and should, like its predecessors, be a useful work of reference to many others engaged in the study of theology, philosophy, ecclesiastical history, and related subjects.

Dr. Williams's Library

14, GORDON SQUARE, LONDON, W.C.1.H. 0.A.G.

Dr. Williams's Library, founded under the will of the Rev. Daniel Williams, D.D. (d.1716), is primarily a theological library intended for the use of ministers, students, and other persons engaged in the study of theology, religion, and ecclesiastical history. It will also be found useful for the study of philosophy, history, literature, and kindred subjects. There is a large collection on Byzantine history and culture, the bulk of which was bequeathed by Professor Norman H. Baynes. The considerable holdings of pre-nineteenth century works relating to English Nonconformity, together with the accumulation of manuscripts largely, though not exclusively, of Nonconformist interest, augmented in 1976 by the donation of books and manuscripts from New College, London, render the Library a pre-eminent research library in this field of study.

CONDITIONS OF ADMISSION

Books may be consulted by persons duly introduced and guaranteed in accordance with the regulations laid down by the Trustees.

READERS' TICKETS. Applicants are admitted to read in the Library free of charge.

BORROWERS' TICKETS. An annual subscription entitles a reader to borrow up to three books at a time. The present annual subscription is £4.00 (£2.00 to ministers and clergy). Books on loan are returnable within one month but may be renewed if not required by another reader. A postal service is available for readers living at a distance from the Library.

Copies of the regulations, guarantee forms, forms of application for admission, may be had on application personally or by post to the Librarian.

LIBRARY HOURS

Monday, Wednesday and Friday 10 to 5; Tuesday and Thursday 10 to 6.30.

The Library is closed from the Thursday before Good Friday to the following Tuesday inclusive; during the first half of August; from Christmas Eve to the day after the New Year Bank Holiday, inclusive; and on Saturdays and Bank Holidays.

CATALOGUES

The following printed catalogues are out of print but may be borrowed from the Library:—

Vol. I.—Author catalogue of books in the Library down to 1841.

Vol. II.—Author catalogue of tracts, pamphlets, sermons, etc., placed in the Library down to 1841.

Vol. III.—Author catalogue of books, pamphlets, etc., placed in the Library from 1842 to 1885.

There was no printed catalogue for the years 1886 to 1899.

Complete author and partial subject catalogues, to the present date, may be seen at the Library; also a special catalogue of books relating to early Non-conformity (1566-1799) with author, subject, and chronological sections; a catalogue of the Norman H. Baynes Byzantine collection; and a Handlist of Manuscripts with Index of names.

PUBLICATIONS ON SALE

Dr. Williams's Library Catalogue of Accessions, 1900-1950. Price £10.00

Dr. Williams's Library Catalogue of Accessions, 1951-1960. Price £7.50

Dr. Williams's Library Catalogue of Accessions, 1961-1970. Price £7.50.

Bulletin of Dr. Williams's Library. Published annually. Price 50p.

Guide to the Manuscripts in Dr. Williams's Library. *By Kenneth Twinn.* 1969. Price 30p.

Nonconformist Congregations in Great Britain: a list of histories and other material in Dr. Williams's Library. 1974. Price £1.50.

New College, London, and its Library. *By G. F. Nuttall.* 1977. Price 75p.

Dr. Williams's Library Occasional Papers.

The following are available.

1. The manuscript of the *Reliquiae Baxterianae.* *By Geoffrey F. Nuttall. Duplicated.* 1954. *Included in No. 8 below.* .. 5p

2. A. G. Matthews' *Walker Revised*—Supplementary index of 'Intruders' and others. *Compiled by Charles E. Surman.* 1956 20p

6. "An Essay of Accommodation" being a scheme for uniting Presbyterians and Congregationals drawn up c. 1680. 1957 .. 20p

8. The Baxter Treatises: a catalogue of the Richard Baxter papers (other than the Letters) in Dr. Williams's Library. 1959 30p

9. An earlier version of the "Essay of Accommodation." *Duplicated.* 1960. .. .. 10p

10. Index to the Henry Crabb Robinson letters in Dr. Williams's Library; being a supplement to the index in Edith Morley's *Henry Crabb Robinson on books and their writers. Compiled by Inez Elliott.* 1960 .. .. 30p

11. Index to the John Evans *List of Dissenting Congregations and Ministers,* 1715-1729, in Dr. Williams's Library. *Compiled by John Creasey.* 1964 .. .. 40p

THE DR. WILLIAMS LECTURES

The following are in print.

1947 Dr. Williams and his Library. *By Stephen Kay Jones* .. 30p

1953 Organic Design: scientific thought from Ray to Paley. *By C. E. Raven.* 1954 .. .. 30p

1954 The True and the Valid. *By Richard I. Aaron.* 1955 .. 30p

1956 The Religious Philosophy of Dean Mansel. *By W. R. Matthews.* 1956 .. .. 30p

1957 Sir Robert Walpole, Samuel Holden, and the Dissenting Deputies. *By Norman C. Hunt.* 1957 .. .. .. 30p

1958 Facts and Obligations. *By Dorothy Emmet.* 1958 .. .. 30p

1959 Ascetics and Humanists in Eleventh-Century Byzantium. *By Joan M. Hussey.* 1960 .. .. 30p

1960 The Essene Problem. *By Matthew Black.* 1961 .. .. 50p

1962 Daniel Williams—Presbyterian Bishop. *By Roger Thomas.* 1964 .. .. 50p

1963 A Mirror of Elizabethan Puritanism: The Life and Letters of "Godly Master Dering". *By Patrick Collinson.* 1964 .. 50p

FRIENDS OF DR. WILLIAMS'S LIBRARY

The Friends of Dr. Williams's Library was founded in 1946 and since then has done much to help the Library. The Dr. Williams Lectures are sponsored by the Friends.

Particulars of Membership may be had on application from the Secretary, Friends of Dr. Williams's Library, c/o the Library.

Catalogue of Accessions

1971 — 1980

[**Abel** (G. C.)] And it came to pass: the story of the development of Salisbury U.R.C. 8vo. *Duplicated.* n.p., 1978. [Pamph.]
—— A history of the Presbyterian Congregational United Reformed Church in Salisbury, 1662-1978. fol. *Duplicated.* n.p., 1978. [Pamph.]
Abelard (Peter) Ethics. Ed. with introd. and Eng. trans. and notes by D. E. Luscombe. [Oxford Medieval Texts.] 8vo. Oxf., 1971.
—— *See* Suppt. Historical Assn. Gen. Ser., 95.
Aboux (Marie-Louise) *ed. See* Teilhard de Chardin (P.) [Misc.]
Abraham, *Kidunaya. See* Suppt. Corpus Script. Christ. Orient., Syri, 140-141.
Abramowski (Luise) and **Goodman** (A. E.) *ed.* A Nestorian collection of christological texts. [Univ. of Cambridge Oriental Publs., 18-19] 2 vols. 8vo. Camb., 1972.
   1. Syriac text.
   2. Introd., trans., and indexes.
[**Absalom** (J.H.)] Unitarianism in Preston. A booklet written to commemorate the two hundred and fiftieth anniversary of the opening of Preston Unitarian Chapel, 1716-1966. 8vo. [Preston, 1966.] [Pamph.]
Accrington. *Unitarian Free Church.* Unitarianism in Accrington, 1859-1959. 8vo. [Accrington, 1959.] [Pamph.]
Adams (James Luther) On being human—religiously. Selected essays in religion and society. Ed. and introd. by Max L. Stackhouse. 8vo. Boston (Mass.), 1976.
Adams (W.G.S.) *See* Papers for War Time, 22.
Adamson (J. H.) *See* Hunter (W. B.) *and others.*
Addams (Jane) *See* Tims (M.)
Adderley (J. G.) Francis: the little poor man of Assisi. A short story of the founder of the Brothers Minor. Introd. by Paul Sabatier. 8vo. Lond., 1900.
Addison (James T.) Life beyond death in the beliefs of mankind. 8vo. Lond., 1933.
Addison (Joseph) *See* Bloom (E. A.) and Bloom (L. D.)
Addleshaw (G. W. O.) The beginnings of the parochial system. [St. Anthony's Hall Publs., 3.] 8vo. Lond., [1953]. [Pamph.]
Afrahat, *the Persian Sage. See* Suppt. Corpus Script. Christ. Orient., Armen., 7-10.
Agate (L. D.) Luther and the Reformation. [People's Books.] 12mo. Lond., [1914].
Agee (James) and **Evans** (Walker) Let us now praise famous men: three tenant families. (1941.) repr. 8vo. Boston (Mass.), 1960.
Agrippa (Henry Cornelius) His fourth book of occult philosophy.—Of geomancy.—Magical elements of Peter de Abano.—Astronomical geomancy.—The nature of spirits.—Arbatel of magick. Trans. Robert Turner. (1665.) facsim. repr. [Source Works of Medieval and Renaissance Magic, 4.] 8vo. Lond., 1978.
Ahlström (G. W.) *See* Suppt. Vetus Testamentum. Suppts., 21.
Ahrweiler (Hélène) Études sur les structures administratives et sociales de Byzance. Préface de Paul Lemerle. [Variorum Reprs.] 8vo. Lond., 1971.
—— Byzance: les pays et les territoires. [Variorum Reprs.] 8vo. Lond., 1976.
Al-'Alawi (Ahmad ibn Mustafa) *See* Lings (M.)
Aland (Kurt) *ed.* Die alten Übersetzung des Neuen Testaments die Kirchenväterzitate und Lektionare. [Arbeiten zur N.T. Textforschung, 5.] 8vo. Berlin, 1972.
A Lasco (John) *See* Bartel (O.); Hall (B.)
Albright (W. F.) New horizons in biblical research. [Whidden Lects., 1961.] 8vo. Lond., 1966.
—— *ed. See* Bible. Commentaries. Anchor Bible.
Albright (W. F.) and **Mann** (C. S.) *See* Bible. Commentaries. Anchor Bible, 26.

Alcuin Club. *See* Suppt.

Alden (E. C.) The old church at New Road: a contribution to the history of Oxford Nonconformity. 12mo. OXF. & LOND., [1904]. [Pamph.]

Alderley Edge and Knutsford Methodist Circuit. Centenary, 1864-1964: a brief history of the Circuit. 8vo. KNUTSFORD, [1964]. [Pamph.]

Aldwinckle (R. F.) Death in the secular city: a study of the notion of life after death in contemporary theology and philosophy. 8vo. LOND., 1972.

Alexander (J. J. G.) *See* Catalogues. *Brussels. Royal Lib.*

Alexander (P. J.) Religious and political history and thought in the Byzantine Empire. Collected studies. [Variorum Reprs.] 8vo. LOND., 1978.

Alexander (Samuel) *See* Wickham (H.)

Alexandra Park. *Congregational Church.* Alexandra Park Congregational Church (Whitefield Memorial), Alexandra Park Road, London N.22. 8vo. LOND., [1970]. [Pamph.]

Alington (C. A.) A Dean's apology: a semi-religious autobiography. 8vo. LOND., 1952.

Allchin (A. M.) Alexander Penrose Forbes: the search for integrity. A lecture, Univ. of Dundee, 19 Nov. 1975. 8vo. [DUNDEE, 1975.] [Pamph.]

—— *ed. See* Coulson (J.) and Allchin (A. M.) *ed.*

Allegro (J. M.) The Dead Sea Scrolls. (1956.) repr. 8vo. HARMONDSWORTH, 1956.

Allen (A. V. G.) Phillips Brooks, 1835-1893: memories of his life with extracts from his letters and note-books. 8vo. LOND., 1908.

Allen (E. L.) The purpose of Jesus. 8vo. LOND., 1951.

Allen (Helen M.) Erasmus on peace. 8vo. 's GRAVENHAGE, [1936]. [Pamph.]

Allen (Hope E.) The authorship of the Prick of Conscience. 8vo. BOSTON (Mass.) & LOND., 1910. [Pamph.]

Allen (Leslie C.) *See* Suppt. Vetus Testamentum. Suppts., 25, 27.

Allen (Paul M.) *comp.* The writings and lectures of Rudolf Steiner: a chronological bibliography of his books, lectures, addresses, courses, cycles, essays and reports as publ. in Eng. trans. 8vo. NEW YORK, 1956.

Allen (Paul M.) and **Pietzner** (C.) *comp.* A Christian Rosenkreutz anthology. 4to NEW YORK, 1968.

Allen (Reginald E.) Plato's 'Euthyphro' and the earlier theory of forms. [Internat. Lib. of Philos.] 8vo. LOND. & NEW YORK, 1970.

Allen (*Sir* Ronald Wilberforce) Methodism and modern world problems. Introd. by Sir Josiah Stamp. 8vo. LOND., 1926.

Allen (William) *Cardinal.* A true, sincere and modest defence of English Catholics that suffer for their faith both at home and abroad. (1584.) repr. [Catholic Lib., 2, 4.] 2 vols. 8vo. LOND., 1914.

—— *See* Haile (M.)

Allmen (Jean-Jacques von) Le saint ministère selon la conviction et la volonté des Réformés du XVIe siècle. [Bibliothèque Théologique.] 8vo. NEUCHATEL & PARIS, 1968.

—— *See* Dictionaries. Biblical.

Allshorn (Florence) Notebooks. Selected and arranged by a member of St. Julian's Community. 8vo. LOND., 1957.

—— *See* Oldham (J. H.)

Almedingen (E. M.) Dom Bernard Clements: a portrait. (1945.) repr. 8vo. LOND., 1946.

Althaus (Heinz) Die Heilslehre des heiligen Gregor von Nazianz. (Münsterische, Beiträge zur Theologie, 34.] 8vo. MÜNSTER, 1972.

Altmann (Alexander) Moses Mendelssohn: a biographical study. [Littman Lib. of Jewish Civilization.] 8vo. LOND., 1973.

Alves (R.A.) A theology of human hope. 8vo. NEW YORK & CLEVELAND (Ohio), 1969.

Amand de Mendieta (E.) *See* Suppt. Texte u. Untersuchungen, 5te. Reihe, 123.

Ambrose, *Saint, Bp. of Milan.* [Works. *Latin.*] *See* Suppt. Corpus Script. Eccles. Lat., 82.

Ambrose (Alice) and **Lazerowitz** (M.) *ed.* Ludwig Wittgenstein: philosophy and language. [Muirhead Lib. of Philos.] 8vo. LOND. & NEW YORK, 1972.

Ambrose (Isaac) *See* Goreham (N. J.)

Ambrosiaster. *See* Suppt. Corpus Script. Eccles. Lat., 81.
Amerbach, *family of.* Die Amerbachkorrespondenz. Im Auftrag der Kommission für die öffentliche Bibliothek der Universität Basel bearb. und hrsg. von Alfred Hartmann. 8vo. BASEL.
    4. Die Briefe aus den Jahren 1531-36. 1953.
    5. —— 1537-43. 1958.
    [*No more in Library.*]
American Congregational Association. *See* Suppt. Bulletin of the Congregational Lib.
American Journal of Semitic Languages and Literature. *See* Suppt. Journal of Near E. Studies.
American Journal of Theology. *See* Suppt. Journal of Religion.
American Schools of Oriental Research. *See* Suppt. Biblical Archaeologist.
American Society of Church History. *See* Suppt. Church History.
Ames (William) A fresh suit against human ceremonies in God's worship. (1633.) facsim. repr. Introd. by R. C. Simmons. 4to. [FARNBOROUGH,] 1971.
—— *See* Horton (D.); Reuter (K.); Sprunger (K.La V.)
Amey (B. W. O.) An account of the New Malden Baptist Church, 1860-1953. 8vo. [NEW MALDEN, 1953.] [Pamph.]
Amphilochius, *Saint, Bp. of Iconium.* Iambi ad Seleucum. Ed. Eberhard Oberg. [Patristische Texte u. Studien, 9.] 8vo. BERLIN, 1969.
Amsterdam. *English Reformed Church.* The English Reformed Church, Begynhof, Amsterdam. 8vo. [AMSTERDAM,] 1958. [Pamph.]
—— —— The English Reformed Church, Begijnhof, Amsterdam. 8vo. [AMSTERDAM,] 1977. [Pamph.]
Amvrosy, *Staretz, formerly A. N. Grenkov.* *See* Dunlop (J. B.)
Amyraut (Moïse) *See* Armstrong (B. G.)
Analecta Bollandiana. *See* Suppt.
—— Subsidia Hagiographica. *See* Suppt.
Anastasius I, *Emperor of the East.* *See* Capizzi (C.); Charanis (P.)
Ancren Riwle. *See* Suppt. Early Eng. Text Soc., O.S. 267, 274.
Anderson (A. A.) *See* Bible. Commentaries. New Century Bible.
Anderson (Hugh) *See* Bible. Commentaries. New Century Bible.
Anderson (John M.) and **Johnstone** (H. W.) Natural deduction: the logical basis of axiom systems. (1962.) repr. 8vo. BELMONT (Calif.), 1963.
Andresen (Carl) *ed.* Zum Augustin-Gespräch der Gegenwart. Mit Bibliographie. [Wege der Forschung, 5.] 8vo. DARMSTADT, 1962.
Andrew, *Father.* *See* Hardy (H.E.) *Father Andrew.*
Andriette (E. A.) Devon and Exeter in the Civil War. 8vo. NEWTON ABBOT, 1971.
Andronicus II, *Paleologus, Emperor of the East.* *See* Laiou (A. E.)
Anglican-Roman Catholic International Commission. The three agreed statements: Eucharistic doctrine (1971); Ministry and ordination (1973); Authority in the Church (1976). 8vo. LOND., 1978. [Pamph.]
Anglican Theological Review. *See* Suppt.
Anglo-American Jewish Historical Conference. *See* Suppt. Jewish Hist. Soc. Publs., 1971.
Anglo-Catholic Congress. *See* Suppt.
Angold (Michael) A Byzantine government in exile: government and society under the Laskarids of Nicaea (1204-1261). [Oxford Historical Monographs.] 8vo. LOND., 1975.
Anne, *Queen of Great Britain and Ireland.* *See* Green (D.); Gregg (E.)
Annual Journal of the Universalist Historical Society. *See* Suppt. Universalist Historical Soc.
Anscombe (G. E. M.) Intention. [Lib. of Philos. and Logic.] (1957.) 2nd ed. (1963.) repr. 8vo. OXF., 1976.
Anselm, *Saint, Abp. of Canterbury.* Memorials. Ed. R. W. Southern and F. S. Schmitt. [Auctores Britannici Medii Aevi, 1.] 8vo. LOND., 1969.
—— *See* Eadmer; Evans (G. R.)
Anskar, *Saint, Abp. of Hamburg.* *See* Dörries (H.) and Kretschmar (G.)
Anstey (Roger) *See* Bolt (C.) and Drescher (S.) *ed.*
Anstruther (Godfrey) *See* Dictionaries. Biography.
Aphraates, *the Persian Sage.* *See* Afrahat.

Apollo, *Archimandrite of the Monastery of Isaac.* *See* Suppt. Corpus Script. Christ. Orient., Copt., 39-40.

Apostolic Church. The Apostolic Church: its principles and practices. (1937.) rev. ed. 8vo. PENYGROES, 1961.

Apostolic Fathers. *See* Kraft (H.) *comp.*

Apostolical Constitutions and Canons. [*Syriac.*] *See* Suppt. Corpus Script. Christ. Orient., Syri, 175-176, 179-180.

Appasamy (A. J.) *Bp. in Coimbatore.* The Christian task in independent India. 8vo. LOND., 1951.

Appleton (N. J. W.) Fifty years of practical Christianity: the story of Bethany Homestead, Northampton. 8vo. NORTHAMPTON, 1974. [Pamph.]

Aquarius. *See* Suppt.

Aquinas (Thomas) *Saint.* Summa Theologiae. Latin text and Eng. trans., introds., notes, appendices and glossaries. ['Blackfriars edition', by the Dominicans of the Eng.-speaking Provinces.] 60 vols. 8vo. LOND. & NEW YORK, 1964-76.

—— *See* Kenny (A. J. P.)

Arbeiten zur Neutestamentlichen Textforschung. *See* Suppt.

Arch (Joseph) *See* Horn (P. L. R.)

[Archbold (John)] Esh Winning (Waterhouses) Baptist Church, 1877-1977: centenary souvenir. 8vo. [ESH WINNING, 1977.] [Pamph.]

Archdale (John) *See* Hood (H. G.)

Archer (R. S.) Trinity Presbyterian Church of England, Claughton, Birkenhead: an historical sketch, 1863-1938. 8vo. BIRKENHEAD, 1938.

Archives de la France monastique. *See* Suppt. Revue Mabillon.

Archivum Franciscanum Historicum. *See* Suppt.

Arias Montano (Benito) *See* Rekers (B.)

Aristeas. Lettre d'Aristée à Philocrate. Introd., texte critique, trad. et notes par André Pelletier. [Sources Chrétiennes, 89.] 8vo. PARIS, 1962.

Aristotelian Society. *See* Suppt.

Aristotle. [Works. *Latin.*] *See* Suppt. Corpus Philos. Medii Aevi. Aristoteles Latinus.

—— [Two or more works. *English.*] De partibus animalium I and De generatione animalium I (with passages from II.1-3). Trans. with notes by D. M. Balme. [Clarendon Aristotle Ser.] 8vo. OXF., 1972.

—— Historia animalium. Trans. A. L. Peck. [Loeb Classical Lib.] 8vo. LOND., 1965-

2. Books 4-6. 1971.

—— *See* Ferguson (J.); Kenny (A. J. P.)

Arminius (Jacobus) *See* Bangs (C.); Bierenga (G. J.) *comp.*

Armstrong (A. Elizabeth) Robert Estienne, royal printer: an historical study of the elder Stephanus. 4to. CAMB., 1954.

Armstrong (B. G.) Calvinism and the Amyraut heresy: Protestant scholasticism and humanism in seventeenth-century France. 8vo. MADISON (Wis.), *etc.*, 1969.

Armstrong (C. J. R.) Evelyn Underhill (1875-1941): an introd. to her life and writings. 8vo. LOND., 1975.

Arnold (Sidney) The imaginative content in aesthetic experience. 8vo. ATHENAI, 1971. [Pamph.]

[Arnold (William)] Bethel Baptist Church and Sunday School [Waterfoot, Lancs.]: historical survey, 1839-1954. 8vo. [WATERFOOT, 1954.] [Pamph.]

Arseniev (Nicholas) and **Martin** (A. von) *ed.* Die Ostkirche. [Sonderh. der Viertelj. schr. "Una Sancta".] 8vo. STUTTGART, 1927.

Arthur, *King of Britain.* *See* Suppt. Early Eng. Text Soc., O.S. 268, 279.

Arthur Stanley Eddington Memorial Lectures. *See* Suppt.

Ashby (G. W. E. C.) Theodoret of Cyrrhus as exegete of the Old Testament. [Rhodes Univ. Publs.] 8vo. GRAHAMSTOWN (S. Afr.), 1972.

Ashley (M. P.) Oliver Cromwell and the Puritan Revolution. [Teach Yourself Hist. Lib.] 8vo. LOND., 1958.

Ashton (Robert) The English Civil War: conservatism and revolution, 1603-1649. [Revolutions in the Modern World.] 8vo. LOND., 1978.

Ashton-Under-Lyne. *Ormonde Street Methodist Church.* The first hundred years: centenary [1851-1951]. 8vo. DUKINFIELD [printed], [1951]. [Pamph.]

Ashworth (Ormerod) *and others.* "A worthy heritage": the 150th anniversary of Bethlehem Unitarian Church, Newchurch-in-Rossendale. 8vo [NEWCHURCH-IN -ROSSENDALE, 1957.[[Pamph.]

Asquith (H. H.) *1st Earl of Oxford and Asquith. See* Jenkins (R. H.)

Assemblies of God. *See* Liturgies. *Pentecostal.*

Associated Councils of Churches in the British and German Empires. Speeches delivered at the inaugural meeting of the British Council at the Queen's Hall, London, Feb. 6th, 1911. 8vo. LOND., [1911]. [Pamph.]

Association de l'Orient Chrétien. *See* Suppt. Patrologia Orientalis.

Association of British Theological and Philosophical Libraries. *See* Suppt. Bulletin of the Association of British Theological and Philosophical Libraries.

Athanasius, *Saint, Patriarch of Alexandria.* Sur l'Incarnation du Verbe. Introd., texte critique, trad., notes et index par Charles Kannengiesser. [Sources Chrétiennes, 199.] 8vo. PARIS, 1973.

—— *See* Suppt. Corpus Script. Christ. Orient., Copt., 37-38; Syri, 142-143, 167-168.

Athenagoras. Legatio and De resurrectione. Ed. and trans. William R. Schoedel. [Oxford Early Christian Texts.] 8vo. OXF., 1972.

—— *See* Barnard (L. W.)

Atkyns (Richard) *See* Young (P.) and Tucker (N.) *ed.*

Atterbury (Francis) *Bp. of Rochester. See* Bennett (G. V.)

Attwater (Donald) The Catholic Church in modern Wales: a record of the past century. 8vo. LOND., 1935.

Aubert (Roger) *See* Rogier (L. J.) *and others, ed.*

Aubineau (Michel) Recherches patristiques: enquêtes sur des manuscrits; textes inédits; études. 8vo. AMSTERDAM, 1974.

—— *ed.* Homélies pascales (cinq homélies inédites): Hésychius de Jerusalem, Basile de Séleucie, Jean de Béryte, Pseudo-Chrysostome, Léonce de Constantinople. Introd., texte critique, trad., commentaire et index de Michel Aubineau. [Sources Chrétiennes, 187.] 8vo. PARIS, 1972.

—— *See* Suppt. Analecta Bollandiana. Subsid. Hagiog., 59.

Auden (Thomas) Shrewsbury: a historical and topographical account of the town. Illus. by Katharine M. Roberts. (1905.) 2nd ed. 8vo. LOND., 1923.

Augustine, *Saint, of Hippo.* [Works. *Latin.*] *See* Suppt. Corpus Script. Eccles. Lat., 77, 84, 85/1.

—— Commentaire de la première épitre de S. Jean. Texte latin, introd., trad. et notes par Paul Agaësse. [Sources Chrétiennes, 75.] 8vo. PARIS, 1961.

—— *See* Andresen (C.) *ed.;* Brown (Peter); Burkill (T. A.); Courcelle (P.); Jaspers (K.); O'Connell (R. J.); Rowe (T. T.); Suppt. Corpus Script. Christ. Orient., Subsid., 55.

Ault (D. D.) Visionary physics: Blake's response to Newton. 8vo. CHICAGO & LOND., 1974.

Aune (Bruce) Kant's theory of morals. 8vo. PRINCETON, 1979.

Aune (D. E.) *See* Suppt. Novum Testamentum. Suppts., 28, 33.

Ausubel (Nathan) Pictorial history of the Jewish people from Bible times to our own day throughout the world. (1953.) repr. 4to NEW YORK, 1976.

Aveling (J. C. H.) Catholic recusancy in the city of York 1558-1791. [Catholic Record Soc. Publs., Monograph Ser., 2.] 8vo. [LOND.,] 1970.

—— The handle and the axe: the Catholic recusants in England from Reformation to emancipation. 8vo. LOND. 1976.

Axminster. *Ecclesiastica. See* Ecclesiastica.

Axon (Ernest) Nonconformity in Lancashire in seventeenth century. 8vo MANCHESTER 1918. [Pamph.]

Ayer (A. J.) The central questions of philosophy. [Gifford Lects., 1972-73.] 8vo. LOND., 1973.

Ayerst (David) Guardian: biography of a newspaper. 8vo. LOND. 1971.

Aylmer (G. E.) The state's servants: the civil service of the English Republic, 1649-1660. 8vo. LOND., 1973.

—— *ed.* The Interregnum: the quest for settlement, 1646-1660. [Problems in Focus.] 8vo. LOND., 1972.

[B. (A. L.)] Ashdon Baptist Church, 1809-1959. 8vo. [ASHDON, 1959.] [Pamph.]

Baarda (T.) *ed.. See* Novum Testamentum Suppts., 47-48.

Babolin (Albino) Joseph Butler: etica e religione. 8vo. PADOVA, 1973.

Babrius and Phaedrus. Newly ed. and trans. into English. With an historical introd. and a comprehensive survey of Greek and Latin fables in the Aesopic tradition by B. E. Perry. [Loeb Classical Lib.] 8vo. LOND., 1965.

Bacchiocchi (Samuele) From Sabbath to Sunday: a historical investigation of the rise of Sunday observance in early Christianity. 4to. ROME, 1977.

Bachofen (J. J.) Mutterecht und Urreligion. Eine Auswahl, hrsg. von Rudolf Marx. 8vo. LEIPZIG, [1926].

Backus (Isaac) Diary. Ed. William G. McLoughlin. 3 vols. 8vo. PROVIDENCE (R. I.), 1979.

Bacon (B. W.) The founding of the Church. [Modern Religious Problems.] 16mo. LOND., 1910.

Badham (Paul) Christian beliefs about life after death. [Lib. of Philos. and Relig.] 8vo. LOND., 1976.

Badius (Conrad) *See* Lupton (L. F.)

Baeck (Leo) *See* Friedlander (A. H.)

Baelz (P. R.) Christian obedience in a permissive context. [John Coffin Memorial Lect., Univ. of London, 13 Mar. 1973.] 8vo. LOND., 1973. [Pamph.]

—— The forgotten dream: experience, hope and God. [Bampton Lects.,] 8vo. LOND., 1975.

Baer (Fritz) Die Juden im christlichen Spanien. Erster Teil: Urkunden und Regesten. (1929-36.) facsim. repr. With an introd. by the author and a select additional bibliog. by H. Beinart. 2 vols. 8vo. [FARNBOROUGH,] 1970.

Bagehot (Walter) *See* Tener (R. H.)

Bagguley (W.H.) *ed.* Andrew Marvell, 1621-1678: tercentenary tributes. 8vo. LOND., *etc.*, 1922.

Bahya Ibn Yusuf, *called Ibn Bakuda.* The book of direction to the duties of the heart. From the original Arabic version. Introd., trans. and notes by Menahem Mansoor, *etc.* [Littman Lib. of Jewish Civilization.] 8vo. LOND., 1973.

Bailey (A. E.) The Gospel in hymns: backgrounds and interpretations. 8vo. NEW YORK, 1950.

Baines (Annie M.) History of Dublin Street Baptist Church, Edinburgh, 1858-1958. 8vo. [EDIN., 1958.]

[**Baines** (Arnold H. J.)] 250 years of Baptist witness: Hinton Baptist Church, Chesham, Bucks. 8vo. [CHESHAM, 1951.] [Pamph.]

[—— *and others.*] Princes Risborough Baptist Church: a short history, 1707-1957. 8vo. [PRINCES RISBOROUGH, 1957.] [Pamph.]

Bainton (R. H.) The Querela Pacis of Erasmus: classical and Christian sources. 8vo. [GÜTERSLOH, 1951.] [Pamph.]

—— The Paraphrases of Erasumus. 8vo. GÜTERSLOH, 1966. [Pamph.]

—— Erasmus and Luther and the Dialog Julius Exclusus. 8vo. BERLIN, 1967. [Pamph.]

—— Erasmus and the Wesen des Christentums. 8vo. [LEIDEN, 1967.] [Pamph.]

Baird (J. Arthur) *ed.* *See* Bible. N.T. Misc. John, Epistles of.

Baker (A. E.) *See* Dark (S.)

Baker (Derek) *ed.* Relations between East and West in the Middle Ages. 8vo. EDIN., 1973.

—— *ed.* *See* Commission Internationale d'Histoire Ecclésiastique Comparée. *British Sub-Commission.;* Suppt. Ecclesiastical Hist. Soc.

Baker (Frank) From Wesley to Asbury: studies in early American Methodism. 8vo. DURHAM (N.C.), 1976.

Baker (Herschel C.) The wars of truth: studies in the decay of Christian humanism in the earlier seventeenth century. 8vo. LOND. & NEW YORK, 1952.

Baker (John Austin) The reconstruction of belief, then and now. [Gore Memorial Lect., 1977.] 8vo. LOND., 1977. [Pamph.]

[**Baker** (Reginald)] For the generation following: a history of the Old Baptist Chapel, Dunstable, 1675-1975. 8vo. CRANLEIGH [printed], [1975]. [Pamph.]

Baker (Robert A.) The Southern Baptist Convention and its people, 1607-1972. 8vo. NASHVILLE (Tenn.), 1974.

Baker (William) *See* Catalogues. *Dr. Williams's Lib.*

[**Baldwin** (F. J.)] Sion Baptist Church, Cloughfold: 300th anniversary handbook, 1672-1972. 8vo. [CLOUGHFOLD, 1972.] [Pamph.]

Balfour (A. J., *1st Earl of*) *See* Clifford (J.); Jenkins (R. H.)

Balfour (R. G.)   Presbyterianism in the Colonies, with special reference to the principles and influence of the Free Church of Scotland.   [Chalmers Lects., 5th ser.] 8vo.   EDIN., 1900.

Ball (Bryan W.)   A great expectation: eschatological thought in English Protestantism to 1660.   [Studies in the Hist. of Christian Thought, 42.]   8vo.   LEIDEN, 1975.

Ballantyne (J. C.)   Liberty, diversity, fraternity: a plea for a new spiritual companionship.   [Religion: its Modern Needs and Problems, 20.]   8vo.   LOND., 1933.

Ballard (A. E.)   *See* Champion (O. C.) and Ballard (A. E.)

Balthasar (Hans Urs von)   La gloire et la croix: les aspects esthétiques de la révélation.   [Théologie, 61, 74, 81.]   8vo.   PARIS, 1965–
2.   ii. Styles. De Jean de la Croix à Péguy. Trad. Robert Givord et Hélène Bourboulon.   1972.

Baltzer (Dieter)   *See* Suppt. Zeitschr. für A. T. Wiss. Beihefte, 121.

Baltzer (Klaus)   The covenant formulary in Old Testament, Jewish and early Christian writings. Trans. David E. Green.   8vo.   OXF., 1971.

Bambrough (J. Renford)   Reason, truth, and God.   [Based on Stanton Lects., 1963.] (1969.) repr.   8vo.   LOND., 1973.

—— Moral scepticism and moral knowledge.   [Studies in Philos. Psychol.]   8vo. LOND. & HENLEY, 1979.

Bampfield (Francis)   *See* Greaves (R. L.)

Bampton Lectures.   *See* Suppt.

Band (Edward)   Barclay of Formosa.   8vo.   TOKYO, 1936.

Bangs (Carl)   Arminius: a study in the Dutch Reformation.   8vo.   NASHVILLE (Tenn.) & NEW YORK, 1971.

Bankes, *family of.*   *See* Suppt. Chetham Soc., 3rd Ser., 21.

Banks (Robert)   Jesus and the Law in the Synoptic tradition.   [Soc. for N.T. Studies, Monograph Ser., 28.]   8vo.   CAMB., 1975.

Banyard (E. A.)   The first 300 years: the unfinished story of Stowmarket Congregational Church.   8vo.   STOWMARKET, 1970.   [Pamph.]   [*Imperfect.*]

Baptist Handbook.   *See* Suppt.

Baptist Historical Society.   *See* Suppt.

Baptist Quarterly.   *See* Suppt.

Baptist Union of Great Britain and Ireland.   A message from the Baptist Union of Great Britain and Ireland to the Baptists of the United States of America.   [By W. Y. Fullerton, John Clifford and J. H. Shakespeare.]   8vo.   BALTIMORE, [1917]. [Pamph.]

—— *See* Suppt. Baptist Handbook; Baptist Union Directory; Baptist Union Handbook.

Baptist Union of Scotland.   See Suppt. Scottish Baptist Yearbook.

Baptist World Alliance.   Golden jubilee congress (ninth world congress), London, England, 16th-22nd July, 1955. Official report, ed. Arnold T. Ohrn asstd. by Geoffrey W. Rusling.   8vo.   LOND., [1955].

Barber (F. Hugh)   The influence of Reformed doctrine on English charity in the sixteenth century.   8vo.   COLCHESTER, 1970. [Pamph.]

[**Barber** (G. J.)]   A peep into Baptist history in Cheshire: Great Warford Chapel (founded 1668) and Bramhall Chapel (founded 1858).   8vo.   MACCLESFIELD, [1936]. [Pamph.]

Barberi (Dominic)   The lamentation of England, or the prayer of the prophet Jeremiah, applied to the same. (1831.)   facsim. repr.   [With introd. by Gerard de Lisle.]   8vo. [WHITWICK (Leics.), priv. printed, 1971.]   [Pamph.]

Barbet (Jeanne)   *See* Gallus (T.)

Barbour (I. G.)   Science and secularity: the ethics of technology.   8vo.   NEW YORK, *etc.*, 1970.

[**Barclay** (R. A.)]   The story of Alva Baptist Church, 1882-1952.   8vo. [ALVA, 1952.] [Pamph.]

Barclay (Thomas) 1849-1935, *Presb. missionary in Formosa.*   *See* Band (E.)

Barkley (J. M.) *and others.*   Henry Bullinger, 1504-1575. Papers read at a colloquium marking the 400th anniversary of his death, Bristol Baptist College, 16-18 Sep. 1975. fol. *Duplicated.*   [BRISTOL,] 1975.   [Pamph.]

[**Barks** (Derek and Mrs.)]   United Reformed Church, Hounslow.   8vo.   *Duplicated.* n.p., [1974].   [Pamph.]

Barlow (Frank) The English Church, 1066-1154. [Hist. of the Anglo-Norman Church.] 8vo. LOND. & NEW YORK, 1979.

Barnabas, *Saint.* Épître de Barnabé. Introd., trad. et notes par Pierre Prigent. Texte grec établi et présenté par Robert A. Kraft. [Sources Chrétiennes, 172.] 8vo. PARIS, 1971.

Barnard (L. W.) C. B. Moss (1888-1964), Defender of the Faith. 8vo. LOND., 1967.

—— Athenagoras: a study in second century Christian apologetic. [Théologie Historique, 18.] 8vo. PARIS, 1972.

Barnard (T. C.) Cromwellian Ireland: English government and reform in Ireland, 1649-1660. [Oxford Historical Monographs.] 8vo. LOND., 1975.

Barnardo (T. J.) *See* Bready (J. W.)

Barnes (Ernest John Ward) Ahead of his age: Bishop Barnes of Birmingham. 8vo. LOND., 1979.

Barnes (Ernest William) *Bp. of Birmingham. See* Barnes (E. J. W.)

Barnes (T. D.) Tertullian: a historical and literary study. 8vo. OXF., 1971.

[Barnett (F. A.) *comp.*] Ruiton Congregational Church: to commemorate the renovation of the church, completed by an act of thanksgiving, 23rd Feb. 1972. 8vo. [RUITON, 1972.] [Pamph.]

Barnett (Henrietta O.) Matters that matter. [Speeches.] 8vo. LOND., 1930.

Barns (J. W. B.) *See* Discoveries in the Judaean Desert.

Barnstaple. *Methodist Church.* Barnstaple Methodist Church (formerly Thorne Memorial Chapel), 1876-1976: centenary brochure. 8vo. [BARNSTAPLE, 1976.] [Pamph.]

Baron (S. W.) A social and religious history of the Jews. (1937.) 2nd ed. rev. and enl. 8vo. NEW YORK, 1953-
15. Resettlement and exploration. 1973.

Barr (A. Margaret) A dream come true: the story of Kharang. Ed. Roy W. Smith. 8vo. LOND., 1974.

Barr (James) 1862-1949. The United Free Church of Scotland. 8vo. LOND., 1934.

Barr (James) *b.*1924. Fundamentalism. 8vo. LOND., 1977.

—— *See* Suppt. Studies in Bibl. Theol., 33*.

[Barraclough (F. T.) *and others.*] The story of a church: Central Congregational Church, Bree Street, Johannesburg, 1889-1949. 8vo. JOHANNESBURG, 1949. [Pamph.]

Barraclough (Peter) John Owen (1616-1683). [Heritage Biographies.] 8vo. LOND., 1961. [Pamph.]

Barrett (C. K.) The Gospel according to St. John: an introd. with commentary and notes on the Greek text. (1955.) 2nd ed. 8vo. LOND., 1978.

—— Luke the historian in recent study. [A. S. Peake Memorial Lect., 6.] 8vo. LOND., 1961.

—— The prologue of St. John's Gospel. [Ethel M. Wood Lect., 1970.] 8vo. LOND., 1971. [Pamph.]

—— New Testament essays. 8vo. LOND., 1972.

—— The Gospel of John and Judaism. [Franz Delitzsch Lects., Univ. of Münster, 1967.] Trans. D. M. Smith. 8vo. LOND., 1975.

—— *See* Bible. N. T. Commentaries. Black's.

[Barrett (Doris A.)] Souvenir of the centenary of Baptist witness in Lydbrook, 1857-1957. 8vo. [LYDBROOK, 1957.] [Pamph.]

Barrett (*Lady* Florence) *ed. See* Barrett (*Sir* W. F.)

[Barrett (Gladys M.)] Westgate Road Baptist Church, Newcastle-upon-Tyne, 1886-1936. 4to. [NEWCASTLE-UPON-TYNE, 1936.] [Pamph.]

Barrett (John Oliver) *See* Payne (E. A.)

Barrett (*Sir* William Fletcher) Death-bed visions. 8vo. LOND., 1926.

—— Personality survives death: messages from Sir William Barrett, ed. by his wife. Foreword by Canon R. J. Campbell. 8vo. LOND., 1937.

Barrowe (Henry) *See* Reason (J.)

Barry (W. F.) Newman. [Literary Lives.] (1904.) 2nd ed. 8vo. LOND., 1904.

Bartel (Oskar) Jan Laski. [Towarzystwo Badán Dziejów Reformacji w Polsce.] Cześć 1, 1499-1556. 8vo. WARSZAWA, 1955.

Barth (Hans-Martin) Atheismus und Orthodoxie: Analysen und Modelle christlicher Apologetik im 17. Jahrhundert. [Forschungen zur systemat. und ökumen. Theologie, 25.] 8vo. GÖTTINGEN, 1971.

Barth (Karl) [Selections. *Englisi.*] God here and now. Trans. Paul M. van Buren. [Religious Perspectives, 9.] 8vc. LOND., 1964.
—— [Two or more works. *German*] Rudolf Bultmann: ein Versuch, ihn zu verstehen. Christus und Adam nach Röm. 5. Zwei theologische Studien. 8vo. ZÜRICH, 1964.
—— Church dogmatics. 8vo EDN., 1936-69.
    1. The doctrine of the Word of God. i. (1936.) 2nd ed. Trans. G. W. Bromiley. 1975.
—— Trouble and promise in the struggle of the Church in Germany. [Philip Maurice Deneke Lect., Mar. 1938.] Trans. P.V. M. Benecke. 8vo. OXF., 1938. [Pamph.]
—— Evangelium und Bildung. (1938) 2te.Aufl. [Theologische Studien, 2.] 8vo. ZOLLIKON-ZÜRICH, 1947. [Pamph.]
—— The Church and the political problem of our day. 8vo. LOND., 1939.
—— A letter to Great Britain from Switzerland. [Christian News-letter Books, 11.] 8vo. LOND., 1941.
—— Deliverance to the captives. [Trans. Marguerite Wieser.] 8vo. LOND., 1961.
—— *See* Busch (E.); Flesseman-Van Leei (E.); Gunton (C. E.); Rumscheidt (H. M.); Sykes (S. W.) *ed.*
Bartha (Tibor) *ed.* A Heidelbergi Káté története Magyarországon. Studia de historia catechismi Heidelbergiensis in Hungar'a collecta, 1563-1965. [Tanulmányok a Magyarországi Református Egyház Négyzázéves Történetéből, 1.] [Studia et Acta Ecclesiastica, 1.] 8vo. BUDAPEST, 1965.
—— *and others.* Der Heidelberger Katechismus in Ungarn. 8vo. BUDAPEST, 1967.
Bartle (G. F.) A history of Borough Road College. 8vo. [ISLEWORTH,] 1976. [Pamph.]
Bartlett (G. W.) The Baptist Church in Darlington: a centenary record of its rise and progress. 8vo. COVENTRY, 1910.
Bartlett (Robert M.) The faith of the Pilgrims: an American heritage. [Pilgrim Book.] 8vo. NEW YORK & PHILADELPHIA, 1978.
Barton (D. A.) Discovering chapels and meeting houses. 8vo. PRINCES RIS-BOROUGH, 1975. [Pamph.]
Barton (Elizabeth) *See* Neame (A.)
Barton (William) c.1598-1678, *hymnwriter.* *See* Welch (C. E.)
Barton (William Eleazar) My faith in immortality. 8vo. LOND., [1927].
Barucq (André) Le livre des Proverbes. [Sources Bibliques.] 8vo. PARIS, 1964.
Basil, *Saint, the Great.* Sur l'origine de l'homme (Hom. X et XI de l'Hexaéméron). Introd., texte critique, trad. et notes par Alexis Smets et Michel van Esbroeck. [Sources Chrétiennes, 160.] 8vo. PARIS, 1970.
—— *See* Berther (K.); Suppt. Texte u. Untersuchungen, 5te. Reihe, 123.
Basil, *Abp. of Seleucia.* *See* Aubineau (M.) *ed.*
Basildon. *Laindon Baptist Church.* Souvenir jubilee brochure, 1909-1959. 8vo. [BASILDON, 1959.] [Pamph.]
Basingstoke. *London Street Congregational Church.* Tercentenary, 1663-1963. 8vo. BASINGSTOKE, [1963]. [Pamph.]
Basnage de Beauval (Henri) Tolérance des religions. (1684.) facsim. repr. Introd. par Elisabeth Labrousse. 12mo. NEW YORK & LOND., 1970.
Bassett (T. Myrfyn) The Welsh Baptists. 8vo. SWANSEA, 1977.
Bate (Walter Jackson) Samuel Johnson. 8vo. LOND., 1978.
Bateman (A. B.) Christianity and spiritualism. 8vo. LOND., 1927.
Bateman (C. T.) John Clifford, Free Church leader and preacher. (1904.) repr. 8vo. LOND., [1908].
Bates (E. Ralph) Methodism in Wokingham, 1817-1967. 8vo. WOKINGHAM, [1967]. [Pamph.]
Batiffol (Pierre) L'abbaye de Rossano: contribution à l'histoire de la Vaticane. (1891.) [Variorum Reprs.] 8vo. LOND., 1971.
Batsford (M. E.) Non-conformity in Walthamstow. [Walthamstow Antiquarian Soc. Monographs, N.S., 19, 22.] 2 pts. 8vo. LOND., 1977-79. [Pamphs.]
    1. Congregationalists & Baptists. 1977.
    2. Methodists and other organisations. 1979.
Battis (Emery) Saints and sectaries: Anne Hutchinson and the Antinomian controversy in the Massachusetts Bay Colony. 8vo. CHAPEL HILL (N.C.), 1962.

Bauckham (Richard) Tudor Apocalypse: sixteenth century apocalypticism, millennarianism and the English Reformation: from John Bale to John Foxe and Thomas Brightman. Illustrative texts. [Courtenay Lib. of Reformation Classics, 8.] 8vo. APPLEFORD, 1978.

Baudrillart (Alfred) *See* Dictionaries. Christianity.

Bauer (Walter) Orthodoxy and heresy in earliest Christianity. 2nd Ger. ed., with added appendices, by Georg Strecker, trans. by a team from the Philadelphia Seminar on Christian Origins, and ed. by Robert A. Kraft and Gerhard Krodel. 8vo. PHILADELPHIA, 1971.

Bauman (Clarence) Gewaltlosigkeit im Täufertum: eine Untersuchung zur theologischen Ethik des oberdeutschen Täufertums der Reformationszeit. [Studies in the Hist. of Christian Thought, 3.] 8vo. LEIDEN, 1968.

[**Baxter** (O. W. M.)] Jubilee, 1909-1959: from Dovecote Hall to Eldon Road [Wood Green]. [8vo. LOND., 1959.] [Pamph.]

Baxter (Richard) The saints' everlasting rest, or a treatise of the blessed state of the saints in their enjoyment of God in glory. (1650). A new ed., ed. William Young. 8vo. LOND., 1907.

—— Poetical fragments: heart-imployment with God and it self. (1681.) facsim. repr. With a biogr. note by V. de S. Pinto. 8vo. FARNBOROUGH, 1971.

—— [Reliquiae Baxterianae. (1696.)] The autobiography of Richard Baxter. Abridged by J. M. Lloyd Thomas. (1925.) Ed. with an introd. by N. H. Keeble. [Everyman's Univ. Lib.] 8vo. LOND., 1974.

—— *See* Harris (W. M.); Lamont (W. M.); Phelan (M. H.)

Bayle (Pierre) Ce que c'est que la France toute catholique, sous le régne [*sic*] de Louis le Grand. (1686.) Texte établi, présenté et annoté par Elisabeth Labrousse, *etc.* [Bibliothèque des Textes Philosophiques.] 4to. PARIS, 1973.

—— *See* Collins (A.); Rétat (P.)

Bayly (Albert F.) *See* Hymns.

Baynes (A. H.) *See* Wheeler (B. R.)

Baynes (Paul) The diocesans tryall, wherein all the sinnews of D. Downams Defence are brought unto three heads, and orderly dissolved. (1621.) facsim. repr. 4to. FARNBOROUGH, 1971.

—— A commentary upon the first and second chapters of Saint Paul to the Colossians. (1635.) facsim. repr. 4to. [FARNBOROUGH,] 1972.

Bazett (L. Margery) Impressions from the unseen. Introd. by Sir William F. Barrett. 8vo. OXF., 1925.

Bea (Augustin) *Cardinal.* The unity of Christians. Ed. Bernard Leeming. Introd. by Archbishop Gerald P. O'Hara. (1963.) repr. 8vo. LOND., 1963.

Beadle (H. L.) *ed.* Centenary souvenir brochure, Wesley Methodist Chapel, Middleton-in-Teesdale. 8vo. MIDDLETON-IN-TEESDALE, 1970. [Pamph.]

Beard (R. W.) *ed. See* Copi (M. I.) and Beard (R. W.) *ed.*

Beards (G. L. W.) "Fellowship in the truth" and "Co-operation in service": a short history of the Devon and Cornwall Baptist Associations. 8vo. PLYMOUTH [printed], [1975]. [Pamph.]

Beasley-Murray (G. R.) *See* Bible. Commentaries. New Century Bible.

Beaton (K. J.) Growing with the years. [The United Church of Canada.] 8vo. TORONTO, [1949].

Beatty (H. M.) A brief history of education. 8vo. LOND., 1922.

Beaulieu, *Abbey. See* Suppt. Royal Hist. Soc. Camden 4th Ser., 16.

Beaumont (R. M.) The Chapter of Southwell Minster: a story of 1,000 years. Foreword by the Bishop of Southwell [F. R. Barry]. 8vo. [SOUTHWELL,] 1956. [Pamph.]

Bebbington (D. W.) A history of Queensberry Street Baptist Church, Old Basford, Nottingham, 1877-1977. 8vo. NOTTINGHAM, 1977. [Pamph.]

Beck (Edmund) *See* Suppt. Corpus Script. Christ. Orient., Subsid., 55.

Beck (Hans-Georg) Res Publica Romana: vom Staatsdenken der Byzantiner. [Bayerische Akademie der Wiss. Philos.-hist. Klasse. Sitzungsberichte 1970, 2.] 8vo. MÜNCHEN, 1970. [Pamph.]

—— Geschichte der Byzantinischen Volksliteratur. [Handbuch der Altertumswiss., 12: Byzant. Handbuch, 2,iii.] 8vo. MÜNCHEN, 1971.

—— Ideen und Realitaeten in Byzanz. Gesammelte Aufsaetze. [Variorum Reprs.] 8vo. LOND., 1972.

Beck (Hans-Georg)—*continued*
—— *ed. See* International Congress of Byzantine Studies. II. [Misc.]
—— *See* Jedin (H.) and Dolan (J.) *ed.*
Beckenham. *United Reformed Church.* Centenary [1878-1978]. 8vo. *Duplicated.* [BECKENHAM, 1978.] [Pamph.]
Becket (Thomas) *Saint. See* Knowles (D.); Smalley (B.)
Beckwith (John) Early Christian and Byzantine art. [Pelican Hist. of Art.] 4to. HARMONDSWORTH, 1970.
Bede, *Venerable, Saint.* [Works. *Latin.*] Opera. Pars II. Opera exegetica. 2A. De tabernaculo.—De templo.—In Ezram et Neemiam. Cura et studio D. Hurst. [Corpus Christianorum, Ser. Latina, 119A.] 8vo. TURNHOUT. 1969.
—— *See* Bonner (G.) *ed.*
Bedford. *Bunyan Meeting.* The minutes of the first Independent Church (now Bunyan Meeting) at Bedford, 1656-1766. Ed. H. G. Tibbutt. [Bedfordshire Historical Record Soc. Publs., 55.] 8vo. [BEDFORD,] 1976.
Bedford (R. D.) The defence of truth: Herbert of Cherbury and the seventeenth century. 8vo. MANCHESTER, 1979.
Bedouelle (Guy) Lefèvre d'Étaples et l'Intelligence des Écritures. [Travaux d'Humanisme et Renaissance, 152.] 4to. GENÈVE, 1976.
Beeston. *Queen's Road Methodist Church.* 1900-1950 Golden Jubilee celebrations May 13th to 18th, 1950. 8vo. [BEESTON, 1950.] [Pamph.]
Beet (J. A.) Holiness symbolic and real: a Bible study. 8vo. LOND., 1910.
Behler (Ernst) *ed. See* Schelling (F. W. J. von)
Belden (A. D.) George Whitefield (1714-1770). [Heritage Biographies.] 8vo. LOND., 1961. [Pamph.]
Belfast. *Great Victoria Street Baptist Church.* Year book, 1952. 8vo. [BELFAST, 1952.] [Pamph.]
Bell (G. K. A.) Randall Davidson, Archbishop of Canterbury. (1935.) 2nd ed. 2 vols. in 1. 8vo. LOND., *etc.*, 1938.
—— The kingship of Christ: the story of the World Council of Churches. 8vo. HARMONDSWORTH, 1954.
—— *See* Rupp (E. G.)
Bell (Gertrude L.) [Selections.] Gertrude Bell (1868-1926). A selection from the photographic archive of an archaeologist and traveller, by Stephen Hill. 8vo. [NEWCASTLE-UPON-TYNE,] 1976.
Bell (Patricia) *See* Bunyan (John) [Misc.]
Bell (R. W.) *See* Gibbon (*Sir* G.) and Bell (R. W.)
Bellah (R. N.) Beyond belief: essays on religion in a post-traditional world. 8vo. NEW YORK, *etc.*, 1970.
Belton (L. J.) World vision. [Uncensored Avowals.] 8vo. LOND., [1937].
Benas (Bertram B.) *See* Temkin (S. D.)
Bender (Gottfried) Die Irenik Martin Bucers in ihren Anfängen (1523-1528). [Studia Irenica, 5.] 8vo. HILDESHEIM, 1975.
Bender (H. S.) The Anabaptist vision. 8vo. GOSHEN (Ind.), 1949. [Pamph.]
Benedict, *Saint, Abbot of Monte Cassino.* La règle de Saint Benoît. [Sources Chrétiennes, 181-6.] 6 vols. 8vo. PARIS, 1971-72.
    1. Prologue-ch.7. Introd., trad., et notes par Adalbert de Vogüé. Texte établi et présenté par Jean Neufville. 1972.
    2. Ch.8-73. Trad. et notes par A. de Vogüé. Texte et concordance par J. Neufville. 1972.
    3. Instruments pour l'étude de la tradition manuscrite par J. Neufville. 1972.
    4. Commentaire historique et critique par A. de Vogüé. i-iii. 1971.
    5. ——iv-vi. 1971.
    6. ——vii-ix, et index. 1971.
Benedikz (Benedikt S.) *ed. See* Blöndal (S. B. B.)
Bengel (Johann Albrecht) *See* Zinzendorf (N. L. von) [Misc.]
Bennett (F. S. M.) The resurrection of the dead. 8vo. LOND., 1929.
Bennett (G. V.) The Tory crisis in church and state, 1688-1730: the career of Francis Atterbury, Bishop of Rochester. 8vo. OXF., 1975.
Bentley (James) Ritualism and politics in Victorian Britain: the attempt to legislate for belief. [Oxford Theological Monographs.] 8vo. OXF., 1978.

Bentwich (Norman) Claude Montefiore and his tutor in Rabbinics [Solomon Schechter]: founders of liberal and conservative Judaism. [Claude Montefiore Lect., 6, 1965.] 8vo. SOUTHAMPTON, 1966. [Pamph.]

Benz (Ernst) Wittenberg und Byzanz: zur Begegnung und Auseinandersetzung der Reformation und der östlich-orthodoxen Kirche. (1949.) 2te Aufl. [Forum Slavicum, 6.] 8vo. MÜNCHEN, 1971.

—— The Eastern Orthodox Church: its thought and life. Trans. Richard and Clara Winston. 8vo. CHICAGO, 1963.

—— Endzeitung zwischen Ost und West: Studien zur christlichen Eschatologie. 8vo. FREIBURG IM B., 1973.

—— Urbild und Abbild: der Mensch und die mythische Welt. Gesammelte Eranos-Beiträge. 8vo. LEIDEN, 1974.

Berdyaev (Nikolai) Aleksei Stepanovich Khomiakov. (1912.) facsim. repr. 8vo. FARNBOROUGH, 1971.

—— The Russian Revolution: two essays on its implications in religion and psychology. Trans. with an introd. by D. B. [Essays in Order, 6.] (1931) repr. 8vo. LOND. & NEW YORK, 1933.

—— See Lowrie (D. A.)

Bereczky (Albert) A magyar protestantizmus a zsidóüldözés ellen. 8vo. BUDAPEST, 1945. [Pamph.]

Berg (Johannes van den) See Van den Berg (J.)

Berger (P. L.) The noise of solemn assemblies: Christian commitment and the religious establishment in America. 8vo. GARDEN CITY (N.Y.), 1961.

Bergin (G. F.) comp. Ten years after: a sequel to the autobiography of George Müller. Being an account of. . .the Ashley Down Orphanage, Bristol, for the ten years following the death of Mr. Müller. (1909.) repr. 8vo. LOND. & BRISTOL, 1911.

Bergson (Henri) An introduction to metaphysics. Authorized trans. by T. E. Hulme, with an introd. by Thomas A. Goudge. [Lib. of Liberal Arts, 10.] (1949.) 2nd ed. 8vo. NEW YORK, 1955.

—— See Gunter (P. A. Y.); Thibaudet (A.); Wickham (H.); Suppt. Études Bergsoniennes.

Berkeley (George) Bp. of Cloyne. See Bracken (H. M.); Catalogues. Yale Univ. Lib.; Gaustad (E. S.); Warnock (G. J.)

Berkhof (Hendrikus) The doctrine of the Holy Spirit. [Annie Kinkead Warfield Lects., 1963-64.] 8vo. LOND., 1965.

Bermant (Chaim) and **Weitzman** (M. P.) Ebla: an archaeological enigma. 8vo. LOND., 1978.

Bernard, Saint, of Clairvaux. See Fechner (H.); Knowles (D.)

Bernhardi (F. A. J. von) See Papers for War Time, 12, 26.

Berofsky (Bernard) ed. Free will and determinism. [Sources in Contemp. Philos.] 8vo. NEW YORK & LOND., 1966.

Berry (Enos) History of the Baptist Church, Worcester. 8vo. WORCESTER, 1914. [Pamph.]

Berry (S. M.) Graces of the Christian character. 8vo. LOND., 1914.

—— Revealing light. 8vo. LOND., 1923.

—— The great issue, and other war-time studies. 8vo. LOND., 1944.

Berther (Karl) Der Mensch und seine Verwirklichung in den Homilien des Basilius von Cäsarea: ein anthropologisch-ethischer Versuch. Dissertation. 8vo. FREIBURG (Schweiz), 1974.

Bertie (Katharine) 1520-80, Baroness of Willoughby de Eresby, Duchess of Suffolk. See Lupton (L. F.)

Bertie (Peregrine) 1555-1601, Lord Willoughby de Eresby. See Lupton (L. F.)

Best (Ernest) See Bible. Commentaries. New Century Bible.

Bethel (Slingsby) The world's mistake in Oliver Cromwell. (1668.) facsim. repr. 8vo. EXETER, 1972. [Pamph.]

Betjeman (Sir John) Nonconformist architecture. [In The Architectural Review, 88, 529.] fol. CHEAM, 1940.

Bevan (Edwyn R.) Christians in a world at war. 8vo. LOND., 1940.

—— See Papers for War Time, 4, 33.

Bevan (Hugh) Morgan Llwyd y llenor. 8vo. CAERDYDD, 1954.

Bevan (Llewelyn David) The life and reminiscences. Comp. and ed. by Louisa Jane Bevan. 8vo. MELBOURNE, 1920.

Bevan (R. J. W.) *ed.* The churches and Christian unity. 8vo. LOND., *etc.*, 1963.
Bevis Marks Synagogue. *See* Suppt. Jewish Hist. Soc. Publs., 1973.
Beyerlin (Walter) *See* Suppt. Zeitschr. für A. T. Wiss. Beihefte, 153.
Beza (Theodore) Correspondence de Théodore de Bèze recueille par Hippolyte Aubert, publieé par Fernand Aubert, Henri Meylan, *etc.* [Travaux d'Humanisme et Renaissance.] 4to. GENÈVE, 1960-
    7. 1566. 1973.
    8. 1567. Avec une table des lettres et documents des tomes 1-8. 1976.
    9. 1568. 1978.
Bezold (Carl) *See* Boll (F.) *and others.*
Bezzant (J. S) The Very Reverend Norman Sykes, 1897-1961. [Repr. from Brit. Acad. Proc., 47, 1961.] 8vo. LOND., [1962]. [Pamph.]
Bhagavadgita. [*English.*] The Bhagavad Gita. A verse translation: Geoffrey Parrinder. 8vo. LOND., 1974.
[**Bibby** (Marjorie) *comp.*] St. Andrew's United Reformed Church, Northey Avenue, Cheam: Golden Jubilee, 1977. 8vo. MITCHAM, [1977]. [Pamph.]
BIBLE.
Under this heading are included: (a) plain texts and versions of the Bible and parts thereof; (b) commentaries in series; and (c), in the 'Miscellaneous' sections, cross references both to other commentaries (whether with or without text) and to other works on particular parts or books of the Bible. (This arrangement differs slightly from that in previous volumes of the catalogue.) Texts and versions of, and texts with commentaries on, books of the Apocrypha are grouped together as a concluding section (as before).
Texts and Versions.
Latin. [Old Latin.] Vetus Latina: die Reste der altlateinischen Bibel nach Petrus Sabatier. Neu gesammelt und hrsg. von der Erzabtei Beuron. fol. FREIBURG IM B., 1949-
    24.ii. Epistulae ad Philippenses et ad Colossenses. Hrsg. J. H. Frede. 1966-71.
    26.i. Epistulae catholicae. Hrsg. W. Thiele. 1956-69.
—— —— —— Aus der Geschichte der lateinischen Bibel. 8vo. FREIBURG IM B. 1-6. *Not in Library.*
    7. Ein neuer Paulustext und Kommentar: H. J. Frede. 1. Untersuchungen. 1973.
    8. —— 2. Texte. 1974.
—— [Vulgate.] Biblia sacra iuxta latinam vulgatam versionem ad codicum fidem, iussu Pii PP.XI, cura et studio Commissionis Pontificae praeside Aidano Gasquet edita. [4+. Cura et studio monachorum Abbatiae Pontificiae S. Hieronymi in urbe Ordinis S. Benedicti edita.] 8vo. ROMA, 1926-
    14. Liber Hieremiae et Lamentationes—Liber Baruch. 1972
English. The New English Bible. 3 vols. 8vo. OXF. & CAMB., 1961-70.
    3. The New Testament. (1961.) 2nd ed. 1970.
—— The Holy Bible. New International Version, containing the Old Testament and the New Testament. 8vo. LOND., 1979.
—— [Concordances.] Cruden's complete concordance to the Old and New Testaments. (1737). With notes and biblical proper names under one alphabetical arrangement. Ed. C. H. Irwin, A. D. Adams, S. A. Waters. (1930.) repr. 8vo. LOND., 1961.
—— [Misc.] *See* Bruce (F. F.); Sparks (H. F. D.)
—— Wycliffe's. [Misc.] *See* Lindberg (C.)
—— Geneva. [Misc.] *See* Lupton (L. F.)
Aramaic. The Bible in Aramaic, based on old manuscripts and printed texts. Ed. Alexander Sperber. 8vo. LEIDEN, 1959-
    4B. The Targum and the Hebrew Bible. 1973.
Commentaries.
ANCHOR BIBLE. [Introductions, translations, and notes.] General editors: W. F. Albright, D. N. Freedman. 8vo. GARDEN CITY (N.Y.)
    1. Genesis: E. A. Speiser. 1964.
    12. I Chronicles: J. M. Myers. 1965.
    13. II Chronicles: J. M. Myers. 1965.
    14. Ezra-Nehemiah: J. M. Myers. 1965.
    15. Job: M. H. Pope. 1965.

BIBLE. Commentaries—*continued*
  16, 17, 17A. Psalms: M. Dahood. 3 vols. 1965-70.
  18. Proverbs: Ecclesiastes: R. B. Y. Scott. 1965.
  21. Jeremiah: J. Bright. 1965.
  26. Matthew: W. F. Albright and C. S. Mann. 1971.
  29, 29A. John: R. E. Brown. (1966.) repr. 2 vols. 8vo. LOND., 1978.
  37. James, Peter, and Jude: B. Reicke. 1964.
INTERNATIONAL CRITICAL COMMENTARY on the Holy Scriptures of the Old and New Testaments. 8vo. EDIN., 1895-
  Romans. 6th ed.: C.E.B. Cranfield. 2 vols. 1975-79.
NEW CENTURY BIBLE [*formerly* CENTURY BIBLE: New edition]. Based on the Revised Standard Version. General editors: H. H. Rowley [*d.*1969], R. E. Clements [1971+] (Old Testament); Matthew Black (New Testament). 8vo. LOND., *etc.*, 1966-
  Old Testament.
    Exodus: J. P. Hyatt. 1971.
    Deuteronomy: A. D. H. Mayes. 1979.
    1 and 2 Samuel: J. Mauchline. 1971.
    Psalms: A. A. Anderson. 2 vols. 1972.
    Isaiah 40-66: R. N. Whybray. 1975.
  New Testament.
    Matthew: D. Hill. 1972.
    Mark: H. Anderson. 1976.
    John: B. Lindars. 1972.
    Acts: W. Neil. 1973.
    Romans: M. Black. 1973.
    1 and 2 Corinthians: F. F. Bruce. 1971.
    Ephesians: C. L. Mitton. 1976.
    Philippians: R. P. Martin. 1976.
NEW CLARENDON BIBLE. 8vo. OXF., 1963-
  New Testament.
    Matthew: H. B. Green. 1975. [Without text.]
    Luke: G. H. P. Thompson. 1972. [With R. S. V. text.]
    Paul's letters from prison (Ephesians, Philippians, Colossians, Philemon): G. B. Caird. 1976. [Without text.]
Miscellaneous.
See Campenhausen (H.von); Frei (H.W.); Hanson (A. T.); Mauser (U. W.); Williams (T. R.);
  Suppt. Bible Translator; Biblica; Biblical Archaeologist; Biblical Research; Expository Times; Forschungen zur Relig. u. Lit.; Interpretation; Journal of Biblical Lit.; Palestine Exploration Quarterly; Revue Biblique; Studies in Bibl. Theol.
OLD TESTAMENT. Texts and Versions.
Hebrew and English. The Holy Scriptures of the Old Testament: Hebrew and English [in parallel columns]. (1870.) repr. 4to. LOND., 1965.
Hebrew. [Misc.] The Hebrew text of the Old Testament: the readings adopted by the translators of the New English Bible: L. H. Brockington. 8vo. OXF. & CAMB., 1973.
Greek. [Concordances. Misc.] *See* Santos (E. C.dos)
Greek. [Misc.] *See* Walters (P.)
PENTATEUCH. *Syriac. See* Suppt. Corpus Script. Christ. Orient., Subsid., 45.
JUDGES. *Syriac.* [Misc.] *See* Dirksen (P. B.)
SAMUEL. *Coptic.* [Misc.] *See* Suppt. Corpus Script. Christ. Orient., Copt., 35-36.
PSALMS. *English.* The Psalter, newly pointed. 8vo. LOND., 1925.
—— —— The Revised Psalter. The final report of the Commission to revise the Psalter appointed by the Archbishops of Canterbury and York, as presented to the Convocations. . .May 1963. 8vo. LOND., 1963.
JONAH. *Hebrew.* [Misc.] *See* Snaith (N. H.)
Commentaries.
DAS ALTE TESTAMENT DEUTSCH: neues Göttinger Bibelwerk. Hrsg. A. Weiser. 8vo. GÖTTINGEN, 1954- [With German text.]
  2.-4. Das erste Buch Mose: G. von Rad. (1949.) 8te. Aufl. 1967.
  18. Der Prophet Jesaja, Kap. 13-39: O. Kaiser. 1973.

BIBLE. OLD TESTAMENT. Commentaries—*continued*
HANDBUCH ZUM ALTEN TESTAMENT. Hrsg. O. Eissfeldt. 8vo. TÜBINGEN, 1934-
[With German text.]
I.4. Leviticus: Karl Elliger. 1966.
18. Die fünf Megilloth. (1940.) 2te. Aufl. Ruth, Das Hohelied, Esther: Ernst
Würthwein.—Der Prediger: Kurt Galling.—Die Klagelieder: Otto Plöger.
1969.
Miscellaneous.
See Bright (J.); Childs (B. S.); Clements (R. E.); Davies (G. H.) [Misc.]; Fohrer (G.);
Gooding (D. W.); Harrison (R. K.); Hayes (J. H.) and Miller (J. M.) *ed.;* Herrmann
(S.); Kaiser (O.); Kippenberg (H. G.); Martin (A. D.); Noth (M.); Preus (J. S.);
Pritchard (J. B.); Robinson (T. H.); Vaughan (P. H.); Zimmerli (W.);
Suppt. Journal of Near Eastern Studies; Journal of Semitic Studies; Old Test.
Lib.; Society for O. T. Study; Vetus Testamentum; Zeitschr. für A. T. Wiss.
PENTATEUCH. [Misc.] *See* Noth (M.); Suppt. Novum Testamentum. Suppts., 42;
Studies in Bibl. Theol., 2nd Ser., 27; Zeitschr. für A. T. Wiss. Beihefte, 146,147.
HISTORICAL BOOKS. [Misc.] *See* Suppt. Studies in Bibl. Theol., 2nd Ser., 26; Vetus
Testamentum. Suppts., 30.
HAGIOGRAPHA. [Misc.] *See* Rad (G. von); Ranston (H.)
GENESIS. [Misc.] *See* Kronholm (T.); Todd (W.); Suppt. Forschungen zur Relig. u.
Lit., 115, 116; Novum Testamentum. Suppts., 46; Zeitschr. für A. T. Wiss. Beihefte,
133, 143, 154.
EXODUS. [Misc.] *See* Childs (B. S.); Coates (C. A.); Suppt. Forschungen zur Relig.
u. Lit., 114; Zeitschr. für A. T. Wiss. Beihefte, 126,145.
DEUTERONOMY. [Misc.] *See* Suppt. Forschungen zur Relig. u. Lit., 108; Zeitschr.
für A. T. Wiss. Beihefte, 139.
JOSHUA. [Misc.] *See* Origen; Soggin (J. A.); Suppt. Studies in Bibl. Theol., 2nd Ser.,
21.
JUDGES. [Misc.] *See* McKenzie (J. L.); Suppt. Studies in Bibl. Theol., 2nd Ser., 29.
KINGS. [Misc.] *See* Gooding (D. W.)
CHRONICLES. [Misc.] *See* Suppt. Forschungen zur Relig. u. Lit., 106; Vetus Testa-
mentum. Suppts., 25, 27,
ISAIAH. [Misc.] *See* Bonnard (P.-E.); Henry (M.-L.); Kaiser (O.); Whedbee (J. W.);
Whybray (R. N.); Suppt. Vetus Testamentum. Suppts., 24; Zeitschr. für A. T. Wiss.
Beihefte, 119, 121, 136, 137, 141.
JEREMIAH. [Misc.] *See* Kraus (H.-J.); Nicholson (E. W.); Suppt. Corpus Script.
Christ. Orient., Syri, 146-147; Forschungen zur Relig. u. Lit., 118; Zeitschr. für
A. T. Wiss. Beihefte, 122, 132.
EZEKIEL. [Misc.] *See* Eichrodt (W.); Zimmerli (W.); Suppt. Corpus Script. Christ.
Orient., Syri, 146-147; Studies in Bibl. Theol., 2nd Ser., 31; Zeitschr. für A. T. Wiss
Beihefte, 121.
DANIEL. [Misc.] *See* Suppt. Corpus Script. Christ. Orient., Syri, 146-147.
HOSEA. [Misc.] *See* Suppt. Zeitschr. für A. T. Wiss. Beihefte, 119.
EZRA-NEHEMIAH. [Misc.] *See* Bede; Suppt. Forschungen zur Relig. u. Lit., 104.
JOB. [Misc.] *See* Gordis (R.); Gregory I, *Pope.;* Kraeling (E. G. H.); Suppt. For-
schungen zur Relig. u. Lit., 121; Zeitschr. für A. T. Wiss. Beihefte, 143.
PSALMS. [Misc.] *See* Kraus (H.-J.); Weatherhead (L. D.); Suppt. Studies in Bibl.
Theol., 2nd Ser., 32; Zeitschr. für A. T. Wiss. Beihefte, 117, 153.
PROVERBS. [Misc.] *See* Barucq (A.)
ECCLESIASTES. [Misc.] *See* Suppt. Zeitschr. für A. T. Wiss. Beihefte, 130, 148, 152.
SONG OF SOLOMON. [Misc.] *See* Gallus (T.); Origen; William, *of St.-Thierry.*
PROPHETS. [Misc.] *See* Bright (J.); Carroll (R. P.); Kraus (H.-J.); Suppt. For-
schungen zur Relig. u. Lit., 107; Vetus Testamentum. Suppts., 26; Zeitschr. für A. T.
Wiss. Beihefte, 124, 150.
JOEL. [Misc.] *See* Suppt. Vetus Testamentum. Suppts., 21.
AMOS. [Misc.] *See* Hammershaimb (E.); Suppt. Zeitschr. für A. T. Wiss. Beihefte,
119, 123, 140.
JONAH. [Misc.] *See* Cohn (G. H.); Suppt. Studies in Bibl. Theol., 2nd Ser., 18;
Zeitschr. für A. T. Wiss. Beihefte, 143.
MICAH. [Misc.] *See* Mayes (J. L.); Suppt. Zeitschr. für A. T. Wiss. Beihefte, 123.
NAHUM. [Misc.] *See* Suppt. Zeitschr. fur A. T. Wiss. Beihefte, 129.
ZECHARIAH. [Misc.] *See* Cunliffe-Jones (H.)

BIBLE—*continued*
NEW TESTAMENT. Texts and Versions.
Greek. [Misc.] *See* Metzger (B. M.); Moulton (J. H.)
English. The New Testament in modern English: a trans. by J. B. Phillips. 8vo. LOND., 1958.
GOSPELS. *English.* The Gospel. [*Contents:* Mark, Luke, Matthew, John, Thomas, Dialogue of the Saviour, Philip the Evangelist, Gospel of Truth, On the three Essences, Thunder! the perfect mind, The book of the holy one.] 4to. n.p., [1975].
—— —— [Selections.] The Gospel according to Thomas. With an introd. by Will Hayes. 8vo. LOND., [1921].
—— [Harmonies. *English.*] A synopsis of the Gospels: H. F. D. Sparks. 2 vols. 4to. LOND., 1964-74.
    2. The Gospel according to John with Synoptic parallels. 1974.
EPISTLES. *Syriac.* [Misc.] *See* Suppt. Corpus Script. Christ. Orient., Subsid., 37.
REVELATION. *Syriac. See* Suppt. Corpus Script. Christ. Orient., Subsid., 56.
Commentaries.
BLACK'S NEW TESTAMENT COMMENTARIES. General editor: Henry Chadwick. 8vo. LOND., 1957- [With Eng. text, trans. by the authors.]
    II Corinthians: C. K. Barrett. 1973.
    Johannine Epistles: J. L. Houlden. 1973.
COMMENTAIRE DU NOUVEAU TESTAMENT. Publié sous la direction de Pierre Bonnard, *etc.* 4to. PARIS, 1949- [With French text.]
    6. Romains. (1957.) Complément: F.-J. Leenhardt. 1969.
Miscellaneous.
See Bruce (F. F.) [Misc.]; Burkill (T. A.); Derrett (J. D. M.); Dodd (C. H.); Dunn (J. D. G.); Evans (C. F.) [Misc.]; Ferguson (J.); Fitzmyer (J. A.); Griffiths (D. R.); Hamerton-Kelly (R. G.); Hanson (A. T.); Hill (D.); Hunter (A. M.); Jeremias (J.); Kümmel (W. G.); Marshall (I. H.) *ed.;* Metzger (B. M.); Nineham (D. E.); Olsen (V. N.); Robinson (J. A. T.); Sanders (J. T.); Sandmel (S.); Schweizer (E.); Scott (C. A. A.); Stanton (G. N.); Trites (A. A.); Vielhauer (P.);
    Suppt. Arbeiten zur N.T. Textforschung; New Test. Abstracts; New Test. Lib.; New Test. Studies; Novum Testamentum; Society for N.T. Studies; Texte u. Untersuchungen, 103, 112; Zeitschr. für N. T. Wiss.
GOSPELS. [Misc.] *See* Banks (R.); Bowker (J.); Christ (F.); Cox (E.); Dodd (C. H.); Farmer (W. R.); Perrin (N.); Piper (J.); Reumann (J); Strong (T. B.); Trocmé (E.); Vermes (G.); Suppt. Corpus Script. Christ. Orient., Subsid., 57; Forschungen zur Relig. u. Lit., 120; Studies in Bibl. Theol., 2nd Ser., 18, 28.
MATTHEW. [Misc.] *See* Curtis (A. H.); Goulder (M. D.); Kingsbury (J. D.); Origen; Rist (J. M.); Van Tilborg (S.); Suppt. Corpus Script. Christ. Orient., Syri, 171-2; Novum Testamentum. Suppts., 52.
MARK. [Misc.] *See* Bruce (F. F.); Burkill (T. A.); Evans (C. F.); Farmer (W. R.); Kee (H. C.); Martin (R. P.); Pryke (E. J.); Rist (J. M.); Schramm (T.); Schweizer (E.); Suppt. Novum Testamentum. Suppts., 51; Zeitschr. für N. T. Wiss Beihefte, 42.
LUKE. [Misc.] *See* Barrett (C. K.); Drury (J. H.); Jervell (J.); Marshall (I. H.); Morgan (G. C.); Nuttall (G. F.); Schramm (T.); Taylor (V.); Wilson (S. G.); Suppt. Corpus Script. Christ. Orient., Syri, 171-2.
JOHN. [Misc.] *See* Barrett (C. K.); Braun (F.-M.); Bultmann (R.); Cullmann (O.); Derrett (J. D. M.); Feuillet (A.); Kysar (R.); Morris (L.); Origen; Reim (G.); Schlatter (A.); Suppt. Corpus Script. Christ. Orient., Syri, 165-6; Novum Testamentum. Suppts., 32, 42.
ACTS. [Misc.] *See* Evans (C. F.); Haenchen (E.); Jervell (J.); Wilson (S. G.); Suppt. Forschungen zur Relig. u. Lit., 103; Novum Testamentum. Suppts., 40.
EPISTLES. [Misc.] *See* Gundry (R. H.); Hanson (A. T.); Therrien (G.); Wiles (G. P.); Suppt. Corpus Script. Christ. Orient., Subsid., 49.
—— *See also* Paul, *Saint and Apostle.*
ROMANS. [Misc.] *See* Barth (K.); Evans (C. F.); Murray (J.); Schlatter (A.); Suppt. Corpus Script. Eccles. Lat., 81; Forschungen zur Relig. u. Lit., 112; Studies in Bibl. Theol., 2nd Ser., 19; Zeitschr. für N. T. Wiss. Beihefte, 43.
CORINTHIANS. [Misc.] *See* Collange (J.-F.); Minn (H. R.); Schmithals (W.)
GALATIANS. [Misc.] *See* Howard (P.)
EPHESIANS. [Misc.] *See* Sampley (J. P.); Suppt. Forschungen zur Relig. u. Lit., 111; Novum Testamentum. Suppts., 39.

BIBLE. NEW TESTAMENT. Miscellaneous—*continued*
PHILIPPIANS. [Misc.] *See* Jowett (J. H.)
COLOSSIANS. [Misc.] *See* Baynes (P.); Martin (R. P.); Suppt. Forschungen zur Relig. u. Lit., 109.
THESSALONIANS. [Misc.] *See* Reese (J. M.); Suppt. Forschungen zur Relig. u. Lit., 110; Novum Testamentum. Suppts., 40.
PASTORAL EPISTLES. [Misc.] *See* Dibelius (M.) and Conzelmann (H.); Suppt. Forschungen zur Relig. u. Lit., 122.
HEBREWS. [Misc.] *See* Héring (J.); Horton (F. L.); Hughes (G.)
PETER. [Misc.] *See* Fornberg (T.); Jowett (J. H.)
JOHN. [Misc.] The Johannine Epistles: a critical concordance. Ed. A. Q. Morton, S. Michaelson. General editors: J. A. Baird, D. N. Freedman. [The Computer Bible, 3.] fol. *Duplicated.* EDIN., 1971.
—— *See* Augustine, *Saint, of Hippo.;* Feuillet (A.)
REVELATION. [Misc.] *See* Court (J. M.); Quispel (G.); Suppt. Novum Testamentum. Suppts., 27; Studies in Bibl. Theol., 2nd Ser., 23.
APOCRYPHA.
NEW TESTAMENT. *Ethiopic. See* Suppt. Corpus Script. Christ. Orient., Aethiop., 66-69.
GOSPELS. *English. See above,* New Testament Texts and Versions, Gospels.
ECCLESIASTICUS. *Arabic and English. See* Suppt. Corpus Script. Christ. Orient., Arab., 30-31.
ELIJAH, APOCALYPSE OF. *French.* L'Apocalypse d'Élie: introd., trad. et notes: Jean-Marc Rosenstiehl. [Textes et Études pour Servir à l'Hist. du Judaisme Intertestamentaire, 1.] 8vo. PARIS, 1972.
JUBILEES. [Misc.] *See* Davenport (G. L.)
JUDITH. *Greek and English.* The book of Judith. Greek text with an Eng. trans., commentary and critical notes: Morton S. Enslin. Ed. with a general introd. and appendices by Solomon Zeitlin. [Jewish Apocryphal Lit., Dropsie Univ.] 8vo. LOND., 1972.
Bible Translator. *See* Suppt.
Biblica. *See* Suppt.
Biblical Archaeologist. *See* Suppt.
Biblical Research. *See* Suppt.
Bibliographical Society. *See* Suppt. Bibliographical Soc.; Library.
Bibliographie de la Philosophie. *See* Suppt.
Bibliography of Denbighshire. *See* Catalogues. *Denbighshire County Lib.*
Bickley (Harold) John Milton (1608-1674). [Heritage Biographies.] 8vo. LOND., 1961. [Pamph.]
Bielby (A. Ronald) Churches and chapels of Kirklees. 8vo. KIRKLEES, 1978.
Biemel (Walter) Martin Heidegger: an illus. study. Trans. J. L. Mehta. 8vo. LOND. & HENLEY, 1977.
[Bierenga (G. J.) *comp.*] Jacobus Arminius, 1560-1960: Arminius tentoonstelling Oudewater Waagebouw, 3 juni- 17 september 1960. obl.8vo. [OUDEWATER, 1960.]
Bietenholz (P. G.) Der italienische Humanismus und die Blütezeit des Buchdrucks in Basel: die Basler Drucke italienischer Autoren von 1530 bis zum Ende des 16. Jahrhunderts. [Basler Beiträge zur Geschichtswiss., 73.] 8vo. BASEL, 1959.
—— Basle and France in the sixteenth century: the Basle humanists and printers in their contacts with Francophone culture. [Travaux d'Humanisme et Renaissance, 112.] 4to. GENÈVE, 1971.
Bill (E. G. W.) *See* Catalogues. *Lambeth Palace Lib.*
Billington (R. J.) The liturgical movement and Methodism. 8vo. LOND., 1969.
Binfield (J. C. G.) George Williams and the Y.M.C.A.: a study in Victorian social attitudes. 8vo. LOND., 1973.
—— A man in his setting: the relevance of George Williams. 8vo. LOND., 1975. [Pamph.]
—— So down to prayers: studies in English Nonconformity, 1780-1920. 8vo. LOND., 1977.
Biographical Studies. *See* Suppt. Recusant History.
Birch (John) 1615-91, *Colonel. See* Heath-Agnew (E.)
Birchenough (Charles) History of elementary education in England and Wales from 1800 to the present day. (1914.) 2nd ed., 4th imp. 8vo. LOND., 1927.

Bird (A. H.)   Outreach: the story of one hundred years of Christian witness in London's East End. Old Ford Methodist Mission: centenary brochure, 1870-1970. 8vo. LOND., 1970. [Pamph.]

Birks, *family of.*   Birks family memorials.   [Memorials of fifty years' ministry, by John Birks; Memoir of the Rev. William Birks, Junr.; The story of my life, by Richard Elliott Birks.] 3pts. in 1 vol. 8vo. DERBY, 1923.

Birmingham. *Edward Road Baptist Church.* Centenary souvenir, 1872-1972. 8vo. [BIRMINGHAM, 1972.] [Pamph.]

—— *Moseley Presbyterian Church.* Jubilee, 1896-1946. 8vo. BIRMINGHAM, [1946]. [Pamph.]

Birnbaum (S. A.)   The Hebrew scripts.   2 vols. fol.   LEIDEN   [& LOND.],   1954-71.
  1.   The text.   1971.
  2.   The plates.   1954-57.

Birney (Leroy)   *See* Suppt. Christian Brethren Research Fellowship, Occ. Papers, 4.

Birrell (T. A.)   English Catholic mystics in non-Catholic circles: the taste for Middle English mystical literature and its derivatives from the seventeenth to the twentieth centuries. 3pts. in 1. 8vo. [DOWNSIDE,] 1976. [Pamph.]

—— The library of John Morris: the reconstruction of a seventeenth-century collection. 8vo. LOND., 1976.

Birt (Henry Norbert)   Obit book of the English Benedictines, 1600-1912. (1913.) facsim. repr. With a new introd. by Dom Maurus Lunn. 8vo. FARNBOROUGH, 1970.

Bischoff (Erich)   Babylonisch-Astrales im Weltbilde des Thalmud und Midrasch. 8vo. LEIPZIG, 1907.

Biss (P. H.)   A brief history of the six member churches of the Sussex Unitarian Union, being the Presidential address...to the General Baptist Assembly, 1968, Essex Hall... London. 8vo. *Duplicated.* [LOND., 1968.]

Black (John B.)   The art of history: a study of four great historians of the eighteenth century [Voltaire Hume, Robertson, and Gibbon] 8vo. LOND., 1926.

Black (K. M.)   The Scots churches in England. 8vo. EDIN. & LOND., 1906.

Black (Matthew) *ed.*   *See* Bible. Commentaries. New Century Bible.

Blackburn. *Furthergate United Reformed Church.* Centenary, 1874-1974. 8vo. n.p., [1974]. [Pamph.]

Blackwood (B. G.)   *See* Suppt. Chetham Soc., 3rd Ser., 25.

Blair (*Sir* D. O. Hunter)   In Victorian days, and other papers. 8vo. LOND., 1939.

Blake (William)   Complete writings, with variant readings. Ed. Geoffrey Keynes. 8vo. LOND., 1969.

—— *See* Ault (D. D.); Clark (*Sir* Kenneth); Murry (J. M.); Nurmi (M. K.); Raine (K.); Syamken (G.)

Blanshard (Brand)   Reason and belief. Based on Gifford Lects. at St. Andrews and Nobel Lects. at Harvard. 8vo. LOND., 1974.

Blass (Friedrich)   Grammatik des neutestamentliche Griechisch. (1896.) Bearb. Albert Debrunner. 11.Aufl. 8vo. GÖTTINGEN, 1961.

Blazeby (William)   The story retold of Michael Servetus, in commemoration of the 350th year of his martyrdom on the 27th October, 1553. 8vo. LOND., [1903]. [Pamph.]

Bleackley (J. R.)   Short history of Monton Chapel, Monton Church, 1697-1969. 8vo. [MONTON, 1969.] [Pamph.]

Blenkinsopp (Joseph)   Gibeon and Israel: the role of Gibeon and the Gibeonites in the political and religious history of early Israel. [Soc. for O.T. Study, Monograph Ser., 2.] 8vo. CAMB., 1972.

Bligh (Edward Vesey)   *See* Purey-Cust (A. P.) *comp.*

Bloch (Marc)   The historian's craft. Trans. from the French by Peter Putnam, with an introd. by Joseph R. Strayer. (1954.) repr. 8vo. MANCHESTER, 1967.

Blöndal (S. B. B.)   The Varangians of Byzantium: an aspect of Byzantine military history. Trans., rev. and rewritten by Benedikt S. Benedikz. 8vo. CAMB., 1978.

Bloom (Anthony)   *Metropolitan of Sourozh.*   God and man.   [Ch. 1 with Marghanita Laski.] 8vo. LOND., 1971.

Bloom (Edward A.) and **Bloom** (Lillian D.)   Joseph Addison's sociable animal: in the market place, on the hustings, in the pulpit. 8vo. PROVIDENCE (R.I.), 1971.

Bloomfield (Edward H.)   The opposition to the English Separatists, 1570-1625: a survey of the polemical literature written by the opponents to Separatism. [Ph.D. dissertation, Claremont Graduate School.] 4to. *Duplicated.* [ANN ARBOR, 1974.]

Blount (Charles)   *See* Bonanate (U.)
Blundell (F. O.)   Old Catholic Lancashire, 1550-1850.   vol. 3.   8vo.   LOND., 1941.
Blundell (Nicholas) 1669-1737.   *See* Suppt. Record Soc. of Lancs. and Chesh., 114.
Blunham.   *Old Meeting Baptist Church.*   Church book, 1724-1891.   [Photocopy of transcript.]   fol.   BEDFORD, 1976.
Blunt (A. W. F.) *Bp. of Bradford.*   *See* Peart-Binns (J. S.)
Bodenstein (Andreas) *von Karlstadt.*   *See* Karlstadt (A. Bodenstein von)
Bodleian Library.   *See* Catalogues; Suppt. Bodleian Library Record.
Boehme (Jakob)   [Selections.]   Glaube und Tat: eine Auswahl aus dem Gesamtwerk. Mit Einleitung und Nachwort, hrsg. Eberhard Hermann Pältz. (1957.)   2te. Aufl. 8vo.   BERLIN, 1976.
Boethius.   [De consolatione. *Latin.*]   Philosophiae consolatio.   Ed. Ludovicus Bieler. [Corpus Christianorum, Ser. Latina, 94.]   8vo.   TURNHOUT, 1957.
—— *See* Suppt. Corpus Philos. Medii Aevi. Aristoteles Latinus, Opera, VI.
Boggess (Elwood C.)   *See* Church of South India.
Boisset (Jean) *ed.*   Réforme et humanisme. Actes du IVe Colloque, Centre d'Histoire de la Réforme et du Protestantisme, Université Paul Valéry, Montpellier, Oct. 1975. 8vo.   MONTPELLIER, 1977.
[**Bolam** (C. G.)]   The story of High Pavement Chapel, Nottingham.   8vo.   RAMS-GATE, [196-].   [Pamph.]
Bolingbroke (Henry St. John, *Viscount*)   *See* St. John (Henry) *Viscount Bolingbroke.*
Boll (Franz) *and others.*   Sternglaube und Sterndeutung: die Geschichte und das Wesen Astrologie: Franz Boll, Carl Bezold, Wilhelm Gundel. (1917.)   6te. Aufl. Mit einem bibliog. Anhang von Hans Georg Gundel.   8vo.   DARMSTADT, 1974.
Bollandist Fathers   [i.e. Société des Bollandistes].   *See* Suppt. Analecta Bollandiana.
Bolt (Christine) and **Drescher** (Seymour) *ed.*   Anti-slavery, religion and reform. Essays in memory of Roger Anstey.   8vo.   FOLKESTONE & HAMDEN (Conn.), 1980.
Bolton (J. D. P.)   Glory, jest and riddle.   8vo.   LOND., 1973.
[**Bolton** (R. C.)]   175 years of history: Ilford High Road Baptist Church, 1801-1976. 8vo.   [BASILDON, printed, 1976.]   [Pamph.]
Bomford (Frances E.)   A history of the Worcestershire Baptist Association, 1836-1936. 8vo.   WORCESTER & LOND.,[1936].   [Pamph.]
Bonanate (Ugo)   Charles Blount: libertinismo e deismo nel Seicento inglese.   [Pubbl. del "Centro di Studi del Pensiero Filosofico del Cinquecento e del Seicento in Relazione al Problemi della Scienza" del Consiglio Nazionale delle Richerche, Serie 1, Studi 3.]   8vo.   FIRENZE, 1972.
Bonaventura, *Saint.* [Two or more works. *English.*]   The soul's journey into God.— The life of St. Francis.   Trans. and introd. by Ernest Cousins.   Preface by Ignatius Brady.   [Classics of Western Spirituality.]   8vo.   LOND., 1978.
[**Bond** (C. D.) *and others.*]   Adnitt Road Baptist Church, Northampton, 1889-1974. 8vo.   [NORTHAMPTON, 1974.]   [Pamph.]
Bondfield (Margaret G.)   A life's work.   [Autobiography.]   8vo.   LOND.,   [1948].
Bone (G. D.)   *See* Greenslade (S. L.)
Bonhoeffer (Dietrich)   [Nachfolge. (1937.) *English.*]   The cost of discipleship. Trans. R. H. Fuller. Foreword by the Bishop of Chichester [G. K. A. Bell] and memoir of the author by G. Leibholz.   8vo.   LOND., 1948.
—— *See* Dumas (A.); Smith (R. G.) *ed.*
Boniface, *Saint, Abp. of Mainz.*   *See* Reuter (T.) *ed.*
Bonnard (P.-E.)   Le seconde Isaïe: son disciple et leurs éditeurs: Isaïe 40-66.   [Études Bibliques.]   8vo.   PARIS, 1972.
Bonner (Gerald) *ed.*   Famulus Christi: essays in commemoration of the thirteenth centenary of the birth of the Venerable Bede.   8vo.   LOND., 1976.
Bonsall (H. E.) and **Robertson** (E. H.)   The dream of an ideal city: Westbourne Park [Baptist Church], 1877-1977.   8vo.   LOND., 1978.
Booth (Catherine Bramwell)   Bramwell Booth. (1933.)   3rd imp.   8vo.   LOND., 1933.
Booth (William) 1829-1912, *'General'.*   *See* Collier (R.)
Booth (William Bramwell) 1856-1929.   These fifty years.   Foreword by Mrs. Bramwell Booth.   8vo.   LOND., 1929.
—— *See* Booth (Catherine Bramwell); Salvation Army.
Bošnjak (Branko) *ed.*   *See* Supek (R.) and Bošnjak (B.) *ed.*
Borg (Marcus)   Conflict and social change   8vo.   MINNEAPOLIS, 1971.

Borham (D. H.) *comp.* The Nicoll Road story: Willeden Presbyterian Church, 1874—St. Margaret's United Reformed Church, 1974. 8vo. [LOND., 1974.] [Pamph.]

Bornhaeuser (Karl) The death and resurrection of Jesus Christ. Trans. A. Rumpus. 8vo. BANGALORE, 1958.

Bornkamm (Günther) Paul. Trans. D. M. G. Stalker. 8vo. LOND., 1971.

Borth. *Libanus.* 1866-1966. Centenary meetings of Libanus, Borth. . .Sep. 1966. 8vo. [BORTH, 1966.] [Pamph.]

Borth (Wilhelm) Die Luthersache (Causa Lutheri), 1517-1524: die Anfänge der Reformation als Frage von Politik und Recht. [Historische Studien, 414.] 8vo. LÜBECK & HAMBURG, 1970.

Bossy (John) The English Catholic community, 1570-1850 (1975.) repr. 8vo. LOND., 1976.

[**Boston,** *Mass. Holy Transfiguration Monastery.*] A history of the Russian Church abroad and the events leading to the American Metropolia's autocephaly. 4to. *Duplicated.* SEATTLE, 1972.

Bottoms (W. W.) "Fifty years of faith and works": Belle Vue Baptist Church. . . Southend-on-Sea, Jubilee, 1902-1952. 8vo. [SOUTHEND-ON-SEA, 1952.] [Pamph.]

Bottyán (János) Rombadöntött és felépített templomaink, 1944-1950. fol. BUDA- PEST, 1950.

—— Hitünk hösei. 8vo. BUDAPEST, 1971.

[**Bounds** (Kenneth)] 175 years of Methodist witness in Stamford Street, Ashton- Under-Lyne, 1799-1974. 8vo. ASHTON-UNDER-LYNE, [1974]. [Pamph.]

Bourne (F. W.) Billy Bray: the King's son. Comp. largely from his own memoranda. (1871.) repr. 8vo. LOND., 1937.

Bournemouth. *Rosebery Park Baptist Church.* Year book, 1952, recording the history of the church since its foundation in 1891. 8vo. [BOURNEMOUTH, 1952.] [Pamph.]

Bousset (Wilhelm) *See* Suppt. Novum Testamentum Suppts., 50.

Bousset (Wilhelm) and **Gunkel** (Hermann) *ed. See* Suppt. Forschungen zur Religion und Lit.

[**Bouvy** (D.) *ed.*] Vromen & verlichten: twee eeuwen protestantse geloofsbeleving, 1650-1850. 8vo. UTRECHT, 1974.

Bowder (Diana R.) The age of Constantine and Julian. 8vo. LOND., 1978.

Bowersock (G. W.) Julian the Apostate. [Classical Life and Letters.] 8vo. LOND., 1978.

Bowes (Pratima) The Hindu religious tradition: a philosophical approach. 8vo. LOND., 1977 [1978].

[**Bowie** (W. C.) *ed.*] Unto this generation: ten essays, with prayers and hymns. 8vo. LOND., 1914.

Bowker (J. W.) Jesus and the Pharisees. 8vo. CAMB., 1973.

—— The sense of God: sociological, anthropological and psychological approaches to the origin of the sense of God. [Wilde Lects., 1972.] 8vo. OXF., 1973.

—— The religious imagination and the sense of God. 8vo. OXF., 1978.

Bowker (Mollie) 'Therefore—forward!' The story of Carey Church, Calcutta. 8vo. CALCUTTA, n.d. [Pamph.]

Bowle (John) Viscount Samuel: a biography. 8vo. LOND., 1957.

Bowmer (J. C.) Pastor and people: a study of Church and ministry in Wesleyan Methodism from the death of John Wesley (1791) to the death of Jabez Bunting (1858). [Fernley-Hartley Lect., 1975.] 8vo. LOND., 1975.

Bowra (*Sir* Cecil Maurice) Inspiration and poetry. [Rede Lect., 1951.] 8vo. CAMB., 1951.

Boylan (Henry) *See* Dictionaries. Biography.

Boyle (Robert) [Selections.] Selected philosophical papers of Robert Boyle. Ed. with an introd. by M. A. Stewart. [Philosophical Classics.] 8vo. MANCHESTER & NEW YORK, 1979.

Brabazon (James) Albert Schweitzer: a biography. 8vo. LOND., 1976.

Bracken (Harry M.) Berkeley. [Philosophers in Perspective.] 8vo. LOND., 1974.

[**Bradbury** (W. J.) and **Hitchin** (H. S.) *ed.*] Mansfield Road Baptist Church, Notting- ham: centenary brochure, 1849-1949 8vo. [NOTTINGHAM, 1949.] [Pamph.]

Bradford (Gary) Dissent in Eden: the history of the Nonconformists in Edenbridge. 8vo. EDENBRIDGE, 1972. [Pamph.]

Bradford (William) Of Plymouth Plantation, 1620-1647. A new ed. The complete text with notes and introd. by Samuel Eliot Morison. 8vo. NEW YORK, 1952.

[Bradley (F. E.)]** Cemetery Road Baptist Church, Sheffield: souvenir of the 100th anniversary, Nov. 1939. 8vo. [SHEFFIELD, 1939.] [Pamph.]

Bradley (R. A.) Albermarle Baptist Church, Taunton: the first 100 years. 8vo. [TAUNTON, 1974.] [Pamph.]

Bradley (W. L.) P. T. Forsyth: the man and his work. 8vo. LOND., 1952.

Bradshaw (Brendan) The dissolution of the religious orders in Ireland under Henry VIII. 8vo. LOND., 1974.

Bradshaw (P. F.) *See* Suppt. Alcuin Club. Collections, 53; Misc. Publs., 1978.

Bradshaw (William) 1571-1618. English Puritanism and other works. facsim. reprs. With a new introd. by R. C. Simmons. 6pts. in 1 vol. 8vo. FARNBOROUGH, 1972.

—— Puritanism and Separatism. A collection of works. facsim. reprs. With a new introd. by R. C. Simmons. 4pts. in 1 vol. 8vo. FARNBOROUGH, 1972.

Brady (W. M.) The episcopal succession in England, Scotland and Ireland, A.D. 1400 to 1875. (1876-77.) facsim. repr. With a new introd. by A. F. Allison. 3 vols. 8vo. [FARNBOROUGH,] 1971.

Brake (G. T.) Inside the Free Churches. 8vo. LOND., 1964.

—— Drink: ups and downs of Methodist attitudes to temperance. 8vo. LOND., 1974.

Braley (Evelyn F.) A policy in religious education. 8vo. LOND., 1941.

—— The school without the parson: religious instruction in the council schools. 8vo. WALINGTON, 1945.

Brauer (Jerald C.) *ed.* Reinterpretation in American church history. [Essays in Divinity, 5.] 8vo. CHICAGO & LOND., 1968.

Brauer (Karl) Die Unionstätigkeit John Duries unter dem Protektorat Cromwells: ein Beitrag zur Kirchengeschichte des siebzehnten Jarhhunderts. 8vo. MARBURG, 1907.

Braun (F.-M.) Jean le théologien. [Études Bibliques.] 8vo. PARIS, 1959- 3.ii. Sa théologie—le Christ, notre seigneur hier, aujourd'hui, toujours. 1972.

Braun (Rainer) *See* Suppt. Zeitschr. für A. T. Wiss. Beihefte, 130.

Brawner (D. H.) *See* Stearns (R. P.) and Brawner (D. H.)

Bray (Billy) *See* Bourne (F. W.)

Braybrooke (M. C. R.) Faiths in fellowship: a short history of the World Congress of Faiths and its work. 8vo. LOND., 1976. [Pamph.]

Bready (J. Wesley) Doctor Barnardo: physician, pioneer, prophet. Child life, yesterday and to-day. 8vo. LOND., 1930.

Breitsohl-Klepser (Ruth) Heiliger ist mir die Wahrheit: Johannes Kepler. Aus dem Nachlass hrsg. von Martha List. 8vo. STUTTGART, 1976.

Brenan (John) [Misc.] A bishop of the penal times, being letters and reports of John Brenan, Bishop of Waterford (1671-93) and Archbishop of Cashel (1677-93). Ed. with introd. and notes by P. Canon Power. 8vo. CORK, 1932.

Brendan, *Saint, Abbot of Clonfert. See* Little (G. A.)

Brendon (Piers) Hawker of Morwenstow: portrait of a Victorian eccentric. 8vo. LOND., 1975.

Brennan (T.) *and others.* Social change in South-West Wales: T. Brennan, E. W. Cooney, H. Pollins. 8vo. LOND., 1954.

Brereton (William) c.1490-1536. *See* Suppt. Record Soc. of Lancs. and Chesh., 116.

Brett (Martin) The English Church under Henry I. [Oxford Historical Monographs.] 8vo. LOND., 1975.

Brewer (Joseph) An outline history of the General Baptists of Loughborough, 1760 to 1975. 8vo. *Duplicated.* LOUGHBOROUGH, 1979.

Brewster (P. S.) *ed.* Pentecostal doctrine. 8vo. n.p.[the editor], 1976.

Breymayer (Reinhard) Die Beredsamkeit einer Taubstummen: zur Bedeutung des Ethos-Bereichs für die Rhetorik der pietistischen Leichenrede. 8vo. MARBURG, 1979. [Pamph.]

Bridge (Abel) and **Lee** (George) *ed.* A centenary history of Queen Street Congregational Church and Sunday School, Oldham, 1816-1920. 8vo. BOLTON, 1921.

Bridget, *Saint, of Sweden. See* Williamson (B.)

Brierley (Jonathan) *See* Jeffs (H.)

[Briggs (D. H. C.)]** A merchant, a banker, and the coal trade, 1693-1971. 8vo. [LEEDS, 1971.] [Pamph.]

Briggs (E. R.) Pierre Cuppé's debts to England and Holland. 8vo. GENÈVE, [1958]. [Pamph.]
—— Mysticism and rationalism in the debate upon eternal punishment. 8vo. GEN-ÈVE, [1963]. [Pamph.]
—— Le débat sur les peines éternelles parmi les Huguenots au XVIIe siècle. 8vo. PARIS, 1969. [Pamph.]
—— Les libertins à Bâle au milieu du XVIe siècle: Celio Secondo Curione, 1503-1569. 8vo. n.p., [1974]. [Pamph.]
—— Un pionnier de la pensée libre au XVe siècle: Galeotto Marzio de Narni (1427?-1497?) 8vo. PARIS, 1974. [Pamph.]
Briggs (G. H.) A history of the Lancaster Baptist Church. 8vo. [LANCASTER, 1962.] [Pamph.]
Briggs (J. H. Y.) A hundred years and more: Baptists in Newcastle-under-Lyme. 8vo. [NEWCASTLE-UNDER-LYME, 1972.] [Pamph.]
—— The burning of the Meeting House, July 1715: Dissent and faction in late Stuart Newcastle. 8vo. [KEELE, 1974.] [Pamph.]
Briggs (J. H. Y.) and **Sellers** (Ian) ed. Victorian Nonconformity. [Documents of Modern History.] 8vo. LOND., 1973.
Bright (John) 1811-89. See Robbins (K.)
Bright (John) b.1908. A history of Israel. [Old Test. Lib.] (1960.) 2nd ed. 8vo. LOND., 1972.
—— Covenant and promise. 8vo. LOND., 1977.
—— See Bible. Commentaries. Anchor Bible, 21.
Bright (William) 1824-1901. Selected letters. Ed. B. J. Kidd, with an introd. memoir by P. G. Medd. 8vo. LOND., 1903.
Brinkmann (Günter) Die Irenik des David Pareus: Freiden und Einheit in ihrer Relevanz zur Wahrheitsfrage. [Studia Irenica. 14.] 8vo. HILDESHEIM, 1972.
Brinton (Anna) ed. See Cadbury (H. J.) [Misc.]
Bristol. Baptist College. See Barkley (J. M.) and others; Moon (N. S.)
Bristol. Broadmead Church. The records of a church of Christ in Bristol, 1640-1687. Ed. Roger Hayden. [Bristol Record Soc. Publs., 27.] 8vo. [BRISTOL,] 1974.
Bristol. Society of Friends. Men's Meeting. Minute Book, 1667-1686. Ed. Russell Mortimer. [Bristol Record Soc. Publs., 26] 8vo. BRISTOL, 1971.
Bristol. Southmead Baptist Church. Silver jubilee, 1933-1958. 8vo. [BRISTOL, 1958.] [Pamph.]
Bristow (James) comp. Stamford Hill Congregational Church: centenary, 1871-1971. 8vo. LOND., 1971. [Pamph.]
British Academy. See Suppt.
British and Foreign Unitarian Association. One hundred years, 1825-1925: centenary of the British and Foreign Unitarian Association. 8vo. LOND., 1925. [Pamph.]
—— See Suppt. Unitarian Hist. Soc. Trans. Suppt.
British Institute of Philosophy. See Suppt. Philosophy.
British Journal for the Philosophy of Science. See Suppt.
British Journal of Aesthetics. See Suppt.
British Museum. Treasures of Tutankhamun. [Catalogue of an exhibition at the B. M., 1972.] 4to. LOND., 1972
—— See also Catalogues.
British School of Archaeology in Jerusalem. See Suppt. Palestine Exploration Quarterly.
Briton Ferry, Glam. Jerusalem English Baptist Church. 1859-1959: the story of a hundred years. Centenary celebrations, Oct. 1959. 8vo. [BRITON FERRY, 1959.] [Pamph.]
Brittain (Frederick) Arthur Quiller-Couch: a biographical study of Q. 8vo. CAMB., 1947.
Brittain (Vera) In the steps of John Bunyan: an excursion into Puritan England. 8vo. LOND., etc., [1950].
Broad (C. D.) Broad's critical essays in moral philosophy. Ed. David R.Cheney. [Muirhead Lib. of Philos.] 8vo. LOND. & NEW YORK, 1971.
—— Leibniz: an introduction. Ed. C. Lewy. 8vo. CAMB., 1975.

Broadbent (Arnold) The first hundred years of the Sunday School Association,. 1833-1933. With a footnote on the next hundred years by Bertram Lister. 8vo. LOND., [1933]. [Pamph.]

Brock (Peter) Pacifism in the United States from the colonial era to the First World War. 8vo. PRINCETON, 1968.
—— Pacifism in Europe to 1914. 8vo. PRINCETON, 1972.

Brockbank (Elizabeth) Edward Burrough: a wrestler for the truth, 1634-1662. 8vo. LOND., 1949.

Brocklesby (Joan) Finsbury Park Methodist Church centenary, 1875-1975. 8vo. [LOND., 1975.] [Pamph.]

Brockett (A. A.) The political and social influence of Exeter Dissenters and some notable families. 8vo. n.p., 1961. [Pamph.]
—— Witnesses: a history of the six members of the Exeter Council of Congregational Churches and their forerunners: Southernhay, Heavitree, Ide, Pinhoe, St. Thomas, Topsham. 8vo. [DAWLISH, priv. printed,] 1962. [Pamph.]
—— Index to papers on Nonconformist history published in the Trans. of the Devonshire Assn. for the Advancement of Science, Lit. and Art, vols. 1-95. 8vo. n.p., 1964. [Pamph.] [Photocopy.]

Brockington (L. H.) See Bible. Old Testament. Hebrew. [Misc.]

Brockway (A. F.) Bermondsey story: the life of Alfred Salter. (1949.) 2nd imp. 8vo. LOND., 1951.

Bromiley (G. W.) ed. See Dictionaries. Languages. Greek.

Bromsgrove. Baptist Church. Church record book, vol. 1, 1670-1715. [Transcript, issued by Bromsgrove Baptist Church and the Baptist Historical Soc.] fol. Duplicated. [BROMSGROVE,] 1974. [Pamph.]

Bronner (E. B.) See Suppt. Friends' Hist. Soc. Journal Suppt. 34.

Brontë (Patrick) See Lock (J.) and Dixon (W. T.)

Brook (Michael) Confederate sympathies in North East Lancashire, 1862-1864. 8vo. MANCHESTER, 1969. [Pamph.]

Brooks (Peter N.) ed. See Dickens (A. G.) [Misc.]; Rupp (E. G.) [Misc.]

Brooks (Phillips) Bp. of Massachusetts. See Allen (A. V. G.)

Broomfield (G. W.) Colour conflict: race relations in Africa. 8vo. LOND., 1943.

Brose (Olive J.) Frederick Denison Maurice: rebellious conformist. 8vo. ATHENS- (Ohio), 1971.

[Broster-Temple (F.)] The story of St. Mary's. Being the history of St. Mary's Congregational Church at Devizes, 1772-1972. 8vo. [TROWBRIDGE, printed, 1972.] [Pamph.]

Brown (Cecil L.) and **Parry** (L. L.) A short history of Beaconsfield and Hotspur United Reformed Church, 1704-1974. 8vo. [BEACONSFIELD, 1974.] [Pamph.]

Brown (Charles) 1855-1947, Baptist Minister. See Cook (H.)

Brown (Charles Armitage) Life of John Keats. Ed. with an introd. and notes by Dorothy Hyde Bodurtha and Willard Bissell Pope. (1937.) 2nd. imp. 8vo. LOND., etc., 1937.
—— Some letters and miscellanea of Charles Brown, the friend of John Keats and Thomas Richards. Ed. Maurice Buxton Forman. 8vo. LOND., 1937.

Brown (Charles K. F.) The Church's part in education, 1833-1941, with special reference to the work of the National Society. 8vo. LOND., 1942.

Brown (Delwin) and others, ed. Process philosophy and Christian thought. Ed. Delwin Brown, Ralph E. James, Gene Reeves. 8vo INDIANAPOLIS & NEW YORK,. 1971.

Brown (Harold F.) The story of Methodism in Hessle, 1820-1977. 8vo. Duplicated. [HESSLE, 1977.] [Pamph.]

Brown (James Henderson) Eternity: is it a biblical idea? A suggestion on the 'larger hope' question. 8vo. LOND., [1926].

Brown (Leslie W.) Relevant liturgy. [Zabriskie Lects., 1964.] 8vo. LOND.,. 1965.

Brown (Peter) Religion and society in the age of St. Augustine. 8vo. LOND., 1972.

Brown (Raymond E.) See Bible. Commentaries. Anchor Bible, 29, 29A.

Brown (Richard Maxwell) ed. See Olson (A. G.) and Brown (R. M.) ed.

Brown (Stuart C.) Do religious claims make sense? [Lib. of Philos. and Theol.] 8vo. LOND., 1969.
—— ed. See Suppt. Royal Inst. of Philos. Lects., 12.

Brown (Wallace) An Englishman views the American Revolution: the letters of Henry Hulton, 1769-1776. 8vo. SAN MARINO (Calif.), 1972. [Pamph.]
Brown (William E.) Robert Heywood of Bolton. 8vo. WAKEFIELD, 1970.
—— The history of Bolton School. With an extended essay by F. R. Poskitt. 8vo. BOLTON, 1976.
Brown (William L.) The story of the Dorset Congregational Association. 8vo. BRIDPORT, 1971.
Browne (Peter) *Bp. of Cork. See* Winnett (A. R.)
Browne (Robert) *See* Reason (J.)
Browne (*Sir* Thomas) *See* Finch (J. S.)
Browning (Robert) Justinian and Theodora. 4to. LOND., 1971.
—— Byzantium and Bulgaria: a comparative study across the early medieval frontier. 8vo. LOND., 1975.
—— The Emperor Julian. 8vo. LOND., 1976.
—— Studies on Byzantine history, literature and education. [Variorum Reprs.] 8vo. LOND., 1977.
Bruce (F. F.) The English Bible: a history of translations. (1961.) repr. 8vo. LOND., 1963.
—— The 'secret' Gospel of Mark. [Ethel M. Wood Lect., 1974.] 8vo. LOND., 1974. [Pamph.]
—— [Misc.] Apostolic history and the Gospel. Biblical and historical essays presented to F. F. Bruce on his 60th birthday. Ed. W. Ward Gasque and Ralph P. Martin. 8vo. [EXETER,] 1970.
—— *See* Bible. Commentaries. New Century Bible.
Bruce (J. C.) Old Newcastle. Lectures. Preface by Thomas Hodgkin. 8vo. NEW-CASTLE-UPON-TYNE, 1904.
Bruges (William) *See* Suppt. Harleian Soc. Publs., 111-112.
Bruin (C. C. de) Woorden voor het onzegbare. College op. 12 Dec. 1975 gegeven . . . aan de Rijksuniversiteit te Leiden. 8vo. LEIDEN, 1976. [Pamph.]
Brumback (Carl) "What meaneth this?" A Pentecostal answer to a Pentecostal question. 8vo. LOND., [1946].
Brunner (Heinrich Emil) The Church and the Oxford Group. Trans. David Cairns. 8vo. LOND., 1937.
—— I believe in the living God: sermons on the Apostles' Creed. Trans. and ed. John Holden. 8vo. LOND., 1961.
Bryer (A. A. M.) The Empire of Trebizond and the Pontos. [Variorum Reprs.] 8vo. LOND., 1980.
Buber (Martin) Briefwechsel aus sieben Jahrzehnten. Hrsg. und eingeleitet von Grete Schaeder. 3 vols. 8vo. HEIDELBERG, 1972-75.
   1. 1897-1918. 1972.
   2. 1918-1938. 1973.
   3. 1938-1965. 1975.
Bucer (Martin) [Works.] Opera omnia. Series I. Martin Bucers deutsche Schriften. 8vo. GÜTERSLOH & PARIS, 1960-
   4. Zur auswärtigen Wirksamkeit, 1528-1533. 1975.
   5. Strassburg und Münster im Kampf um den rechten Glauben, 1532-1534. 1978.
—— [Selections.] Common places of Martin Bucer. Trans. and ed. D. F. Wright. [Courtenay Lib. of Reformation Classics, 4.] 8vo. APPLEFORD, 1972.
—— *See* Bender (G.); Collinson (P.); Rott (J.); Stephens (W. P.); Suppt. Alcuin Club. Collections, 58.
Buchanan (C. O.) *ed.* Further Anglican liturgies, 1968-1975. 8vo. NOTTINGHAM, 1975.
Buchdahl (Gerd) Metaphysics and the philosophy of science: the classical origins, Descartes to Kant. 8vo. OXF., 1969.
Bucking (Jürgen) and **Rublack** (Hans-Christoph) Der Bauernkrieg in der vorder- und oberösterreichischen Ländern und in der Stadt Würzburg: Ansätz zu einer Theorie Bauernkrieges. 8vo. GÜTERSLOH, 1975. [Pamph.]
[Buckley (George)] Salem Baptist Church, Longford, Coventry: third jubilee volume, 1759-1909. 8vo. LOND., [1909].
Bucsay (Mihály) *and others.* A Második Helvét Hitvallás Magyarországon és Méliusz életműve. Studia de historia confessionis Helveticae posterioris in Hungaria et de

Bucsay (Mihály) *and others.—continued*
vita operibusque Petri Melii collecta. [Tanulmányok és Okmányok a Magyarországi Református Egyház Történetéböl a Négyszázéves Jubileum Alkalmából, 2.] [Studia et Acta Ecclesiastica, 2.] 8vo. BUDAPEST, 1967.

Budd (K. G.) The story of Donald Hankey, a student in arms. 8vo. LOND., 1931.

Budd (Susan) Varieties of unbelief: atheists and agnostics in English society, 1850-1960. 8vo. LOND., 1977.

Buddha. The gospel of Buddha. Comp. from ancient records by Paul Carus. (1894.) repr. 8vo. LA SALLE (Ill.), 1943.

Buffard (F. J.) James Castleden (1778-1854), Bethel Baptist Church, Hampstead. 8vo. [LOND.,] 1975. [Pamph.]

Buijtenen (Mari P. van) *and others, ed.* Unitas fratrum: Moravian studies. Ed. Mari P. van Buijtenen, Cornelius Dekker and Huib Leeuwenberg. 8vo. UTRECHT, 1975.

Bull (P. B.) Science and faith on life, death and immortality. 8vo. LOND., [1931].

Bulletin of . . . *See* Suppt.

Bullinger (Heinrich) Epistola ad ecclesias hungaricas earumque pastores scripta. (1551.) [Textum Latinum curavit, Hungarice reddidit, praefatione et annotationibus instruxit Barnabas Nagy.] 8vo. BUDAPEST, 1967.

—— *See* Barkley (J. M.) *and others.*; Gäbler (U.) and Zsindely (E.) *ed.*

Bullock (F. W. B.) A history of training for the ministry of the Church of England and Wales from 1875 to 1974. 8vo. LOND., 1976.

Bulmer (J. R.) Monumental inscriptions of the Unitarian Burial Ground, Lady Lane, Croft, near Warrington. fol. *Duplicated.* n.p., 1971. [Pamph.]

—— Risley Presbyterian Chapel, Cross Lane, Risley, near Warrington. obl. fol. *Duplicated.* n.p., 1972. [Pamph.]

Bultmann (Rudolf) The Gospel of John: a commentary. Trans. G. R. Beasley-Murray, R. W. N. Hoare and J. K. Riches. 8vo. OXF., 1971.

—— *See* Barth (K.)

Bunting (Jabez) [Letters. 1820-29.] *See* Suppt. Royal Hist. Soc. Camden 4th Ser., 11.

—— [Letters. 1830-58.] Early Victorian Methodism: the correspondence of Jabez Bunting, 1830-1858. Ed. W. R. Ward. [Univ. of Durham Publs.] 8vo. OXF., 1976.

—— *See* Sellers (I.)

Bunyan (John) Miscellaneous works. General editor: Roger Sharrock. [Oxford English Texts.] 8vo. OXF.
    1. Some Gospel-truths opened; A vindication of Some Gospel-truths opened; A few sighs from Hell. Ed. T. L. Underwood with the assistance of Roger Sharrock. 1980.
    No more yet in Library, 1980.

—— The Pilgrim's progress from this world to that which is to come. (1678.) facsim. repr. [Noel Douglas Replica.] 8vo. LOND., 1928.

—— [Misc.] The John Bunyan Lectures, 1978, to mark the 350th anniversary of the birth of John Bunyan and the tercentenary of the publication of The Pilgrim's Progress. [By Roger Sharrock, Christopher Hill, Patricia Bell, and E. A. James.] 8vo. [BEDFORD, 1978.] [Pamph.]

—— *See* Brittain (V.); Dix (K.); Greaves (R. L.); Griffith (G. O.); Knott (J. R.); Newey (V.) *ed.*; Sharrock (R. I.); Towers (L. T.)

Burchard (Christoph) *See* Suppt. Forschungen zur Religion u. Lit., 103.

Burchfield (R. W.) *ed.* *See* Dictionaries. Languages. *English.*

Burder (George) *See* Sell (A. P. F.)

Burgess (W. H.) Sir Ferdinando Gorges and Plymouth Fort in Elizabethan times. 8vo. [PLYMOUTH, 1916.] [Pamph.]

Buri (Fritz) Dogmatik als Selbstverständnis des christlichen Glaubens. 2 vols. 8vo. BERN & TÜBINGEN, 1956-62.
    1. Vernunft und Offenbarung. 1956.
    2. Der Mensch und die Gnade. 1962.

—— Der Pantokrator: Ontologie und Eschatologie als Grundlage der Lehre von Gott. [Theologische Forschung, 47.] 8vo. HAMBURG-BERGSTEDT, 1969.

—— Zur Theologie der Verantwortung. Hrsg. Günter Haff. 8vo. BERN & STUTTGART 1971.

Burke (Peter) *ed.* *See* Cambridge Modern Hist.
Burkill (T. A.) The condemnation of Jesus: a critique of Sherwin-White's thesis. 8vo. LEIDEN, 1970. [Pamph.]
—— The causes of laughter. 8vo. SALISBURY (Rhod.), 1971. [Pamph.]
—— The evolution of Christian thought. 8vo. ITHACA & LOND., 1971.
—— Faith, knowledge and cosmopolitanism. An inaugural lect., Univ. of Rhodesia, 6th May 1971. 8vo. SALISBURY (Rhod.), 1971. [Pamph.]
—— Two into one: the notion of carnal union in Mark 10:8, 1 Kor. 6:16, Eph. 5:31. 8vo. BERLIN & NEW YORK, 1971. [Pamph.]
—— New light on the earliest Gospel: seven Markan studies. 8vo. ITHACA & LOND., 1972.
—— St. Augustine's notion of nothingness in the light of some recent cosmological speculation. 8vo. n.p., [1974]. [Pamph.]
—— Blasphemy: St. Mark's Gospel as damnation history. 8vo. [LEIDEN, 1975.] [Pamph.]
Burne (Alfred H.) and **Young** (Peter) The Great Civil War: a military history of the first Civil War, 1642-1646. 8vo. LOND., 1959.
Burne (Kathleen E.) *ed.* *See* Hardy (H. E.) *Father Andrew.*
Burney (Lester) Cross Street Chapel Schools, Manchester, 1734-1942. 8vo. MANCHESTER, 1977. [Pamph.]
Burnley. *Sion Baptist Church.* Souvenir brochure, 1828-1962. 4to. [BURNLEY, 1962.] [Pamph.]
Burns (F. V.) From the rock to the hill: a short history of Methodism in Salcombe, 1807-1978. 8vo. ASHBURTON, [1978]. [Pamph.]
[**Burns** (J. H. L.) *and others.*] The Scottish Congregational College, 1811-1961. 8vo. [EDIN., 1961.] [Pamph.]
Burns (N. T.) Christian mortalism from Tyndale to Milton. 8vo. CAMB. (Mass.), 1972.
Burr (David) The persecution of Peter Olivi. [Trans. of the Amer. Philos. Soc., N. S., 66, 5.] fol. PHILADELPHIA, 1976.
Burrough (Edward) *See* Brockbank (E.)
[**Burton** (John) *and others.*] A brief historical account of the Union Congregational Church, Plaistow, Essex, 1807-1907. 8vo. PLAISTOW, 1907. [Pamph.]
Busch (Eberhard) Karl Barth: his life from letters and autobiographical texts. [Trans. John Bowden.] 8vo. LOND., 1976.
Bush (M. L.) The government policy of Protector Somerset. 8vo. LOND., 1975.
Bushby (D. W.) Two hundred years of Methodism in St. Neots and district, 1775-1975. fol. *Duplicated.* n.p., 1975. [Pamph.]
Bushrod (Emily) The Birmingham Unitarians, 1692-1973. 8vo. [BIRMINGHAM, 1974.] [Pamph.]
Butler (David M.) Quaker meeting houses of the Lake counties: a history and description of all the Quaker meeting houses in the former counties of Cumberland and Westmorland and in the Furness and Sedburgh districts, now the County of Cumbria. 4to. LOND., 1978.
Butler (Joseph) *Bp. of Durham.* *See* Babolin (A.)
[**Butt** (A. W. G.)] Yeovil Baptist Church: celebration of the 250th anniversary, Oct. 1938. 4to. [YEOVIL, 1938.] [Pamph.]
Butterfield (*Sir* Herbert) Writings on Christianity and history. Ed. with an introd. by C. T. McIntire. 8vo. NEW YORK, 1979.
Butterworth (G. W.) Spiritualism and religion. 8vo. LOND., [1944].
Buxbaum (Melvin H.) Benjamin Franklin and the zealous Presbyterians. 8vo. UNIVERSITY PARK (Pa.) & LOND., 1975.
Buxton (R. F.) *See* Suppt. Alcuin Club. Collections, 58.
Byrne (Muriel St. Clare) and **Thomson** (Gladys Scott) "My lord's books": the library of Francis, second Earl of Bedford, in 1584. 8vo. LOND., [1931]. [Pamph.]
Byrom (John) *See* Hoyles (J.)
Byrt (G. W.) Stream of the river: an attempt to tell the story of West End Baptist Church, Hammersmith, 1793-1943. 8vo. LOND., 1944.
—— John Clifford, a fighting Free Churchman. 8vo. LOND., 1947.
Bysshe (*Sir* Edward) *See* Suppt. Harleian Soc. Publs., 117.
Bywater (Margaret) Joseph Parker (1830-1902). [Heritage Biographies.] 8vo. LOND., 1961. [Pamph.]

Byzantina Chronica. *See* Suppt. Vizantijskij Vremennik.
Byzantinische Zeitschrift. *See* Suppt.
Byzantinoslavica. *See* Suppt.
Byzantion. *See* Suppt.

Cabot (Philip) The sense of immortality. [Ingersoll Lect., 1924.] 8vo. CAMB. (Mass.), 1924.
Caccamo (Domenico) Eretici italiani in Moravia, Polonia, Transilvania (1558-1611). Studi e documenti. [Biblioteca del Corpus Reformatorum Italicorum.] 8vo. FIRENZE & CHICAGO, 1970.
Cadbury (Geraldine S.) *See* Whitney (J.)
Cadbury (Henry J.) *See* Suppt. Friends' Hist. Soc. Journal Suppt., 32.
—— [Misc.] Then and now: Quaker essays, historical and contemporary. By friends of Henry Joel Cadbury. Ed. Anna Brinton. 8vo. PHILADELPHIA, 1960.
Cadoux (C. J.) The resurrection and second advent of Jesus. 8vo. [LOND.,] 1927. [Pamph.]
Caird (G. B.) Charles Harold Dodd, 1884-1973. [Repr. from Brit. Acad. Proc., 60, 1974.] 8vo. LOND., 1975. [Pamph.]
—— *See* Bible. Commentaries. New Clarendon.
Cairns (D. S.) *See* Papers for War Time, 12.
Calder-Marshall (Arthur) The enthusiast: an enquiry into the life, beliefs and character of the Rev. Joseph Leycester Lyne, alias Fr. Ignatius, O. S. B., Abbot of Elm Hill, Norwich, and Llanthony, Wales. 8vo. LOND., 1962.
Calvin (Jean) Sermons on the epistle to the Ephesians. [Eng. trans. by Arthur Golding (1577), rev. by Leslie Rawlinson and S. M. Houghton.] 8vo. EDIN., 1973.
—— *See* Armstrong (B. G.); Kendall (R. T.); Lupton (L. F.); Parker (T. H. L.); Partee (C.); Plath (U.); Rotondò (A.); Vinay (V.)
Cambridge. *University Press.* A brief history of the Cambridge University Press. 8vo. CAMB., 1955. [Pamph.]
Cambridge. *Westminster College. See* Knox (R. B.)
Cambridge Modern History (The New) Planned by Sir George Clark. 14 vols. 8vo. CAMB., 1957-79.
   13. Companion volume. Ed. Peter Burke. 1979.
Camden (William) *See* Trevor-Roper (H. R.)
Camden Society. *See* Suppt. Royal Historical Society.
Cameron (Alan D. E.) Bread and circuses: the Roman Emperor and his people. Inaugural lect. in Latin lang. and lit. at King's Coll., London, May 21st 1973. 8vo. [LOND., 1973.] [Pamph.]
—— Porphyrius the charioteer. 8vo. OXF., 1973.
—— The authenticity of the letters of St. Nilus of Ancyra. 8vo. [DURHAM (N.C.),] 1976. [Pamph.]
—— Circus factions: blues and greens at Rome and Byzantium. 8vo. OXF., 1976.
—— Theodorus triseparchos. 8vo. [DURHAM (N.C.),] 1976. [Pamph.]
Cameron (George C.) The Scots Kirk in London. 8vo. OXF., 1979.
Cameron (Kenneth) *ed. See* Suppt. English Place-Name Soc. Publs.
Caminos (R. A.) *See* Suppt. Egypt Exploration Soc. Arch. Survey, 32.
Cammaerts (Emile) *See* Lindley (J.)
Campbell (R. J.) New Theology sermons. 8vo. LOND., 1907.
—— Thursday mornings at the City Temple. 8vo. LOND., 1908.
Campbell (W. A.) Did the Jews kill Jesus? 8vo. LOND., 1927. [Pamph.]
Campenhausen (Hans, *Freiherr* von) The formation of the Christian Bible. Trans. John Austin Baker. 8vo. LOND., 1972.
Campion (Edmund) Ten reasons proposed to his adversaries for disputation in the name of the faith. [Latin text (1581) with Eng. trans. by Joseph Rickaby and introd. by J. H. Pollen.] [Catholic Lib., 6.] 8vo. LOND., 1914.
Canadian Unitarian Council. Centennial yearbook, 1967. Ed. Ralph A. Greer. 8vo. [TORONTO, 1967.]
Canivet (Pierre) Le monachisme syrien selon Théodoret de Cyr. [Théologie Historique, 42.] 8vo. PARIS, 1977.
Canterbury. *Union Church.* Landmarks in the history of Congregationalism at Canterbury, 1645-1945. 8vo. [CANTERBURY, 1945.] [s.sh.fold.]
Canterbury and York Society. *See* Suppt.

Capito (Wolfgang)   *See* Kittelson (J. M.)
Capizzi (Carmelo)   L'imperatore Anastasio I (491-518): studio sulla sua vita, la sua opera e la sua personalità.   [Orientalia Christiana Analecta, 184.]   8vo.   ROMA, 1969.
Caplan (Niel)   The Sussex Catholics, c.1660-1800.   4to.   [CHICHESTER,]   1978. [Pamph.]
Capp (B. S.)   The Fifth Monarchy men: a study in seventeenth-century millenarianism.   8vo.   LOND., 1972.
—— Astrology and the popular press: English almanacs, 1500-1800.   8vo.   LOND. & BOSTON, 1979.
Cappelli (Adriano)   *See* Dictionaries. Abbreviations.
Cardiff. *Bethany Baptist Church.*   1806-1956: 150th anniversary celebrations, Oct. 1956.   8vo.   [CARDIFF, 1956.]   [Pamph.]
Carey (K. M.) *ed.*   The historic episcopate.   *See* Fairweather (E. R.)
Carey (S. P.)   The story of Stockton Baptists from about 1775 to 1941.   8vo.   LOND., 1941.
Carey (William)   *See* Clement (A. S.)
Carington (W. Whatley) *pseud.*   *See* Smith (Walter Whatley)
Carleton Rode. *Baptist Church.*   Ter-jubilee, 1812-1962: souvenir booklet.   8vo. [CARLETON RODE, 1962.]   [Pamph.]
Carley (K. W.)   *See* Suppt. Studies in Bibl. Theol., 2nd Ser., 31.
Carlile (J. C.)   My life's little day.   8vo.   LOND. & GLASGOW, 1935.
Carlson (Leland H.)   [Misc.]   Essays for Leland H. Carlson: the Dissenting tradition. Ed. C. Robert Cole and Michael E. Moody.   8vo.   ATHENS (Ohio), 1975.
Carlson (Leland H.) and **Paulson** (Ronald)   English satire.   [Clark Lib. Seminar Papers.]   8vo.   LOS ANGELES, 1972.   [Pamph.]
Carmen de Hastingae Proelio.   *See* Guy, *Bp. of Amiens.*
Carnap (Rudolf)   *See* Suppt. Library of Living Philosophers, 11.
Carnes (Paul N.)   Longing of the heart: prayers and invocations.   16mo.   BUFFALO, 1978.   [Pamph.]
Carpenter (Edward)   The drama of love and death: a study of human evolution and transfiguration.   8vo.   LOND., 1912.
Carpenter (Joseph Estlin)   The place of Christianity among the religions of the world (1904.)   2nd ed.   8vo.   LOND., 1911.
Carpenter (Mary)   *See* Manton (J.)
[**Carpenter** (W. H.) *ed.*]   A memento of the Revd. John Stephen Mummery, Unitarian minister at Peckham, 1885-1891, and Wood Green, 1891-1910. Died 31st Aug. 1910 in his 86th year.   8vo.   LOND., 1910.   [Pamph.]
Carr (E. H.)   A history of Soviet Russia.   10 vols. in 14.   8vo.   LOND., 1950-78.
   8.i. Foundations of a planned economy, 1926-1929.   1 ,i.   With R. W. Davies. 1969.
   8.ii. —— 1,ii. ——.   1969.
   9. —— 2.   1971.
   10.i. —— 3,i.   1976.
   10.ii. —— 3,ii.   1976.
   10.iii. —— 3,iii.   1978.
Carritt (E. F.)   The theory of morals: an introduction to ethical philosophy.   8vo. OXF. & LOND., 1928.
Carroll (K. L.)   *See* Suppt. Friends' Hist. Soc. Journal Suppt., 33.
Carroll (Robert P.)   When prophecy failed: reactions and responses to failure in the Old Testament prophetic traditions.   8vo.   LOND., 1979.
Carroll (Robert Todd)   The common-sense philosophy of religion of Bishop Edward Stillingfleet, 1635-1699.   [Internat. Archives of the Hist. of Ideas, 77.]   8vo. THE HAGUE, 1975.
Carruthers (S. W.)   The Solemn League and Covenant: its text and translations. 8vo.   [EDIN., 1924.]   [Pamph.]
Carshalton Beeches. *Baptist Free Church.*   Carshalton Beeches Baptist Free Church, 1931-1952.   8vo.   [CARSHALTON BEECHES, 1952.]   [Pamph.]
Carswell (John)   *See* Discoveries in the Judaean Desert.
Carter (Charles)   A brief historical sketch of the Northumberland and Durham Unitarian Christian Association, 1813-1916.   8vo.   NEWCASTLE [printed], 1916. [Pamph.]

Carter (Charles Frederick) On having a sense of all conditions. [Swarthmore Lect., 1971.] 8vo. LOND., 1971.

Carter (Charles Sydney) The Reformation and reunion. With an appreciation by E. A. Knox and a foreword by F. S. Guy Warman. 8vo. LOND., [1935].

Carter (Henry) The English Temperance Movement: a study in objectives. [Beckly Social Service Lect., 1932.] 1. The formative period, 1830-1899. 8vo. LOND., 1933.

—— Liberty and authority in the modern world. [Merttens Lect., 1939.] 8vo. LOND., [1939]. [Pamph.]

—— *See* MacLachlan (L.); Urwin (E. C.)

Carter (J. W.) Taste and technique in book-collecting: a study of recent developments in Great Britain and the United States. [Sandars Lects. in Bibliography, 1947.] (1948.) 2nd imp. 8vo. CAMB., 1949.

Carus (Paul) *comp. See* Buddha.

Caruthers (J. Wade) Octavius Brooks Frothingham, gentle radical. 8vo. UNIVERSITY (Ala.), 1977.

Cary (Lucius) *2nd Viscount Falkland. See* Tanner (J.)

Case (H. B.) The history of the Baptist Church in Tiverton, 1607 to 1907. 8vo. LOND. & TIVERTON, [1907]. [Pamph.]

Casella (M. C.) Religious liberalism in modern Italy. 2 vols. 8vo. LOND., 1965-66.

Casey (John) *ed.* Morality and moral reasoning. Five essays in ethics. 8vo. LOND., 1971.

Cass (A. J.) The Congregational Church, Blackheath, London, S.E.3: the first 100 years, 1854-1954. 8vo. LOND., 1954. [Pamph.]

Cassara (Ernest) *ed.* Universalism in America: a documentary history. 8vo. BOSTON (Mass.), 1971.

Cassian (John) *See* Rousseau (P.)

Cassiodorus. *See* O'Donnell (J. J.)

Castelli (Enrico) *and others.* Herméneutique de la sécularisation. Actes du colloque organisé par le Centre International d'Études Humanistes, et par l'Institut d'Études Philosophiques de Rome, Rome, 3-8 janvier 1976. 4to. PARIS, 1976.

Castellion (S.) *See* Châteillon (S.)

Castleden (James) *See* Buffard (F. J.)

Catalogues. *Bibliothèque Nationale.* Le livre anglais: trésors des collections anglaises. 8vo. PARIS, 1951.

—— *Birmingham. Museum and Art Gallery.* An exhibition to commemorate the bicentenary of the Lunar Society of Birmingham, Oct. 13th to Nov. 27th 1966. 8vo. BIRMINGHAM, [1966]. [Pamph.]

—— *Birmingham. University Library.* The Lunar Society: an exhibition in connection with the bicentenary celebrations, Oct. 12th to Nov. 26th 1966. 8vo. BIRMINGHAM, 1966. [Pamph.]

—— *Bodleian Library.* Notes on Bodleian MSS. relating to Cambridge. 1. Town and university. By Falconer Madan. 2. County. By W. M. Palmer. Index by J. H. Bullock and G. J. Gray. [Cambridge Antiquarian Soc. Octavo Publs., 52.] 8vo. CAMB., 1931.

—— *British Museum. Dept. of MSS.* Catalogue of additions to manuscripts. 8vo. LOND., 1889-
[11.] 1931-1935. 1967.
[12-13.] 1936-1945. 2 vols. 1970.

—— *Brussels. Royal Library.* Le cinquième centenaire de l'imprimerie dans les anciens Pays-Bas: exposition à la Bibliothèque royale Albert 1er. Catalogue. 4to. BRUXELLES, 1973.

—— —— English illuminated manuscripts, 700-1500. Catalogue by J. J. G. Alexander and C. M. Kauffmann. 4to. BRUXELLES, 1973.

—— *Cheshire County Record Office and Chester Diocesan Record Office.* [Lists of records held.] fol. *Duplicated.* [CHESTER, 1978.] [Pamph.]

—— *Cheshunt College, Cambridge.* List of college papers. 4to. *Duplicated.* n.p., 1969. [Pamph.]

—— —— Report on the archives and related papers. [Royal Comm. on Hist. MSS.] 4to. *Duplicated.* LOND., 1972. [Pamph.]

Catalogues—*continued*

—— *Denbighshire County Library.* Llyfryddiaeth y Sir. Bibliography of the County. (—Bibliography of Denbighshire.) [Compiled by Owen Williams.] 3 pts. 8vo. [RUTHIN,] 1935-37.

—— —— Pt.2. (1935.) rev. and enl. ed. [by R. G. ab Iorweth]. 8vo. [RUTHIN,] 1951.

—— *Dickinson College.* The Priestley family collection: the gift of Mrs. Temple Fay. 8vo. CARLISLE (Pa.), 1965. [Pamph.]

—— —— Archives and manuscript collections: a guide. Compiled by Charles Coleman Sellers and Martha Calvert Slotten. 8vo. CARLISLE (Pa.), 1972. [Pamph.]

—— *Dr. Williams's Library.* Guide to the manuscripts. By Kenneth Twinn. 8vo. LOND., 1969. [Pamph.]

—— —— Catalogue of accessions, vol.3: being a catalogue of books published in the twentieth century and added to the Library, 1961-1970. Ed. for the Trustees by John Creasey. 8vo. LOND., 1972.

—— —— Nonconformist congregations in Great Britain: a list of histories and other material in Dr. Williams's Library. 8vo. LOND., 1973.

—— —— The George Eliot—George Henry Lewes library: an annotated catalogue of their books at Dr. Williams's Library. [Compiled by] William Baker. [Garland Reference Lib. of the Humanities, 67.] 8vo. NEW YORK & LOND., 1977.

—— *Edmund Jones Library, Pontnewenydd, Gwent.* [A catalogue, compiled by Trevor Watts.] 8vo. [ABERYSTWYTH, 1976.] [Pamph.]

—— *Exeter. University Library.* Devon union list. (Catalogue of books on Devon known to be in the five main libraries of Exeter.) Subject list 3. Nonconformity in Devon. fol. *Duplicated.* [EXETER, 1973?] [Pamph.]

—— *Gospel Standard Baptists' Library.* Catalogue. 8vo. [HOVE,] 1952. [Pamph.]

—— —— Supplemantary catalogue. 8vo. [HOVE,] 1977. [Pamph.]

—— *House of Lords Record Office.* Handlist of the papers of Reginald, Lord Sorensen (the Rev. R. W. Sorensen, M.P.). Complied by S. K. Ellison. [House of Lords Record Office Memorandum, 49.] fol. LOND., 1973. [Pamph.]

—— *Lambeth Palace Library.* A catalogue of manuscripts, MSS.1222-1860: E. G. W. Bill. With a suppt. to M. R. James's Descriptive catalogue of the MSS. in the Lib. of Lambeth Palace, by N. R. Ker. 8vo. OXF., 1972.

—— *Leeds. University. Brotherton Library.* Erasmus: an exhibition held 24 Nov. 1969 to 31 Jan. 1970. [Catalogue.] 4to. [LEEDS, 1969.] [Pamph.]

—— *London. Guildhall Library.* Parish registers: a handlist. 8vo. LOND. [Pamphs.]
  1. Church of England parishes within the City of London. (1963.) 4th ed. 1979.
  2. Church of England parishes outside the City—Non-parochial and foreign denominations—Burial ground records. (1964.) 2nd ed. 1970.
  2. —— 3rd ed. 1978.

—— *London. New College.* Additional report on the records of New College, London: being the literary remains of the Simpson family, 19th and early 20th century (L249). [Royal Comm. on Hist. MSS.] fol. *Duplicated.* LOND., 1976. [Pamph.]

—— —— *University College.* Manuscript collections: a handlist. (1975.) 2nd ed. [Compiled by Janet Percival.] [U.C.L. Lib. Occ. Publs., 1.] fol. LOND., 1978. [Pamph.]

—— *London University.* Incunabula in the libraries of the University of London: a hand-list. 8vo. LOND., 1963. [Pamph.]

—— *Manchester. Central Library. Archives Dept.* Report on the papers of the Widows' Fund Association (for the benefit of Protestant Dissenting Ministers, their widows and orphans in Lancashire and Cheshire), 1764-1967. [Royal Comm. on Hist. MSS.] fol. *Duplicated.* LOND., 1978. [Pamph.]

—— *Oxford University Press.* John Fell, 1625-1686: bishop, printer and typefounder. [Catalogue of an exhibition at O.U.P., London.] 8vo. LOND., 1967. [Pamph.]

—— *St. David's University College, Lampeter.* A catalogue of the tract collection. [Ed. with an introd. by Brian Ll. James.] fol. LOND., 1975.

—— *St. Mary's Seminary, Oscott.* Catalogue of the Bible collections in the Old Library at St. Mary's, Oscott, c.1472-c.1850. 4to. NEW OSCOTT, 1971.

—— *Sheffield. University Library.* Henry Joseph Wilson (1833-1914). [List of papers in Sheffield Univ. Lib., compiled by G. A. Dyer.] fol. *Duplicated.* [SHEFFIELD, 1978.] [Pamph.]

Catalogues—*continued*
—— *Shrewsbury Unitarian Church Library.* [Catalogue of books, on permanent loan to] Shropshire County Library. 4to. *Duplicated.* [SHREWSBURY, 1977.]
—— *Victoria and Albert Museum.* The Festival of Britain: exhibition of books, arranged by the National Book League at the Victoria and Albert Museum, 1951. 8vo. LOND., 1951.
—— *Yale. University Library.* Bishop Berkeley's gift of books in 1733. [Introd. and short catalogue, with transcript of Berkeley's letters in Yale Univ. Lib.] 8vo. YALE, 1933. [Pamph.]
—— *Miscellaneous.* The annual catalogue, 1736-37. (1737-38.) facsim. repr. [English Bibliographical Sources, I, 5.] 8vo. LOND., 1965.
—— —— The lists of books from the British Magazine, 1746-50, collected with annual indexes. facsim. repr. [English Bibliographical Sources, I, 8.] 8vo. LOND., 1965.
—— —— A catalogue [—The general catalogue] of all the books printed in England since the dreadful Fire of London, 1666. Collected by Robert Clavel. (1673-96.) facsim. reprs. [English Bibliographical Sources, II, 3-6.] 4 vols. fol. FARNBOROUGH, 1965.
—— —— Original parish registers in record offices and libraries. 8vo. MATLOCK, 1974. [Pamph.]
—— —— —— 1st suppt. 1976. [Pamph.]
—— —— —— 2nd Suppt. 1978. [Pamph.]
—— —— Book subscription lists: a revised guide. By F. J. G. Robinson and P. J. Wallis. obl. fol. NEWCASTLE-UPON-TYNE, 1975.
—— —— *See* Gulik (E. van) and Vervliet (H. D. L)
Catechisms. *Heidelberg. See* Bartha (T.)
—— *Roman Catholic.* [De nieuwe katechismus. *English.*] A new catechism: Catholic faith for adults. [Trans. Kevin Smyth.] 8vo. LOND., 1967.
Catherall (G. A.) A short history of the Baptist Church in Alnwick, 1883-1957. 4to. *Duplicated.* [ALNWICK, 1957.] [Pamph.]
Catholic Record Society. *See* Suppt.
[**Caton** (Dora M.)] A short history of the Avenue Congregational Church, Southampton. 8vo. *Duplicated.* SOUTHAMPTON, [1968]. [Pamph.]
Causebrook (Arthur) College Chapel echos. 8vo. ILFRACOMBE, [1942.]
Cavenagh (F. A.) The life and work of Griffith Jones of Llanddowror. 8vo. CARDIFF, 1930.
Caxton (William) *See* Suppt. Early Eng. Text Soc., Suppt. Texts, 2.
Cazelles (Henri) *See* Dictionaries. Biblical.
C.B.R.F. *See* Suppt. Christian Brethren Research Fellowship.
Cecil (Robert) *1st Earl of Salisbury. See* Tyacke (N. R. N.)
Cely, *family of. See* Suppt. Early Eng. Text Soc., O. S., 273.
Cerutti (Toni) Antonio Gallenga: an Italian writer in Victorian England. [Univ. of Hull Publs.] 8vo. LOND., *etc.*, 1974.
Chadwick (Henry) Priscillian of Avila: the occult and the charismatic in the early Church. 8vo. OXF., 1976.
—— *ed. See* Bible. N.T. Commentaries. Black's.
Chadwick (John) *See* Ventris (M.) and Chadwick (J.)
Chadwick (Owen) The secularization of the European mind in the nineteenth century. [Gifford Lects., 1973-74.] 8vo. CAMB., 1975.
—— Catholicism and history: the opening of the Vatican archives. [Herbert Hensley Henson Lects., Univ. of Oxford, 1976.] 8vo. CAMB., 1978.
Chadwick (Samuel) *See* Dunning (N. G.)
Chalford. *France Congregational Church.* A record of two and a half centuries [1662-1919]. 8vo. [CHALFORD, 1919.] [Pamph.]
Chalice. *See* Suppt.
Challaye (Charles Alexandre, *Comte de*) 1816-55. Mémoire sur l'état actuel et l'avenir de la religion catholique et des missions lazaristes et protestantes en Perse. Texte publié, introd. et annoté par J.-M. Hornus. [Cahier d'Études Chrétiennes Orientales, 8-11, 1970-73.] 8vo. STRASBOURG, [1976].
Challoner (Richard) *R.C. Bp. of Debra. See* Mathew (D.) *and others.*
Chamberlain (John) *See* Notestein (W.)

Chambers (*Sir* Edmund K.) Sir Henry Lee: an Elizabethan portrait. 8vo. OXF., 1936.

Chambers (R. F.) The Strict Baptist Chapels of England. 8vo. THORNTON HEATH [1-3], LOND. [4+], 1952-
5. The chapels of Wiltshire and the West. By Robert W. Oliver. 1968.

Champion (L. G.) *comp.* Tyndale Baptist Church, Bristol, 1868-1968. 8vo. BRISTOL, [1968]. [Pamph.]

[**Champion** (O. C.) and **Ballard** (A. E.)] A brief survey of the history of the church worshipping at Mount Zion Chapel, London, E.C.1., between the years 1851 and 1951. 8vo. LOND., [1951]. [Pamph.]

Chandos (John) *ed.* In God's name: examples of preaching in England from the Act of Supremacy to the Act of Uniformity, 1534-1662. 8vo. LOND., 1971.

[**Channon** (W. G.) *and others.*] Fifty years on: a record of the foundation and growth of the Baptist Church in Banstead Road, Purley, Surrey. 8vo. [PURLEY, 1957.] [Pamph.]

Chaplin (W. K.) and **Street** (M. Jennie) *ed.* Fifty years of Christian Endeavour: a jubilee record and forecast, 1881-1931. 8vo. LOND., [1931].

Chapple (Stewart) Streatham Baptist Church, Lewin Road, London, S.W.: the story of our church. The origin of Nonconformity in Streatham. Ed. and brought up to 1962 by his daughter. 8vo. [LOND., 1962.] [Pamph.]

Charanis (Peter) Social, economic and political life in the Byzantine Empire. Collected studies. [Variorum Reprs.] 8vo. LOND., 1973.

——— Church and state in the later Roman Empire: the religious policy of Anastasius the First, 491-518. (1939.) 2nd ed. [Byzantine Texts and Studies, 11.] 8vo. [THESSALONIKI,] 1974.

Charles I, *King of Great Britain and Ireland.* See Wingfield-Stratford (E. C.); Young (G. M.)

Charles (Amy M.) The Williams manuscript and "The Temple". 8vo. n.p., [1971]. [Pamph.]

——— A life of George Herbert. 8vo. ITHACA (N.Y.) & LOND., 1977.

Charles (Thomas) See Pritchard (R. A.)

Charles Lamb Bulletin. See Suppt.

Charley (R. M.) Stafford Baptist Church (the Green): some notes on its century of history. 8vo. [STAFFORD,] 1958. [Pamph.]

Chartier (Alain) See Suppt. Early Eng. Text Soc., O.S., 270, 281.

Châteillon (Sébastien) See Plath (U.)

Chatteris. *Zion Strict Baptist Chapel.* These 100 years: a brief record of the goodness and mercy of a covenant keeping God in connection with Zion Strict Baptist Chapel, Chatteris, Cambridgeshire, 1839-1939. 8vo. [CHATTERIS, 1939.] [Pamph.]

Chaudhuri (N. C.) Scholar extraordinary: the life of Professor the Rt. Hon. Friedrich Max Müller, P. C. 8vo. LOND., 1974.

Chauliac (Guy de) See Suppt. Early Eng. Text Soc., O.S., 265.

Chauncy (*Sir* Henry) See Gerish (W. B.)

Checkland (S. G.) The Gladstones: a family biography, 1764-1851. 8vo. CAMB., 1971.

Cheltenham. *Gas Green Chapel.* A history of Gas Green Chapel, Cheltenham, 1849-1949. 8vo. [CHELTENHAM, 1949.] [Pamph.]

Cheltschizki (Peter) See Zinzendorf (N. L. von) [Misc.]

Cheney (C. R.) Medieval texts and studies. 8vo. OXF., 1973.

Cherry (Conrad) The theology of Jonathan Edwards: a reappraisal. 8vo. NEW YORK, 1966.

Chesham. *Broadway Baptist Church.* A brief history of 250 years of Christian witness, 1706-1956. 8vo. [CHESHAM, 1956.] [Pamph.]

Cheshire. See Suppt. Record Society of Lancashire and Cheshire.

Chesnut (Glenn F.) The first Christian histories: Eusebius, Socrates, Sozomen, Theodoret and Evagrius. [Théologie Historique, 46.] 8vo. PARIS, 1977.

Chesnut (Roberta C.) Three Monophysite christologies: Severus of Antioch, Philoxenus of Mabbug, and Jacob of Sarug. [Oxford Theological Monographs.] 8vo. LOND., 1976.

Chester Mystery Cycle. See Suppt. Early Eng. Text Soc., Suppt. Texts, 3.

Chesterman (A. de M.) Axholme Baptists: heralds of Christian freedom. 8vo. CROWLE (Lincs.), 1949. [Pamph.]

Chetham Society. *See* Suppt.
Chevrolet (Jean-Pierre) Le sacré dans la philosophie de Max Scheler. Thèse. 8vo. FRIBOURG (Suisse), 1970.
Chicago Society of Biblical Research. *See* Suppt. Biblical Research.
Child (R. L.) and **Shipley** (C. E.) Broadmead origins: an account of the rise of Puritanism in England, and of the early days of Broadmead Baptist Church, Bristol, issued for the tercentenary, 1940. 8vo. LOND., 1940.
Childs (B. S.) Exodus: a commentary. [Old Test. Lib.] 8vo. LOND., 1974.
—— Introduction to the Old Testament as scripture. 8vo. LOND., 1979.
[Chivers (J. Stanley)] Histon Baptist Church, 1858-1958. 8vo. [HISTON, 1958.] [Pamph.]
Chrimes (S. B.) Henry VII. 8vo. LOND., 1972.
Christ (Felix) Jesus Sophia: die Sophia-Christologie bei den Synoptikern. [Abhandlungen zur Theol. des A. u. N. Test., 57.] 8vo. ZÜRICH, 1970.
Christensen (Torben) The divine order: a study in F. D. Maurice's theology. [Acta Theologica Danica, 11.] 8vo. LEIDEN, 1973.
Christian Believing. *See* Church of England. *Reports.*
Christian Brethren Research Fellowship. *See* Suppt.
Christian Centuries. *See* Rogier (L. J.) *and others, ed.*
Christian Endeavour. Eighteenth British National C.E. Convention, Nottingham, June 6th-10th, 1908. Programme. [With 'Hymn Supplement', from the Christian Endeavour Hymnal, ed. J. Brown Morgan and Carey Bonner.] 8vo. [NOTTINGHAM, 1908.] [Pamph.]
Christian Irishman. *See* Suppt.
Christianity Today. *See* Suppt.
Christianson (P. K.) English Protestant apocalyptic visions, c.1536-1642. [Univ. of Minnesota Ph.D. thesis, 1971.] 4to. *Duplicated.* ANN ARBOR, 1971.
—— Reformers and Babylon: English apocalyptic visions from the Reformation to the eve of the Civil War. 8vo. TORONTO, 1978.
Christie-Murray (D. H. A.) A history of heresy. 8vo. LOND., 1976.
Chrysos (Evangelos K.) He ekklesiastike politike tou Ioustinianou kata ten erin peri ta tria kephalaia kai ten e oikoumeniken synodon. [Analecta Blatadon, 3.] 8vo. THESSALONIKA, 1969.
Chrysostom (John) *Saint, Patriarch of Constantinople.* Sur la providence de Dieu. Introd., texte critique, trad. et notes de Anne-Marie Malingrey. [Sources Chrétiennes, 79.] 8vo. PARIS, 1961.
—— Sur l'incomprehensibilité de Dieu. Tom. 1. Homeliés I-V. 2e éd. Introd. de Jean Daniélou, texte critique et notes de Anne-Marie Malingrey, trad. de Robert Flacelière. [Sources Chrétiennes, 28.] 8vo. PARIS, 1970.
—— *See* Aubineau (M.) *ed.*; Ritter (A. M.); Suppt. Analecta Bollandiana. Subsid. Hagiog., 60.
Chrysostomides (Julian) Venetian commercial privileges under the Palaeologi. 8vo. FIRENZE, 1970. [Pamph.]
Church (Roy A.) Kenricks in hardware: a family business, 1791-1966. 8vo. NEWTON ABBOT, 1969.
Church History. *See* Suppt.
Church of England. *Constitutions and Canons.* The canons of the Church of England: canons ecclesiastical promulged by the Convocations of Canterbury and York in 1964 and 1969. 8vo. LOND., 1969.
—— *See* Lyndwood (W.)
—— *Convocation.* The Church of South India: being the united report of the joint Committees of the Convocations of Canterbury and York. 8vo. LOND., 1950. [Pamph.]
—— *See* Gibson (E.) *Bp. of London.*
—— *Reports.* The fourth R: the report of the Commission on Religious Education in Schools appointed in 1967 under the chairmanship of the Bishop of Durham. 8vo. LOND., 1970.
—— —— The central records of the Church of England: a report and survey presented to the Pilgrim and Radcliffe Trustees. 8vo. LOND., 1976.
—— —— Christian believing: the nature of the Christian faith and its expression in Holy Scripture and creeds. A report by the Doctrine Commission of the Church of England. (1976.) 2nd imp. 8vo. LOND., 1976.

Church of India, Burma and Ceylon. *See* Plan of church union; Proposed scheme of union.

Church of Ireland. *See* Hurley (M.) *ed.*

Church of South India. [Misc.] The Church of South India, 1947-1949. Prepared for the Joint Committee on Doctrine of the American Church Union and the Clerical Union. Elwood C. Boggess, Chairman. 8vo. n.p., n.d. [Pamph.]

—— *See* Church of England. *Convocation;* Davidson (W. J. H.); Fisher (G. F.); Haselmayer (L. A.); Hodgson (L.); Horsley (C. D.); Palmer (E. J.); Proposed scheme of union; Warren (M. A. C.)

Churches' Council for Covenanting. *Report.* Towards visible unity: proposals for a covenant. 8vo. LOND., 1980. [Pamph.]

Churchill (*Sir* Winston L. S.) Great contemporaries. (1937.) 2nd ed. 8vo. LOND., 1941.

Churchman. *See* Suppt.

Churm (F.) North Cheshire Unitarian Sunday School Union. "Something attempted": a history of the Union, 1863-1963. 8vo. DUKINFIELD [printed], [1963]. [Pamph.]

Cirket (A. F.) The 1830 riot in Bedfordshire: background and events. 8vo. [BEDFORD, 1978.] [Pamph.]

Citron (Bernhard) New birth: a study of the evangelical doctrine of conversion in the Protestant fathers. [Edinburgh Univ. Publs. Theology, 1.] 8vo. EDIN., 1951.

Clamp (A. L.) The story of Elburton village chapel. 4to. n.p. [the author, 1976.] [Pamph.]

Clap (Thomas) *See* Tucker (L. L.)

Clapton (Upper) *Congregational Church.* A short history of 150 years [1812-1962]. 8vo. [LOND., 1962.] [Pamph.]

Clapton Park. *Congregational Church.* An account of the meetings held on March 5th, 6th and 10th, 1904, in celebration of the 100th anniversary of the formation of the church. 8vo. [LOND., 1904.]

—— [List of records now depositied at Shoreditch District Lib.] fol. *Duplicated.* n.p., 1972. [Pamph.]

Clarendon (Edward Hyde, *1st Earl of*) *See* Hyde (Edward) *1st Earl of Clarendon.*

[Clark (A. D. W.) *and others.*] Newhaven Baptist Church, 1901-1961. 8vo. *Duplicated.* [NEWHAVEN, 1961.] [Pamph.]

Clark (Elmer T.) The small sects in America. (1937.) rev. ed. (1949.) repr. 8vo. NEW YORK, [1965].

Clark (F. L.) Two hundred and fifty years of Epsom Congregationalism, being a history of Epsom Congregational Church, 1688-1938. 8vo. EPSOM, [1938]. [Pamph.]

Clark (*Sir* George N.) *See* Cambridge Modern Hist.

Clark (Henry E.) *ed.* Memorials of Elgin Place Congregational Church, Glasgow: a centenary volume, 1803-1903. 8vo. GLASGOW, 1904.

Clark (*Sir* Kenneth) *Baron Clark of Saltwood.* Blake and visionary art. [W. A. Cargill Memorial Lect. in Fine Art, 2.] 8vo. GLASGOW, 1973. [Pamph.]

Clark (Peter A.) English provincial society from the Reformation to the Revolution: religion, politics and society in Kent, 1500-1640. 8vo. HASSOCKS (Sx.), 1977.

—— *ed. See* Hurstfield (J.) [Misc.]

Clark (Walter E.) Indian conceptions of immortality. [Ingersoll Lect., 1934.] 8vo. CAMB. (Mass.), 1934.

Clark-Lewis (W. R.) The foundation and history of Beaumont Street Church, Gainsborough [1688-1912]. 8vo. GAINSBOROUGH, [1912.] [Pamph.]

Clarke (Adam) *See* Sellers (I.)

Clarke (Samuel) *See* Ferguson (J. P.)

Clarkson (George E.) William Law, John Wesley, and Quakerism. 4to. n.p., 1971. [Pamph.] [Photocopy.]

—— John Wesley and William Law's mysticism. 8vo. [NASHVILLE (Tenn.),] 1973. [Pamph.]

—— A Northamptonshire pilgrimage ... concerning William Law, writer and mystic. 4to. ST. IVES (Hunts.), 1973. [Pamph.]

Clarkson (John) 1764-1828. *See* Wilson (E. G.)

Clarkson (Laurence) The lost sheep found: or, the prodigal returned to his fathers house, after many a sad and weary journey through many religious countreys. (1660.) facsim. repr. 8vo. EXETER, 1974. [Pamph.]

Clasen (Claus-Peter) Anabaptism: a social history, 1525-1618: Switzerland, Austria, Moravia, South and Central Germany. 8vo. ITHACA (N.Y.) & LOND., 1962.

Claude, *Saint, of Antioch.* See Suppt. Patrologia Orientalis, XXXV.4.

Clavier (Henri) See Suppt. Novum Testamentum. Suppts., 43.

Clayton (J. C.) *ed.* See Sykes (S. W.) and Clayton (J. C.) *ed.*

Cleaves (R. W.) Congregationalism, 1960-1976: the story of the Federation. 8vo. SWANSEA, 1977.

Clegg (James) The diary of James Clegg of Chapel en le Frith, 1708-1755. Ed. Vanessa S. Doe. [Derbyshire Record Soc. Publs.] 3 vols. 8vo. MATLOCK, 1978-
    1. [Introd. Diary 1708-36.] 1978.
    2. [Diary 1737-47.] 1979.
    3. *Not yet published,* 1980.

Clement, *of Alexandria.* See Ferguson (J.); Floyd (W. E. G.); Lilla (S. R. C.)

Clement, *of Rome.* Epître aux Corinthiens. Introd., texte, trad., notes et index par Annie Jaubert. [Sources Chrétiennes, 167.] 8vo. PARIS, 1971.
—— See Suppt. Novum Testamentum Suppts., 34, 38.

[Clement (A. S.)] Baptist Church, Madeley: centenary brochure, 1858-1958. 4to. [BIRMINGHAM, 1958.] [Pamph.]
—— William Carey (1761-1834). [Heritage Biographies.] 8vo. LOND., 1961. [Pamph.]

Clements (Bernard) A monk in Margaret Street. [Sermons and addresses.] 8vo. LOND. & OXF., 1941.
—— Speaking in parables: last broadcasts. (1943.) 2nd ed. 8vo. LOND., 1943.
—— See Almedingen (E. M.)

Clements (R. E.) Old Testament theology: a fresh approach. [Marshall's Theol. Lib.] 8vo. LOND., 1978.
—— See Bible. Commentaries. New Century Bible.

Cleobury (F. H.) A study in Christian apologetic. [Suppt. to Faith and Thought, 100.] 8vo. LOND., 1972. [Pamph.]
—— From clerk to cleric. Foreword by Edward Carpenter, Dean of Westminster. 8vo. CAMB., 1976. [Pamph.]

Clifford (*Lady* Anne) *Countess of Dorset, Pembroke & Montgomery.* See Notestein (W.); Williamson (G. C.)

Clifford (John) 1836-1923, *Baptist minister.* [Selections.] Extracts from sermons and lectures. Compiled by H. Edgar Bonsall. 8vo. LOND., 1973. [Pamph.]
—— Brotherhood and the war in South Africa. 8vo. LOND., [1900]. [Pamph.]
—— The call of the new century to temperance workers. 8vo. LOND., 1900. [Pamph.]
—— The demands of the twentieth century. An address to the Baptist Union. 8vo. LOND., 1900. [Pamph.]
—— The call of the new century: the sphere of the church in the coming social regeneration. 4to. n.p., n.d. [1900?] [Pamph.]
—— The great awakening in 1900. 8vo. LOND., 1901. [Pamph.]
—— The living message of the church for to-day. 8vo. LOND., n.d. [1901?] [Pamph.]
—— Making Anglicans at the cost of the ratepayers. 8vo. LOND., n.d. [1901?] [s.sh.]
—— Clericalism in British politics: letters on the Education Bill of 1902. 8vo. LOND., [1902]. [Pamph.]
—— The fight against the Education Bill: what is at stake. [National Reform Union Pamphs.] 8vo. MANCHESTER, [1902]. [Pamph.]
—— The housing of the poor. 8vo. LOND., [1902]. [Pamph.]
—— What hinders national education? [Liberation Society's Education Tracts, 10.] 8vo. LOND., [1902]. [s.sh.]
—— Imprisonment by the bishops. 8vo. LOND., [1903]. [s.sh.fold.]
—— Mr. Balfour's defence of the Education Act of 1902. 8vo. LOND., [1903]. [Pamph.]
—— [National Passive Resistance Committee Tracts. 8vo. LOND., [1903]. [s.shs. fold.]

Clifford (John)—*continued*
1. Why refuse the Rate seeing you have paid the tax?
2. Is it unconstitutional to refuse to pay the Rate?
3. Ought a Protestant to pay the Rate for teaching Romanism?
4. The teaching profession and the Education Act, 1902.
5. The Education Act, 1902, and the higher life of the state.
—— [National Free Church Council Leaflets.] 8vo. LOND., [1903-4]. [s.shs.fold.]
4. The Bishop of London's great hoax. n.d.
9. Rome on the rates: the London Education Bill. 1903.
12. Board school teaching: is it Free Church or not? n.d.
13. Bible or no Bible in state schools. [1904.]
—— Dr. Clifford as a passive resister: statement to the Paddington magistrates, July 1st, 1904. 8vo. LOND., 1904. [s.sh.]
—— Funeral of the late Mrs. Cayford. 8vo. EASTBOURNE, [1904]. [Pamph.]
—— Passive resistance, June 1903-June 1904: the story of the first year's sales in aid of the new Church Rate. 8vo. LOND., 1904. [s.sh.fold.]
—— The revival of religion in the churches. 8vo. LOND., [1904]. [Pamph.]
—— Disestablishment a question of practical politics. 8vo. LOND., [1905]. [s.sh. fold.]
—— Passive resistance in England and Wales. 8vo LOND., 1905. [Pamph.]
—— Conversion to Rome: as seen in the recent case of Princess Ena. 8vo. LOND., [1906]. [Pamph.]
—— General election, 1906: Dr. Clifford and secular education. 8vo. LOND., [1906]. [s.sh.]
—— George Jacob Holyoake. A sermon preached at Westbourne Park Chapel. 12mo. LOND., [1906]. [Pamph.]
—— The battle at the General Election. 8vo. LOND., [1906]. [s.sh.fold.]
—— Primary conditions of social progress. 8vo. LOND., 1907. [Pamph.]
—— Socialism and the churches. [Fabian Tract, 139.] 8vo. LOND., 1908. [Pamph.]
—— What passive resisters really want. 12mo. LOND., [1909]. [s.sh.fold.]
—— Why are we afraid of Rome? 8vo. LOND., [1909]. [Pamph.]
—— Is England to be converted to Rome? Passive resistance, June 1909-June 1910. LOND., 1910. [Pamph.]
—— The attitude of Baptists to Catholicism—Roman and Greek. 8vo. [LOUIS-VILLE (Ky.),] 1911. [Pamph.]
—— Comparative religion and missions to non-Christian peoples. [Carey Lect., 3, 1912.] 8vo. LOND., [1912]. [Pamph.]
—— The peers' veto gone: what next? Passive resistance, June 1910-July 1911. 8vo. LOND, 1911. [Pamph.]
—— Clericalism in state education. Passive resistance, June 1911-July 1912. 8vo. LOND., [1912]. [Pamph.]
—— Temperance reform and the ideal state. [Lees and Raper Memorial Lect., 12, 1913.] 8vo. LOND., [1913]. [Pamph.]
—— Ten years of protest against the intrusion of churches into state schools. Passive resistance, June 1912-June 1913. 8vo. LOND., [1913]. [Pamph.]
—— Fifty years in a London pastorate. Delivered in Westbourne Park Chapel, London, Oct. 18th, 1914. 8vo. LOND., 1914. [Pamph.]
—— The political crisis and passive resisters. Passive resistance, June 1913-June 1914. 8vo. LOND., [1914]. [Pamph.]
—— The reign of war and the rule of God. 8vo. LOND., 1914. [Pamph.]
—— The War and public opinion. 8vo. LOND., [1914]. [Pamph.]
—— The War and the churches. 8vo. LOND., [1914]. [Pamph.]
—— The European War as a conflict of ideas. 8vo. [LOUISVILLE (Ky.),] 1915. [Pamph.]
—— The Great War and passive resisters. Passive resistance, June 1914-June 1915. 8vo. LOND., [1915]. [Pamph.]
—— The new world after the War. 8vo. [LOND., 1915?] [Pamph.]
—— Brotherhood in ideal and in action. 8vo. LOND., [1916]. [Pamph.]
—— Brotherhood of nations: a plea for high aims in the coming peace. 8vo. LOND., [1916]. [s.sh.fold.]

Clifford (John)—*continued*

—— State education after the War. Passive resistance, June 1915-June 1916. 8vo. LOND., [1916]. [Pamph.]

—— The League of Free Nations: facing the facts. 8vo. LOND., 1918. [Pamph.]

—— Our fight for Belgium and what it means. 8vo. LOND., *etc.*, 1918. [Pamph.]

—— An appeal to young England. 8vo. LOND., 1919. [s.sh.fold.]

—— The place of industry in the plan of God for the education of the world. 8vo. LOND., 1919. [Pamph.]

—— The political situation: the last conspiracy against freedom. 16mo. LOND., [1919?]. [Pamph.]

—— Baptist work in Europe. 12mo. LOND., [1920]. [Pamph.]

—— Dr. Clifford's optimistic outlook. 4to. LOND., [*c.*1920]. [s.sh.fold.]

—— *See* Baptist Union; Bateman (C. T.); Byrt (G. W.); Education Act, 1902-3.

Clogan (P. M.) *ed.* Transformation and continuity. [Medievalia et Humanistica: Studies in Medieval and Renaissance Culture, N.S., 8.] 8vo. CAMB., 1977.

Cloud of unknowing. A book of contemplation the which is called The cloud of unknowing, in the which a soul is oned with God. Ed. from the B.M. MS. Harl.674 with an introd. by Evelyn Underhill. (1912.) 3rd ed. 8vo. LOND., 1934.

Clouse (Robert G.) Millennialism and America. [Bueermann-Champion Lect., Western Conservative Baptist Seminary, 1976.] 8vo. PORTLAND (Or.), 1977. [Pamph.]

Clover (B. W.) Faithfulness and fruit at Fressingfield: a short history of the Strict Baptist Church, Fressingfield [1835-1935]. 8vo. [FRESSINGFIELD, 1935.] [Pamph.]

Clowes (J. E.) *comp.* Chronicles of the Old Congregational Church at Great Yarmouth, 1642 to 1858. (1906.) repr. 8vo. [GREAT YARMOUTH,] 1912.

Clowes (William) *See* Wilkinson (J. T.)

Cloyd (Royal) Theodore Parker: a Unitarian conscience. [Script for a dramatic presentation.] 8vo. BOSTON (Mass.), 1960. [Pamph.]

Clutterbuck (Nesta) *ed.* William Wordsworth, 1770-1970: essays of general interest on Wordsworth and his time. 8vo. GRASMERE, 1970. [Pamph.]

Clutton-Brock (Arthur) *See* Papers for War Time, 18, 26, 32.

Coad (F. Roy) *See* Suppt. Christian Brethren Research Fellowship, Occ. Papers, 2.

[Coates (C. A.)] An outline of the Book of Exodus. The substance of a series of readings. 8vo. LOND., [192-].

Cocks (H. F. Lovell) The wondrous cross. 8vo. LOND., 1957.

—— The religious life of Oliver Cromwell. [Congregational Lects.] 8vo. LOND., 1960.

Codex Brucianus. [*Coptic and English.*] The Books of Jeu and the Untitled Text in the Bruce Codex. Text ed. by Carl Schmidt. Trans. and notes by Violet Mac-Dermot. Volume ed. R. McL. Wilson. [Nag Hammadi Studies, 13.] [Coptic Gnostic Lib.] 8vo. LEIDEN, 1978.

[Coffin (W. T.) *and others.*] "These 150 years": being a brief history of Poole Baptists, 1804-1954. 8vo. [LOND., 1954.] [Pamph.]

Cofiadur (Y) *See* Suppt.

Coggan (F. Donald) *ed.* Christ and the colleges: a history of the Inter-Varsity Fellowship of Evangelical Unions. 8vo. LOND., 1934.

Coggins (R. J.) Samaritans and Jews: the origins of Samaritanism reconsidered. [Growing Points in Theol.] 8vo. OXF., 1975.

Cohen (Abraham) An Anglo-Jewish scrapbook, 1600-1840: the Jew through English eyes. (1943.) facsim. repr. 8vo. FARNBOROUGH, 1969.

Cohen (Arthur A.) *ed.* Arguments and doctrines: a reader of Jewish thinking in the aftermath of the holocaust. 8vo. NEW YORK, *etc.*, 1970.

Cohn (G. H.) Das Buch Jona im Lichte der biblischen Erzählkunst. [Studia Semitica Neerlandica, 12.] 8vo. ASSEN, 1969.

Coillard (François) *See* Shillito (E.)

Coke (Thomas) *See* Vickers (J. A.)

Cole (C. Robert) and **Moody** (M. E.) *ed.* *See* Carlson (L. H.) [Misc.]

Cole (Margaret I.) The story of Fabian socialism. [Kingswood Books on Social Hist.] 8vo. LOND., 1961.

Coleman (B. I.) *See* Suppt. Historical Assn. Gen. Ser., 98.

Coleman (J. A.) The evolution of Dutch Catholicism, 1958-1974. 8vo. BERKELEY (Calif.), *etc.*, 1978.

Coleman (T. W.) The Free Church sacrament and Catholic ideals: a plea for reunion. 8vo. LOND., 1930.

Coleridge (Samuel Taylor) Collected works. General editor: Kathleen Coburn; associate editor: Bart Winer. [Bollingen Ser., 75.] 8vo. LOND. & PRINCETON, 1969-
    1. Lectures, 1795, on politics and religion. 1971.
    3. Essays on his times in The Morning Post and The Courier. 3 vols. 1978.
    6. Lay sermons. 1972.
   10. On the constitution of the church and state. 1976.
—— Collected letters. Ed. Earl Leslie Griggs. 6 vols. 8vo. OXF., 1956-71.
    5. 1820-1825. 1971.
    6. 1826-1834. 1971.
—— Notebooks. Ed. Kathleen Coburn. 8vo. LOND., 1957-
    3. 1808-1819. Text and notes [in sep. volumes]. 2 vols. 1973.
—— *See* Prickett (S.); Willey (B.)

Coles (R. A.) *See* Suppt. Egypt Exploration Soc. Graeco-Rom. Memoirs, 59.

Coles (V. S. S.) Letters, papers, addresses, hymns and verses, with a memoir. Ed. J. F. Briscoe. Preface by Charles Gore. 8vo. LOND., 1930.

Colgrave (Hilda) Saint Cuthbert of Durham. Foreward by C. A. Alington. 8vo. DURHAM, 1947.

Collange (J.-F.) Enigmes de la deuxième épître de Paul aux Corinthiens: étude exégétique de 2 Cor. 2:14 - 7:4 [Soc. for N.T. Studies, Monograph Ser., 18.] 8vo. CAMB., 1972.

College of the Bible Quarterly. *See* Suppt. Lexington Theological Quarterly.

Collier (D. W.) The Baptist cause in Kings Heath, 1811-1914. Notes from the minutes of church meetings comp. for the ter-jubilee of the church, 1961. 8vo. [BIRMINGHAM, 1961.] [Pamph.]

Collier (Richard) The General next to God: the story of William Booth and the Salvation Army. (1965.) 3rd imp. 8vo. LOND., 1966.

Collingwood (R. G.) *See* Suppt. Historical Assn. Leaflets, 79.

Collins (Anthony) Determinism and freewill: Anthony Collins' A philosophical inquiry concerning human liberty. [Facsim. repr. of 2nd ed. (1717.)] Ed. and annot., with a discussion of the opinions of Hobbes, Locke, Pierre Bayle, William King and Leibniz, by J. O'Higgins. [Internat. Archives of the Hist. of Ideas, Ser. Minor, 18.] 8vo. THE HAGUE, 1976.
—— *See* O'Higgins (J.)

Collins (William) The Congregational Church, Hereford, past and present, founded A.D. 1662. 8vo. HEREFORD, 1913.

Collinson (Patrick) The Reformer and the Archbishop: Martin Bucer and an English Bucerian [Edmund Grindal]. 8vo. [SYDNEY, 1971.] [Pamph.]
—— Archbishop Grindal, 1519-1583: the struggle for a reformed Church. 8vo. LOND., 1979.

Coltman (Irene) Private men and public causes: philosophy and politics in the English Civil War. 8vo. LOND., 1962.

Comenius (John Amos) Orbis sensualium pictus. Trans. Charles Hoole. (1659.) facsim. repr. MENSTON, 1970.

Comfort (W. W.) William Penn, 1644-1718: a tercentenary estimate. 8vo. PHILA-DELPHIA, 1944.

Commemoration of the 350th anniversary of the Newbury Martyrs, July 15 & 16, 1906. 8vo. NEWBURY, [1906]. [Pamph.]

Commission Internationale d'Histoire Ecclésiastique Comparée. *British Sub-Commission.* The bibliography of the Reform, 1450-1648, relating to the United Kingdom and Ireland for the years 1955-70. Ed. Derek Baker. Comp. D. M. Loades, J. K. Cameron, Derek Baker. 8vo. OXF., 1975.

Communio Viatorum. *See* Suppt.

Condon (Kevin) *See* McCormack (J.) and Condon (K.)

Congar (Yves M. J.) L'ecclésiologie du haut Moyen Age: de Saint Grégoire le Grand à la désunion entre Byzance et Rome. 8vo. PARIS, 1968.

Congregational Federation. *See* Cleaves (R. W.)

Congregational Historical Society. *See* Suppt.

Congregational Union of England and Wales. The report of the Commission on the Sacraments of Baptism and the Lord's Supper. 8vo. LOND., [1933]. [Pamph.]
—— *See* Suppt. Congregational Year Book.
Congregational Year Book. *See* Suppt.
Conn (Charles W.) Like a mighty army: a history of the Church of God. (1955.) rev. ed. 8vo. CLEVELAND (Tenn.), 1977.
[Connolly (C. V.)] The uniquiet grave: a word cycle by Palinurus. 8vo. LOND., 1944.
Constantine, *Bp. of Assiou. See* Suppt. Corpus Script. Christ. Orient., Copt., 37-38.
Constantine I, *Emperor of Rome, 'the Great'. See* Ruhbach (G.) *ed.*
Constantine V, *Emperor of the East, 'Copronymus'. See* Suppt. Corpus Script. Christ. Orient., Subsid., 52.
Constantine VII, *Porphyrogenitus. See* Toynbee (A. J.)
Constantine-Cyril, *Saint. See* Cyril, *Saint, Apostle of the Slavs.*
Contarini (Gasparo) *Cardinal. See* Jedin (H.); Matheson (P.)
Conzelmann (Hans) *See* Dibelius (M.) and Conzelmann (H.)
[Cook (E. J. R.)] Bradford Unitarian Church, Chapel Lane Chapel, 1719-1969. 8vo. [BRADFORD, 1969.] [Pamph.]
Cook (Henry) Charles Brown 8vo. LOND., 1939.
Cook (Michael J.) *See* Suppt. Novum Testamentum. Suppts., 51.
Cooke (Alice M.) *See* Horner (I. B.) and Haworth (E. A.)
Coomer (Duncan) *See* Suppt. Methodist Sacramental Fellowship. M.S.F. Booklets, N.S., 2.
Cooney (E. W.) *See* Brennan (T.) *and others.*
[Cooper (Cyril J.)] Centenary celebrations of the Baptists now worshipping at City Road Baptist Church, Winchester. A short history of the cause, 1861-1961. 8vo. [WINCHESTER, 1961.] [Pamph.]
Cooper (F. W.) The Wilts and East Somerset Association of Baptist Churches, 1862-1975. fol. [YEOVIL, 1975.] [Pamph.]
Cooper (Margaret E.) The history of Methodism in Beeston, and The story of Chilwell Road Methodist Church, 1902-1952. 8vo. [BEESTON, 1952.] [Pamph.]
Coornhert (Dirck Volckertszoon) A l'aurore des libertés modernes: Synode sur la liberté de conscience. (1582.) Avant-propos de Pierre Brachin. Introds., trad. et notes par Joseph Lecler et Marius-François Valkhoff. 8vo. PARIS, 1979.
Cope (Gilbert Frederick) *ed.* Dying, death, and disposal. 8vo. LOND., 1970.
Cope (Gilbert Frederick) *and others.* An experimental liturgy. By G. Cope, J. G. Davies, D. A. Tytler. [Ecumenical Studies in Worship, 3.] (1958.) 4th imp. 8vo. LOND., 1963.
Copi (I. M.) and **Beard** (R. W.) *ed.* Essays on Wittgenstein's Tractatus. 8vo. LOND., 1966.
Copleston (Frederick Charles) A history of philosophy. [Bellarmine Series.] 8vo. LOND., 1946-
   9. Maine de Biran to Sartre. 1975.
—— The history of philosophy: relativism and recurrence. An inaugural lect., Heythrop Coll., Univ. of London, 8 March, 1973. 8vo. LOND., 1973. [Pamph.]
—— Philosophy and religion in Judaism and Christianity. Maynard-Chapman Divinity Lect., Westfield Coll., Univ. of London, 26 June, 1973. 8vo. [LOND., 1973.] [Pamph.]
—— Religion and philosophy. 8vo. DUBLIN, 1974.
—— On the history of philosophy, and other essays. 8vo. LOND. & NEW YORK, 1979.
Coppe (Abiezer) A fiery flying roll: a word from the Lord to all the great ones of the earth . . . With another flying roll ensuing (to all the inhabitants of the earth). (1649.) facsim. repr. 8vo. EXETER, 1973. [Pamph.]
Copping (Alice M.) The story of College Hall. 8vo. LOND., 1974.
Cordeaux (E. H.) *See* Suppt. Oxford Hist. Soc., N.S., 25.
Corpus Philosophorum Medii Aevi. *See* Suppt.
Corpus Scriptorum Christianorum Orientalium. *See* Suppt.
Corpus Scriptorum Ecclesiasticorum Latinorum. *See* Suppt.
Corrie (Andrew) An illustrated history of Methodism in Bramhall [1871-1971]. 8vo. BRAMHALL, 1971. [Pamph.]

Coster (G. T.) Points from my journal. 8vo. LOND., 1908.

Cotgrove (Barbara) *See* Pert (K. G.) and Cotgrove (B.)

Cottier (Fred) The story of Gorton Chapel and Brookfield Church, 1703-1871-1953. 8vo. [MANCHESTER, 1953.] [Pamph.]

Cotton (John) 1584-1652. [Two or more works.] John Cotton on the Churches of New England. Ed. Larzer Ziff. [John Harvard Lib.] 8vo. CAMBRIDGE (Mass.), 1968.

Coulson (John) and **Allchin** (A. M.) *ed.* The rediscovery of Newman: an Oxford symposium. 8vo. LOND. & MELBOURNE, 1967.

Courcelle (Pierre) Recherches sur les Confessions de saint Augustin. (1950.) Nouvelle éd., augmentée et illus. 8vo. PARIS, 1968.

Court (J. M.) Myth and history in the Book of Revelation. 8vo. LOND., 1979.

Coutts (Frederick) *See* Sandall (R.)

Coverdale (Miles) *Bp. of Exeter*. *See* Lupton (L. F.)

Cowan (I. B.) *See* Suppt. Historical Assn. Gen. Ser., 92.

Cowie (Margaret J.) *comp.* The London Missionary Society in South Africa: a bibliography. 8vo. CAPE TOWN, 1969. [Pamph.]

Cowley (R. A.) They built in faith. [Norbury Baptist Church.] 8vo. LOND., [1947]. [Pamph.]

Cox (Edwin) This elusive Jesus: the problem of Gospel teaching. 8vo. LOND., 1975.

Cox (H. G.) The secular city: secularization and urbanization in theological perspective. 8vo. LOND., 1965.

Cox (W. J. B.) Union Church, Totteridge: a history of its first thirty years, 1945-1975. 8vo. TOTTERIDGE, 1974. [Pamph.]

Cozens (H. B.) The church of the vow: a record of Zion Congregational Church, Bedminster, Bristol, 1830-1930. 8vo. BRISTOL, 1930.

Cozens-Hardy (Basil) The Norwich Chapelfield House Estate since 1545 and some of its owners and occupiers. 8vo. [NORWICH, 194-.] [Pamph.]

Crabtree (Herbert) Some religious cults and movements of to-day, and their contribution to the religion of to-morrow. [Religion: its Modern Needs and Problems, 7.] 8vo. LOND., 1932.

Cradley, *Worcs. Baptist Church*. Registers and historical records, 1783-1837. fol. *Duplicated*. BIRMINGHAM, 1978. [Pamph.]

Craig (Robert) William Temple and the prospects of a reasonable Christology. 8vo. n.p., [1959]. [Pamph.]

—— The Church: unity in integrity. [Peter Ainslie Memorial Lect., 1965.] 8vo. GRAHAMSTOWN (S. Afr.), 1966. [Pamph.]

—— Politics and religion: a Christain view. A public lect., Univ. of Rhodesia, 12th April 1972. 8vo. SALISBURY (Rhod.), 1972. [Pamph.]

—— On belonging to a university. Address to first year students . . . Univ. of Rhodesia. 8vo. [ST.ANDREWS, 1974.] [Pamph.]

Cranfield (C. E. B.) *See* Bible. Commentaries. Internat. Crit. Comm.

Cranmer (Thomas) *Abp. of Canterbury*. *See* Williams (C. W. S.)

Crashaw (Richard) *See* Lewalski (B. K.) and Sabol (A. J.) *ed.*

Crawley. *Baptist Church*. Year book and history, 1883-1958. 8vo. [HOVE, 1958.] [Pamph.]

Creasey (J. O.) *ed.* *See* Catalogues. *Dr. Williams's Lib.*

Crenshaw (J. L.) *See* Suppt. Zeitschr. für A. T. Wiss. Beihefte, 124.

Cresswell (M. J.) *See* Hughes (G. E.) and Cresswell (M. J.)

Crighton (J. D.) *See* Suppt. Alcuin Club. Misc. Publs., 1974.

Cripps (Arthur Shearly) *See* Steere (D. V.)

Croft (John) The Northern Sunday School Federation, 1845-1945. 8vo. MANCHESTER, [1945]. [Pamph.]

Crofton (C. Anthony) Pedigrees of the Martineau family: a revision and continuation of pedigrees set forth in 1907 by David Martineau. 8vo. n.p. [priv. printed], 1972.

Croker (W. C.) Penrallt English Baptist Church, Bangor: the story of a hundred years, 1872-1972. 8vo. [BANGOR, 1972.] [Pamph.]

Cromwell (Oliver) *See* Ashley (M.P.); Bethel (S.); Brauer (K.); Cocks (H. F. L.); Johnstone (H.); Paul (R. S.); Woolrych (A. H.); Young (G. M.); Young (P.)

[**Crook** (W. G. S.)] Marlowes Baptist Church, Hemel Hempstead: some account of its history, and to mark the centenary year of its foundation in Marlowes. 8vo. BERKHAMSTEAD, 1961.

Cross (F. L.) *ed.* *See* Dictionaries. Christianity.

Cross (H. G.) By faith also: a short history of the Swallownest Baptist Church. 8vo. [SWALLOWNEST, 1958.] [Pamph.]

Crossman (R. H. S.) A politician's view of Health Service Planning. [Maurice Bloch Lects., 13, 1972.] [Glasgow Univ. Publs.] 8vo. GLASGOW, 1972. [Pamph.]

Crothers (S. M.) The endless life. [Ingersoll Lect., 1905.] 8vo. LOND., 1906.

Crouch (J. E.) *See* Suppt. Forschungen zur Religion u. Lit., 109.

Crowe (S. C.) And they began to build: the story of John Bunyan Baptist Church, Cowley, Oxford, 1939-1949. 8vo. [OXF., 1949.] [Pamph.]

Crowley (Robert) *c.* 1518-88. *See* Peel (A.)

Cruse (J. H.) and **Green** (B. S. W.) Marriage, divorce and repentance in the Church of England. 8vo. LOND., 1949. [Pamph.]

Cuckson (John) Brooke Herford: a memoir. 8vo. BOSTON (Mass.), 1904.

Cudworth (Ralph) *See* Gysi (L.)

Cullmann (Oscar) Jesus and the revolutionaries. Trans. Gareth Putnam 8vo. NEW YORK, *etc.*, 1970.

—— Der johanneische Kreis: sein Platz im Spätjudentum, in der Jüngerschaft Jesu und im Urchristentum. Zum Ursprung des Johannesevangeliums. 8vo. TÜBINGEN, 1975.

—— The Johannine circle: its place in Judaism, among the disciples of Jesus, and in early Christianity. A study in the origin of the Gospel of John. [New Test. Lib.] 8vo. LOND., 1976.

Cuming (G. J.) *ed.* *See* Suppt. Ecclesiastical Hist. Soc.

Cunliffe-Jones (Hubert) Christian theology since 1600. [Duckworth Studies in Theol.] 8vo. LOND., 1970.

—— A word for our time? Zechariah 9-14, the New Testament, and today. [Ethel M. Wood Lect., 1973.] 8vo. LOND., 1973. [Pamph.]

—— *See* Suppt. Methodist Sacramental Fellowship. M.S.F. Booklets, N.S., 5.

Cunningham (Valentine) Everywhere spoken against: Dissent in the Victorian novel. 8vo. OXF., 1975.

Cuppé (Pierre) *See* Briggs (E. R.)

Curio (C. S.) *See* Briggs (E. R.); Plath (U.)

Curle (Adam) Peace and love: the violin and the oboe. [Essex Hall Lect., 1977.] 8vo. LOND., 1977. [Pamph.]

Currie (Robert) *and others.* Churches and churchgoers: patterns of church growth in the British Isles since 1700. By Robert Currie, Alan Gilbert and Lee Horsley. 4to. OXF., 1977.

[**Curtis** (A. H.)] The birth of Jesus: a fresh interpretation of St. Matthew's story. 8vo. BIRMINGHAM, 1943. [Pamph.]

Curtis (S. J.) History of education in Great Britain. (1948.) 2nd ed. 8vo. LOND., 1950.

Curwen (John F.) The ancient parish of Heversham with Milnthorpe, including the hamlets of Leasgill, Ackenthwaite and Rowell. [Village Histories.] 8vo. KENDALL, 1930.

Cuthbert, *Saint, Bp. of Lindisfarne.* *See* Colgrave (H.)

Cymdeithas Hanes Annibynwyr Cymru. *See* Suppt. Cofiadur.

Cymdeithas Hanes Bedyddwyr Cymru. *See* Suppt. Trafodion Cymdeithas Hanes Bedyddwyr Cymru.

Cyprian, *Saint, Bp. of Carthage.* [Works. *Latin.*] Opera. Pars I. Ad Quirinum—Ad Fortunatum. Ed. R. Weber.—De lapsis—De ecclesiae catholicae unitate. Ed. M. Bévenot. [Corpus Christianorum, Ser. Latina, 3.] 8vo. TURNHOUT, 1972.

—— [Two or more works. *Latin and English.*] De lapsis and De ecclesiae catholicae unitate. Text and trans. by Maurice Bévenot. [Oxford Early Christian Texts.] 8vo. OXF., 1971.

—— *See* Suppt. Analecta Bollandiana. Subsid. Hagiog., 54; Zeitschr. für N.T. Wiss. Beihefte, 41.

Cyril, *Saint, Patriarch of Alexandria.* Deux dialogues christologiques. [Dialogue sur l'incarnation du monogène, et Le Christ est un.] Introd., texte critique, trad. et notes par G. M. de Durand. [Sources Chrétiennes, 97.] 8vo. PARIS, 1964.

—— *See* Wilken (R. L.); Suppt. Corpus Script. Christ. Orient., Syri, 157-158.

Cyril, *Saint, Abp. of Jerusalem.* Catéchèses mystagogiques. Introd., texte critique et notes de Auguste Piédagnel. Trad. de Pierre Paris, revue et adaptée. [Sources Chrétiennes, 126.] 8vo. PARIS, 1966.
Cyril, *Saint, Apostle of the Slavs.* *See* Dvornik (F.)
Cyrus, *of Edessa.* *See* Suppt. Corpus Script. Christ. Orient., Syri, 155-156.

Dadišo Qatraya. *See* Suppt. Corpus Script. Christ. Orient., Syri, 144-145.
Dagens (Claude) Saint Grégoire le Grand: culture et expérience chrétiennes. 8vo. PARIS, 1977.
Dagron (Gilbert) *See* Suppt. Analecta Bollandiana. Subsid. Hagiog, 62.
Dahood (Mitchell) *See* Bible. Commentaries. Anchor Bible, 16, 17, 17A.
Dale (R. W.) *See* Myers (S.)
Dale (W. L.) The law of the parish church: an account of the powers, rights and duties of the incumbent, the churchwardens, the parochial church council and the parishioners. (1932.) 2nd ed. 8vo. LOND., 1946.
Dallimore (A. A.) George Whitefield: the life and times of the great evangelist of the eighteenth-century revival. 2 vols. 8vo. LOND., 1970-80.
    2. [1741-1770.] 1980.
Damsteegt (P. Gerard) Foundations of the Seventh-day Adventist message and mission. (1977.) repr. 8vo. GRAND RAPIDS (Mich.), 1978.
Dando (Marcel) The Moralia in Job of Gregory the Great as a source for the Old Saxon Genesis B. 8vo. COPENHAGUE, 1969. [Pamph.]
—— Une énigme le l'église celtique: les culdées. [Cahiers du Cercle Ernest-Renan, 88.] 8vo. PARIS, 1975. [Pamph.]
Daniel-Rops (Henri) Histoire de l'église du Christ. 8vo. PARIS.
    1. L'église des apôtres et des martyrs. 1948.
    2. L'église des temps barbares. 1950.
    3. L'église de la cathédrale et de la croisade. 1952.
    [No more in Library.]
Danish Yearbook of Philosophy. *See* Suppt.
Dante Alighieri. *See* Foster (K.); Herde (P.); Kirkpatrick (R.); Reade (W. H. V.); Vincent (E. R. P.)
Darbishire (Helen) Somerville College Chapel addresses and other papers. With a list of her published writings, 1908-1961. 8vo. LOND., 1962.
Darcy (C. P.) *See* Suppt. Chetham Soc., 3rd Ser., 24.
D'Arcy (M. C.) Communism and Christianity. 8vo. HARMONDSWORTH, 1956.
Dare (Thomas) The Old Baptist Chapel, South Chard, Somerset. obl. 12mo. [SOUTH CHARD, 1909.] [Pamph.]
Dark (Sidney) The people's archbishop: the man and his message. With an appendix, "Dr. Temple as a diocesan", by A. E. Baker, Canon of York. 8vo. LOND., [1942].
Darlaston (G. E.) *See* Pringle (A.) *ed.*
Darling (Edward) *ed.* *See* Raible (C.) and Darling (E.) *ed.*
Darragh (R. E.) *comp.* In defence of His word: being a number of selected testimonies of dire suffering, healed by the power of Christ, under the ministry of Principal George Jeffreys. 8vo. LOND., 1932.
Darrouzès (Jean) Recherches sur les Officia de l'église byzantine. [Archives de l'Orient Chrétien, 11.] 8vo. PARIS, 1970.
—— Le registre synodal du patriarcat byzantin au XIVe siècle: étude paléographique et diplomatique. [Archives de l'Orient Chrétien, 12.] 8vo. PARIS, 1971.
—— Littérature et histoire des textes byzantins. [Variorum Reprs.] 8vo. LOND., 1972.
Dartford Priory. A history of the English Dominicanesses. By the Dominican nuns of Headington. 8vo. OXF., 1945. [Pamph.]
Darwin (F. D. S.) The English mediaeval recluse. 8vo. LOND., [1944].
Dassmann (Ernst) *ed.* *See* Suppt. Jahrbuch für Antike u. Christentum. Erg.Bde., 3, 8.
Daube (David) He that cometh. [St. Paul's Lect., Oct. 1966.] 8vo. [LOND., 1966.] [Pamph.]
Davenport (G. L.) The eschatology of the Book of Jubilees. [Studia Post-Biblica, 20.] 8vo. LEIDEN, 1971.
David (Francis) *d.* 1579, *Transylvanian Unitarian.* *See* Varga (B.)
Davidson (A. Nevile) Reflections of a Scottish churchman. 8vo. LOND., 1965.

Davidson (Hilda R. E.) *ed.* The journey to the other world. [Folklore Soc. Mistletoe Ser.] 8vo. CAMB., 1975.
Davidson (Randall T.) *Abp. of Canterbury. See* Bell (G. K. A.); Education Act, 1902-3.
Davidson (W. J. Havelock) Church union in South India: facts to face. 8vo. LOND., [1943]. [Pamph.]
Davie (D. A.) A gathered church: the literature of the English Dissenting interest, 1700-1930. [Clark Lects., 1976.] 8vo. LOND. & HENLEY, 1978.
Davies (*Sir* Alfred Thomas) *ed.* "O.M." (Sir Owen M. Edwards): a memoir. 8vo. CARDIFF & WREXHAM, 1946.
Davies (Dewi Eirug) Hoff Ddysgedig Nyth: cyfraniad Coleg Presbyteraidd Caerfyrddin i fywyd Cymru. 8vo. ABERTAWE, 1976.
Davies (Ebenezer Thomas) Episcopacy and the royal supremacy in the Church of England in the XVI century. 8vo. OXF., 1950.
Davies (G. I.) The way of the wilderness: a geographical study of the wilderness itineraries in the Old Testament. [Soc. for O.T. Study, Monograph Ser., 5.] 8vo. CAMB., 1979.
Davies (Gwynne Henton) [Misc.] Proclamation and presence. Old Testament essays in honour of Gwynne Henton Davies. Ed. John I. Durham and J. R. Porter. 8vo. LOND., 1970.
Davies (Horton M.) Worship and theology in England. 5 vols. 8vo. PRINCETON & LOND., 1961-75.
   1. From Cranmer to Hooker, 1534-1603. 1970.
   2. From Andrewes to Baxter and Fox, 1603-1690. 1975.
Davies (John Gordon) Every day God: encountering the holy in world and worship. 8vo. LOND., 1973.
—— *See* Cope (G. F.) *and others.*
—— *ed. See* Dictionaries. Liturgiology.
Davies (John Trevor) Lord of all. 8vo. LOND., 1951.
Davies (Rupert Eric) Methodism. (1963.) repr. 8vo. [HARMONDSWORTH,] 1964.
Davies (Rupert Eric) *and others, ed.* A history of the Methodist Church in Great Britain. 2 vols. 8vo. LOND., 1965-78.
   2. Ed. Rupert Davies, A Raymond George and Gordon Rupp. 1978.
Davies (Samuel) 1724-61, *New England divine. See* Gilbourn (C. A.)
Davies (William David P.) The Gospel and the land: early Christianity and Jewish territorial doctrine. 8vo. BERKELEY (Calif.), *etc.*, 1974.
[**Davies** (William Solva)] "In pleasant places." 1767-1967: the story of Tenterden Baptist Church over two centuries. 8vo. [TENTERDEN, 1967.] [Pamph.]
Davies (William T. Pennar) Diwinyddiaeth J. R. Jones: darlith gofa J. R. Jones a draddodwyd yn y Coleg ar Chwefror 21, 1978. 8vo. ABERTAWE, 1978. [Pamph.]
Davis (Charles) Body as spirit: the nature of religious feeling. 8vo. LOND., 1976.
Davis (Charles Henry) The history of the Silver Street Sunday School Society. 8vo. LOND., 1904.
Davis (David Daniel) *See* Jones (G. R.)
Davis (Edward) *See* Jones (G. R.)
[**Davis** (Ernest W.)] Upper Brook Street Free Church and Sunday School. 8vo. MANCHESTER, 1915. [Pamph.]
Davis (Henry W. C.) Regesta regum Anglo-Normannorum, 1066-1154. 4 vols. 8vo. OXF., 1913-69.
   3. Regesta regis Stephani ac Mathildis imperaticis ac Gaufridi et Henrici Ducum Normannorum, 1135-1154. Ed. H. A. Cronne and R. H. Davis. 1968.
   4. Facsimiles of original charters and writs of King Stephen, the Empress Matilda and Dukes Henry and Geoffrey. Ed. H. A. Cronne and R. H. C. Davis. 1969.
Davis (Myer David) *ed.* [Shetaroth.] Hebrew deeds of English Jews before 1290. [Publs. of the Anglo-Jewish Historical Exhibition, 2.] (1888.) facsim. repr. 8vo. FARNBOROUGH, 1969.
Davis (Richard Whitlock) Dissent in politics, 1780-1830: the political life of William Smith, M.P. 8vo. LOND., 1971.
Davis (Thomas W.) *ed.* Committees for repeal of the Test and Corporation Acts: minutes, 1786-90 and 1827-8. [Lond Record Soc. Publs., 14.] 8vo. [LEICESTER,] 1978.
Dawson (Albert) Joseph Parker, D.D.: his life and ministry. Minister of the City Temple, London. [New Century Leaders Ser.] 8vo. LOND., 1901.

Dawson (William Harbutt)   Cromwell's understudy: the life and times of General John Lambert, and the rise and fall of the Protectorate.   8vo.   LOND., *etc.*, 1938.
Day (E. H.)   Renaissance architecture in England.   [Arts of the Church, 6.]   8vo. LOND. & OXF., 1910.
Day (John R.)   *See* Gould (F. J.) and Day (J. R.)
Deacon (Malcolm)   Philip Doddridge of Northampton, 1702-51.   8vo.   NORTHAMPTON, 1980.
Dead Sea Scrolls.   [Collections. *Hebrew and German.*]   Die Texte aus Qumran, hebräisch und deutsch. Mit masoretischer Punktation, Übersetzung, Einführung und Anmerkungen. Hrsg. Eduard Lohse.   8vo.   DARMSTADT, 1964.
—— *See* Allegro (J. M.); Discoveries in the Judaean Desert.
Dearing (V. A.)   *See* Plumb (J. H.) and Dearing (V. A.)
Dearmer (Percy)   *See* Papers for War Time, 13; Suppt. Alcuin Club. Misc. Publs., 1980.
Debrunner (Albert) *ed.*   *See* Blass (F.)
Décarreaux (Jean)   Les Grecs au concile de l'Union Ferrare-Florence, 1438-1439. [Publ. de la Société des Études Italiennes, 6.]   8vo.   PARIS, [1969].
Dee (John)   *See* French (P. J.)
Defoe (Danuel)   *See* Payne (W. L.)
Deimel (P. Anton) *ed.*   *See* Dictionaries. Languages. *Sumerian.*
Dekker (Cornelius) *ed.*   *See* Buijtenen (M.P.van) *and others, ed.*
De La Brosse (Olivier)   *See* Dumeige (G.) *ed.*
Delany (Paul)   British autobiography in the seventeenth century.   8vo.   LOND., 1969.
Delaval (*Lady* Elizabeth) *afterwards Hatcher.*   *See* Suppt. Surtees Soc., 190.
Dell (William)   *See* Sippell (T.); Walker (E. C.)
DeMolen (R. L.) *ed.*   Essays on the works of Erasmus [presented to Craig R. Thompson on his 65th birthday, 1976].   8vo.   NEW HAVEN & LOND., 1978.
Denbighshire County Library.   *See* Catalogues.
De Nerée (Richard Jean)   *See* Posthumus Meyjes (G. H. M.)
Denney (A. H.) *ed.*   The Sibton Abbey estates: select documents, 1325-1509.   [Suffolk Records Soc., 2.]   8vo.   [IPSWICH,] 1960.
Denney (James)   *See* Taylor (J. R.)
Dent (H. C.)   Education in transition: a sociological study of the impact of war on English education, 1939-1943.   [Internat. Lib. of Sociol. and Social Reconstr.] 8vo.   LOND., 1944.
—— Change in English education: a historical survey.   8vo.   LOND., 1952.
Dentz (F. O.)   History of the English Church at The Hague, 1586-1929. Together with a short account of the family Tinne, a member of which, John Abraham Tinne, founded the present church building.   8vo.   DELFT, 1929.
Derby.   *Broadway Baptist Church.*   Silver jubilee, 1939-64.   8vo.   [DERBY, 1964.] [Pamph.]
Derrett (J. D. M.)   La parabola delle vergini stolte.   8vo.   FIRENZE, [1971]. [Pamph.]
—— The Good Shepherd: St. John's use of Jewish halakah and haggadah.   8vo. [OSLO,] 1973.   [Pamph.]
—— Jesus's audience: the social and psychological environment in which he worked: prolegomena to a restatement of the teaching of Jesus. Lects. at Newquay, 1971. 8vo.   LOND., 1973.
—— The footwashing in John XIII and the alienation of Judas Iscariot.   8vo.   [BRUXELLES, 1977.] [Pamph.]
—— Studies in the New Testament.   8vo.   LEIDEN, 1977-
    1.   Glimpses of the legal and social presuppositions of the authors.   1977.
    2.   Midrash in action and as a literary device.   1978.
—— "Domini, tu mihi lavas pedes?" Studio su Giovanni 13, 1-30.   8vo.   BORNATO, 1979.   [Pamph.]
—— Haggadah and the account of the Passion.   8vo.   EXETER [printed], 1979. [Pamph.]
—— Spirit-possession and the Gerasene demoniac.   8vo.   [LOND., 1979.] [Pamph.]
—— The Iscariot, mesira, and the redemption.   8vo.   [SHEFFIELD, 1980.] [Pamph.]
—— Legend and event: the Gerasene demoniac: an inquest into history and liturgical projection.   8vo.   SHEFFIELD, 1980.   [Pamph.]

Descartes (René) Geometry. Trans. from the French and Latin by David Eugene Smith and Marcia L. Latham. [With a facsim. of the 1st ed., 1637.] (1925.) repr. 8vo. NEW YORK, 1954.
—— *See* Weinberg (J. R.)
Detienne (Marcel) and **Vernant** (Jean-Pierre) Cunning intelligence in Greek culture and society. Trans. from the French by Janet Lloyd. [European Philos. and the Human Sciences.] 8vo. HASSOCKS (Sx.) & ATLANTIC HIGHLANDS (N.J.), 1978.
Deutsche Mystiker. 8vo. KEMPTEN & MÜNCHEN.
   1. Seuse. Ausgewahlt und hrsg. von Wilhelm Oehl. [1910].
   2. Mechtild von Magdeburg: Das fliessende Licht der Gottheit. In Auswahl übersetzt von Wilhelm Oehl. [1910.]
   3. *Not in Library.*
   4. Tauler. In Auswahl übersetzt von Wilhelm Oehl. [191-.]
   5. Frauenmystik im Mittelalter. Ausgewählt und hrsg. von M. David-Windstosser. [191-.]
Devon Congregational Union. Annual meetings held at the Congregational Church, Tavistock, April 9th, 10th & 11th, 1923. 8vo. TIVERTON [printed], [1923]. [Pamph.]
De Vooght (Paul) L'hérésie de Jean Huss. (1960.) 2e. éd. [Bibliothèque de la Revue d'Hist. Ecclésiastique, 34-35.] 2 vols. 8vo. LOUVAIN, 1975.
Dewey (John) A common faith. [Based on Terry Lects., Yale Univ.] (1934.) repr. 8vo. NEW HAVEN, 1960.
—— *See* Kestenbaum (V.); Peters (R. S.) *ed.;* Wickham (H.)
De Winton (F. S. W.) "Except the Lord build—", being a history of St. Ninian's Presbyterian Church, Pagham, Sussex, 1963-1972. 8vo. BOGNOR REGIS, [1972]. [Pamph.]
Dibelius (Martin) and **Conzelmann** (Hans) A commentary on the Pastoral Epistles. Trans. Philip Buttolph and Adela Yarbro. Ed. Helmut Koestler. [Hermeneia—a Crit. and Hist. Comm. on the Bible.] 4to. PHILADELPHIA, 1972.
Dickens (A. G.) The Marian reaction in the Diocese of York. [St. Anthony's Hall Publs., 11-12.] 2 pts. 8vo. LOND. & YORK, 1957. [Pamphs.]
   1. The clergy.
   2. The laity.
—— [Misc.] Reformation principle and practice. Essays in honour of Arthur Geoffrey Dickens, ed. Peter Newman Brooks. 8vo. LOND., 1980.
Dickinson (F. H.) *ed. See* Liturgies. *Latin Rite.* [Hours.]
Dickinson (H. T.) Bolingbroke. 8vo. LOND., 1970
Dickinson (J. C.) The later Middle Ages: from the Norman Conquest to the eve of the Reformation. [Ecclesiastical Hist. of England, 2.] 8vo. LOND., 1979.
DICTIONARIES. Abbreviations. Lexicon abbreviaturarum: dizionario di abbreviature latine ed italiane usate nelle carte e codici specialmente del medio-evo riprodotte con oltre 14000 segni incisi. Per cura di Adriano Cappelli. [Manuali Hoepli.] (1899.) 6a. ed. (1929.) repr. 12mo. MILANO, 1961.
—— —— Supplément. Abbréviations latines médiévales: Auguste Pelzer. (1964.) 2e. éd. 12mo. LOUVAIN & PARIS, 1966.
—— **Archaeology.** *Classical. See* Dictionaries. Classical.
—— **Biblical.** Dictionnaire de la Bible [of F. Vigoroux, 1895-1912]. Supplément, commencé par L. Pirot, A. Robert, continué sous la direction de Henri Cazelles et André Feuillet. 4to. PARIS, 1928-
   8. Pithom-Providentissimus. 1972.
   9. Psaumes-Refuge. 1979.
—— —— Vocabulary of the Bible. General editor: J.-J. von Allmen. [Trans. ed. Hilda A. Wilson.] Introd. by H. H. Rowley. (1958.) 2nd imp. 8vo. LOND., 1958.
—— —— The interpreter's dictionary of the Bible. (4 vols., 1962.) Suppt. vol. 4to. NASHVILLE (Tenn.), 1976.
—— **Bibliography.** *See* Suppt. Bibliographical Soc. Publs., 1973-75.
—— **Biography.** Who was who: a companion to Who's who containing the biographies of those who died during the decade... 8vo. LOND., 1920-
   6. 1961-1970. 1972.
—— —— Who's who in philosophy. Ed. Dagobert D. Runes, *etc.* [Vol. 1. Anglo-American philosophers.] (1942.) repr. 8vo. NEW YORK, 1969.

DICTIONARIES—*continued*

—— —— The seminary priests: a dictionary of the secular clergy of England and Wales, 1558-1850: Godfrey Anstruther. 4 vols. 8vo. GREAT WAKERING, *etc.*, 1969-77.

 2. 1603-1659. 1975.

 3. 1660-1715. 1976.

 4. 1716-1800. 1977.

—— —— Y bywgraffiadur Cymreig, 1941-1950, gydag atodiad i'r bwygraffiadur Cymreig hyd 1940. Paratowyd dan nawdd Anrhydeddus Gymdeithas y Cymmrodorion. 8vo. LOND., 1970.

—— —— Dictionary of national biography, 1951-60. Ed. E. T. Williams and Helen M. Palmer. With index, 1901-1960. 8vo. OXF., 1971.

—— —— A dictionary of Irish biography: Henry Boylan. 8vo. DUBLIN, 1978.

—— —— The Oxford dictionary of saints: David Hugh Farmer. 8vo. OXF., 1978.

—— **Christianity.** Dictionnaire d'histoire et de géographie ecclésiastiques. Publié sous la direction de Alfred Baudrillart, *etc.* 4to. PARIS, 1912-

 [*Volumes already in Library:* 1-18 (A-Frères), 1912-77.]

—— —— The Oxford dictionary of the Christian Church. Ed. F. L. Cross. (1957.) 2nd ed., ed. F. L. Cross and E. A. Livingstone. 8vo. OXF., 1974.

—— —— Weltkirchen Lexikon: Handbuch der Ökumene. Im Auftrag des Deutschen Evangelischen Kirchentages. Hrsg. Franklin H. Littell und Hans Hermann Walz. 8vo. STUTTGART, 1960

—— —— Handbuch theologischer Grundbegriffe. Hrsg. Heinrich Fries. 2 vols. 8vo. MÜNCHEN, 1962-3.

—— —— A Catholic dictionary of theology. A work prepared with the approval of the Catholic hierarchy of England and Wales. 4to. LOND., *etc.*, 1962-

 3. Hegel-Paradise. 1971.

—— —— A dictionary of Christian theology. Ed. Alan Richardson. (1969.) repr. 8vo. LOND., 1977.

—— —— The new international dictionary of the Christian Church. General editor: J. D. Douglas. 8vo. EXETER, 1974.

—— —— Concise dictionary of Christian ethics. Ed. Bernhard Stoeckle. 8vo. LOND., 1979.

—— **Classical.** Paulys Realencyclopädie der classischen Altertumswissenschaft. Neue Bearb., hrsg. Georg Wissowa, *etc.* 8vo. STUTTGART, 1894-

 Suppt. Bd. 13. 1973.

 Suppt. Bd. 14. 1974.

—— **Islam.** The encyclopaedia of Islam. New edition, ed. H. A. R. Gibb, *etc.* 8vo. LEIDEN, 1960-

 3. H-Iram. 1971.

—— **Judaism.** Philo-Lexikon: Handbuch des jüdischen Wissens. (1934.) 3te. Aufl. 8vo. BERLIN, 1936.

—— **Languages.** *English.* A supplement to the Oxford English Dictionary. Ed. R. W. Burchfield. 4to. OXF., 1972-

 1. A-G. 1972.

 2. H-N. 1976.

—— —— *Gaelic.* A pronouncing Gaelic-English dictionary. By Neil MacAlpine. (1832.) new ed. (1929.) repr. [With pt.2. An English-Gaelic dictionary. By John MacKenzie. (1845.) new ed. (1930.) repr. 1956.] 8vo. GLASGOW, 1957.

—— —— *Greek.* Theological dictionary of the New Testament. Ed. Gerhard Kittel [and Gerhard Friedrich]. Trans. and ed. Geoffrey W. Bromiley. 10 vols. 8vo. GRAND RAPIDS (Mich.) & LOND., 1964-76.

—— —— *Latin.* Thesaurus linguae latinae. fol. LEIPZIG, 1900-

 [*Volumes already in Library:* 1-5,6.i-iii,7.i,8.]

—— —— —— Oxford Latin dictionary. 4to. OXF., 1968-

 [*Fascicles already in Library:* 1-7, 1968-80.]

—— —— *Latin, Medieval.* Dictionary of medieval Latin from British sources. Prepared by R. E. Latham. 4to. LOND.

 Fasc.1. A-B. 1975.

—— —— *Sumerian.* Sumerisches Lexikon. Hrsg. P. Anton Deimel. [Scripta Pontificii Instituti Biblici.] 2 vols. in 5. 4to. ROME, 1925-33.

DICTIONARIES—*continued*
—— **Liturgiology.** A dictionary of liturgy and worship. Ed. J. G. Davies. (1972.) 4th imp. 8vo. LOND., 1978.
—— **Quotations.** The Oxford dictionary of quotations. (1941.) 3rd ed. 4to. OXF., 1979.
—— **Religion.** An illustrated encyclopaedia of mysticism and the mystery religions: John Ferguson. 8vo. LOND., 1976.
—— —— Dictionary of Asian philosophies: St. Elmo Nauman. 8vo. LOND. & HENLEY, 1979.
—— —— *Christian Church.* See Dictionaries. Christianity.
Didascalia Apostolorum. *See* Suppt. Corpus Script. Christ. Orient., Syri, 175-176, 179-180.
Diels (Hermann) Kleine Schriften zur Geschichte der antiken Philosophie. Hrsg. Walter Burkert. 8vo. DARMSTADT, 1969.
Diem (Hermann) Kierkegaard's dialectic of existence. Trans. Harold Knight. 8vo. EDIN. & LOND., 1959.
—— Sine vi—sed verbo. Aufsätze, Vorträge, Voten. Aus Anlass der Vollendung seines 65. Lebensjahres am 2. Feb. 1965. Hrsg. Uvo Andreas Wolf. [Theologische Bücherei, 25.] 8vo. MÜNCHEN, 1965.
Dieten (J. L. van) Zur Überlieferung und Veröffentlichung der Panoplia Dogmatike des Niketas Choniates. [Zetemata Byzantina, 3.] 8vo. AMSTERDAM, 1970.
—— Niketas Choniates: Erläuterungen zu den Reden und Briefen nebst einer Biographie. [Supplementa Byzantina, 2.] 8vo. BERLIN & NEW YORK, 1971.
Dietrich (Walter) *See* Suppt. Forschungen zur Religion u. Lit., 108.
Dijksterhuis (E. J.) Die Mechanisierung des Weltbildes. Ins deutsche übertragen von Helga Habicht. 8vo. BERLIN, *etc.*, 1956.
Dillistone (F. W.) The Holy Spirit in the life of today. [St. Paul's Lib.] 8vo. LOND., 1946.
—— Revelation and evangelism. 8vo. LOND. & REDHILL, 1948.
—— The structure of the divine society. 8vo. PHILADELPHIA, 1951.
—— Dramas of salvation. 8vo., LOND., 1967.
—— Traditional symbols and the contemporary world. [Bampton Lects., 1968.] 8vo. LOND., 1973.
—— Charles Raven: naturalist, historian, theologian. 8vo. LOND., 1975.
—— C. H. Dodd: interpreter of the New Testament. 8vo. LOND., 1977.
Dilthey (Wilhelm) Einleitung in die Geisteswissenschaften versuch einer Grundlegung für das Studium der Gesellschaft und der Geschichte. 1.Bd. (1883.) 3te. Aufl. [Gesammelte Schriften, 1.] 8vo. LEIPZIG & BERLIN, 1933.
Dinwiddy (J. R.) Christopher Wyvill and reform, 1790-1820. [Borthwick Papers, 39.] 8vo. YORK, 1971. [Pamph.]
Dirksen (P. B.) The transmission of the text in the Peshitta manuscripts of the Book of Judges. [Monographs of the Peshitta Institute of Leiden, 1.] 8vo. LEIDEN, 1972.
Discoveries in the Judaean Desert. ([Sponsored by the] Jordan Department of Antiquities; École Biblique et Archéologique Française; Palestine Archaeological Museum.) 4to OXF., 1955-
 6. Qumrân Grotte 4. II. 1. Archéologie. Par R. de Vaux, avec des contributions de J. W. B. Barns et J. Carswell. 2. Tefillin, mezuzot et targums (4Q128-4Q157). Par J. T. Milik. 1977.
Ditchfield (G. M.) The early history of Manchester College. 8vo. [LIVERPOOL, 1972.] [Pamph.]
—— The parliamentary struggle over the repeal of the Test and Corporation Acts, 1787-1790. 8vo. [HARLOW,] 1974. [Pamph.]
—— The campaign in Lancashire and Cheshire for the repeal of the Test and Corporation Acts, 1787-1790. 8vo. [LIVERPOOL,] 1977. [Pamph.]
—— Debates on the Test and Corporation Acts, 1787-90: the evidence of the division lists. 8vo. [LOND.,] 1977. [Pamph.]
—— Dissent and toleration: Lord Stanhope's Bill of 1789. 8vo. [CAMB.,] 1978. [Pamph.]
—— The Scottish campaign against the Test Act, 1790-1791. 8vo. CAMB., 1980. [Pamph.]
Ditchling. *Old Meeting House.* Records of the Old Meeting House, Ditchling, Sussex. Transcribed by Leonard J. Maguire. 3 vols. 8vo. n.p. [priv. publ.], 1976-79.

Ditchling. *Old Meeting House—continued*
  1. Church memorandum book, 1753-1803. 1976.
  —— enl. ed., 1753-1894. 1977.
  2. Registers and monumental inscriptions. 1978.
  3. Trust deeds. 1979.
Dives and Pauper. *See* Suppt. Early Eng. Text Soc., O.S., 275, 280.
Dix (Gregory) The power and wisdom of God. Broadcast addresses [in Holy Week, 1948]. 8vo. LOND., [1948]. [Pamph.]
Dix (Kenneth) John Bunyan: Puritan pastor. 8vo. [BEDFORD,] 1978. [Pamph.]
Dixon (A. C.) *ed. See* Fundamentals.
[**Dixon** (G. W.)] Castle Street Baptist Church, Calne, Wilts., 1655-1955. 8vo. [CALNE, 1955.] [Pamph.]
Dixon (W. T.) *See* Lock (J.) and Dixon (W. T.)
Djobadze (W. Z.) *See* Suppt. Corpus Script. Christ. Orient., Subsid., 48.
Dobbek (Wilhelm) Johann Gottfried Herders Jugendzeit in Mohrungen und Königsberg, 1744-1764. [Marburger Ostforschungen, 16.] 8vo. WÜRZBURG, 1961.
[**Dobson** (T. B.)] Milford on Sea Baptist Church: a brief account of its history, 1816-1977. Condensed from the full account by T. B. Dobson. 8vo. *Duplicated.* n.p., [1977]. [Pamph.]
Dr. Williams's Library. *See* Catalogues; Payne (E. A.); Twinn (K.); Suppt. Friends of Dr. Williams's Lib. Lectures.
Dodd (C. H.) The Gospel parables. 8vo. MANCHESTER, 1932. [Pamph.]
—— The Gospel and the law of Christ. William Ainslie Memorial Lect., St. Martin-in-the-Fields, 4th June 1946. 8vo. LOND., *etc.*, 1947. [Pamph.]
—— More New Testament Studies. 8vo. MANCHESTER, 1968.
—— The founder of Christianity. 8vo. LOND., 1971.
—— *See* Caird (G. B.); Dillistone (F. W.); Williams (J. T.)
Doddridge (Philip) *See* Deacon (M.); Harris (F. W. P.); Suppt. Historical MSS. Comm. Joint Publs., 26.
Doel (D. C.) I and my Father are one: the struggle for freedom from 'Mother'. [Essex Hall Lect., 1980.] 8vo. LOND., 1980. [Pamph.]
Dölger (Franz J.) Zur Form des Auslandsschreibens der byzantinischen Kaiserkanzlei. 8vo. BELGRADE, 1963. [Pamph.]
——*See* Suppt. Jahrbuch für Antike u. Christentum. Erg.Bd. 7.
Döring-Hirsch (E.) Tod und Jensiets im Spätmittelalter, zugleich ein Beitrag zur Kulturgeschichte des deutschen Bürgertums. [Studien zur Gesch. der Wirtschaft und Geisteskultur, 2.] 8vo. BERLIN, 1927.
Dörries (Hermann) and **Kretschmar** (Georg) Ansgar: seine Bedeutung für die Mission. 8vo. HAMBURG, 1965.
Dolet (Etienne) L'Erasmianus sive Ciceronianus d'Etienne Dolet. (1535.) Introd., facsim. de l'éd. originale du De Imitatione Ciceroniana, commentaires et appendices: Emile V. Telle. [Travaux d'Humanisme et de Renaissance, 138.] 4to GENÈVE, 1974.
Donfried (K. P.) *See* Suppt. Novum Testamentum. Suppts., 38.
Donne (John) *See* Lewalski (B. K.) and Sabol (A. J.) *ed.*
Dooren (J. P. van) *See* Van den Berg (J.) and Dooren (J. P. van)
Doran (H. P.) A century of Presbyterianism in Streatham: Trinity Church, Pendennis Road, Streatham, Lond S.W.16, opened for public worship on 6th June 1877. 8vo. *Duplicated.* [LOND., 1977.] [Pamph.]
Dorset Congregational Association. 129th annual report, 1925. 8vo. n.p., [1925.] [Pamph.]
Dougall (Lily) *See* Papers for War Time, 21.
[**Douglas** (A. Halliday) *ed.*] Westminster College, Cambridge: an account of the opening of the College at Cambridge on 17 October 1899, with a history of the College from its foundation in 1844 to the present time. 8vo. LOND., 1900.
Douglas (David Charles) Alexander Hamilton Thompson, 1873-1952. [Repr. from Brit. Acad. Proc., 38, 1952.] 8vo. LOND., [1953]. [Pamph.]
—— *ed.* English historical documents. 8vo. LOND., 1953-
        3. 1189-1327: Harry Rothwell. 1975.
Douglas (J. D.) *ed. See* Dictionaries. Christianity.
Douglas (Mary T.) Natural symbols: explorations in cosmology. (1970.) **2nd ed.** 8vo. LOND., 1973.

Downame (George) *Bp. of Derry.* *See* Baynes (P.)

Downe. *Baptist Church.* A brief history, 1851-1969. 8vo. [DOWNE, 1969.] [Pamph.]

Downie (J. A.) Robert Harley and the press: propaganda and public opinion in the age of Swift and Defoe. 8vo. CAMB., 1979.

Downing (A. B.) From Max Müller to Karl Marx: a study of E. M. Geldart, Scholar of Balliol. 8vo. LOND., 1970. [Pamph.]

—— Beyond the horizon: Dissent, independence and the future of the free religious tradition. [Essex Hall Lect., 1976.] 8vo. LOND., 1976. [Pamph.]

Downing (F. Gerald) Doing theology thoughtfully is really very like thoughtfully doing all sorts of other things. (The theologians' craft.) 4to. BURY, 1974.

Drake (H. A.) In praise of Constantine: a historical study and new translation of Eusebius' Tricennial Orations. [Univ. of California Publs., Classical Studies.] 8vo. BERKELEY, 1976.

Draper (Martin P.) *See* Suppt. Alcuin Club. Misc. Publs., 1980.

Drescher (Seymour) *ed.* *See* Bolt (C.) and Drescher (S.) *ed.*

Drew (Kate) The life story of Mrs. J. Bellamy Horton, the well-known evangelist. By her late comrade. 8vo. LOND., [1929].

Droz (Eugénie) Chemins de l'hérésie. Textes et documents. 8vo. GENÈVE, 1970-
> 2. 1971.
> 3. 1974.
> 4. 1976.

Drury (J. H.) Tradition and design in Luke's Gospel: a study in early Christian historiography. 8vo. LOND., 1976.

Dublin Review. *See* Suppt. Month.

Duché (Jacob) *See* Garrett (C.)

Duchrow (Ulrich) Christenheit und Weltverantwortung. Traditionsgeschichte und systematische Struktur der Zweireichelehre. [Forschungen u. Berichte der Evang. Studiengemeinschaft im Auftrage des Wissensch. Kuratoriums, 25.] 8vo. STUTTGART, 1970.

Duckett (James) *See* Merrick (M. M.)

Duckworth Studies in Theology. *See* Suppt.

Dugmore (C. W.) Jewish and Christian benedictions. 8vo. PARIS, 1978. [Pamph.]

—— [Misc.] *See* Suppt. Ecclesiastical Hist. Soc. Studies in Church Hist. Subsid., 2.

Duker (A. C.) Gisbertus Voetius. 4 vols. 8vo. LEIDEN, 1897-1915.

Dumas (André) Dietrich Bonhoeffer: theologian of reality. [Trans. Robert McAfee Brown.] 8vo. LOND., 1971.

Dumbarton Oaks: Center for Byzantine Studies. *See* Suppt.

Dumeige (Gervaise) *ed.* Histoire des Conciles Oecuméniques. 4to. PARIS, 1962-
> 3. Constantinople II et Constantinople III: F.-X. Murphy, P. Sherwood. 1974.
> 4. Nicée II: Gervais Dumeige. 1978.
> 10. Latran V et Trente: Olivier de la Brosse, Joseph Lecler, Henri Holstein, Charles Lefebvre. 1975.

Duncan (John) The early record of the Old Congregational Church at Great Yarmouth, 1642-1855, and its influence on local historians. 8vo. *Typescript.* n.p., 1965. [Pamph.]

Dungan (D. L.) The sayings of Jesus in the churches of Paul: the use of the Synoptic tradition in the regulation of early church life. 8vo. OXF., 1971.

[Dunkel (Wilbur)] Brick Presbyterian Church, Rochester, New York, 1825-1950. 8vo. ROCHESTER (N. Y.), 1950. [Pamph.]

Dunkerley (Roderic) Beyond the Gospels. (1957.) repr. 8vo. HARMONDSWORTH, 1961.

Dunkerley (W. A.) *See* Oxenham (J.) *pseud.*

Dunkley (E. H.) The Reformation in Denmark. 8vo. LOND., 1948.

Dunlop (*Sir* Derrick Melville) The problem of modern medicines and their control. [Maurice Bloch Lects., 12, 1971.] [Glasgow Univ. Publs.] 8vo. GLASGOW, 1971. [Pamph.]

Dunlop (J. B.) Staretz Amvrosy. (1972.) repr. 8vo. LOND. & OXF., 1975.

Dunn (J. D. G.) Jesus and the Spirit: a study of the religious and charismatic experience of Jesus and the first Christians as reflected in the New Testament. [New Test. Lib.] 8vo. LOND., 1975.

Dunn (J. D. G.)—*continued*
—— Unity and diversity in the New Testament: an inquiry into the character of earliest Christianity. [New Test. Lib.] 8vo. LOND., 1977.
Dunning (N. G.) Samuel Chadwick. Foreword by David Lloyd George. (1933.) repr. 8vo. LOND., 1935.
Dunning (R. W.) *ed.* Christianity in Somerset. obl. 4to. [TAUNTON,] 1976.
Duns (Johannes) *Scotus.* God and creatures: the quodlibetal questions. Trans. with an introd., notes and glossary by Felix Alluntis and Allan B. Wolter. 8vo. PRINCETON & LOND., 1975.
Dunstan (G. R.) The artifice of ethics. [Moorhouse Lects., 1973.] 8vo. LOND., 1974.
—— 1929-1979: and what have the righteous done? [Maynard Chapman Divinity Lect., 26th Feb. 1979, Westfield Coll. Chapel, Lond.] 8vo. WATFORD [printed], [1979]. [Pamph.]
Dunton (John) *See* McEwen (G. D.)
Dupré La Tour (Marie) *See* Suppt. Analecta Bollandiana. Subsid. Hagiog., 62.
Duquenne (Luc) *See* Suppt. Analecta Bollandiana. Subsid. Hagiog., 54.
Durham (J. I.) and **Porter** (J. R.) *ed. See* Davies (G. H.) [Misc.]
Durie (John) *See* Brauer (K.); Rae (T. H. H.)
Durrant (Michael) The logical status of 'God' and the function of theological sentences. [New Studies in the Philos. of Relig.] 8vo. LOND., *etc.*, 1973.
—— Theology and intelligibility: an examination of the proposition that God is the last end of rational creatures and the doctrine that God is Three Persons in one Substance (the doctrine of the Holy Trinity). [Studies in Ethics and the Philos. of Relig.] 8vo. LOND., 1973.
Duschinsky (Charles) The Rabbinate of the Great Synagogue, London, from 1756-1842. (1921.) facsim. repr. With a new bibliogr. note by Ruth P. Lehmann. 8vo. FARNBOROUGH, 1971.
Dusen (W. M.van) *See* Van Dusen (W. M.)
Dutch Reformed Church in South Africa. The Dutch Reformed Church and the Boers. 8vo. LOND., [c.1900.] [Pamph.]
Duthie (C. S.) Responding to the Gospel. 8vo. BÂLE, [1974]. [Pamph.]
—— *ed.* Resurrection and immortality. A selection from the Drew Lects. on Immortality. 8vo. LOND., 1979.
Dvornik (Francis) Les slaves: Byzance et Rome au IXe siècle. [Travaux publ. par l'Institut d'Études Slaves, 4.] (1926.) With a new introd. by Peter Charanis. 8vo. HATTIESBURG (Miss.), 1970.
—— Byzantine missions among the Slavs: SS. Constantine-Cyril and Methodius. [Rutgers Byzantine Ser.] 8vo. NEW BRUNSWICK (N.J.), 1970.
—— Photian and Byzantine ecclesiastical studies. [Variorum Reprs.] 8vo. LOND., 1974.
Dye (Alfred) *See* Sell (A. P. F.)
Dyer (G. A.) *comp. See* Catalogues. *Sheffield Univ. Lib.*
Dyer (J. W.) The soul of a skunk. The original text of the article submitted to the "Unitarian Ministry" 8vo. [MAIDSTONE, the author, 1971.] [Pamph.]
[Dymond (George)] Carrying the torch: the story of Llanishen Baptist Church, 1909-1959. 8vo. [LLANISHEN, 1959.] [Pamph.]
—— Sixty years on: history of Llanishen Baptist Church, 1909-1969. 8vo. [LLANISHEN, 1969.] [Pamph.]
Dyson (A. O.) We believe. [Mowbrays Lib. of Theol.] 8vo. LOND. & OXF., 1977.

Eadmer. The life of St. Anselm, Archbishop of Canterbury. Ed. with introd., notes and trans. by R. W. Southern. (1962.) repr. [Oxford Medieval Texts.] 8vo. OXF., 1972.
Eaglesham (E. J. R.) From school board to local authority. 8vo. LOND., 1956.
Early English Text Society. *See* Suppt.
Eastern Churches Review. *See* Suppt. Sobornost.
Eastman (A. C.) Gospel ventures: the story of Bookham Congregational Church. 4to. *Duplicated.* BOOKHAM, 1971. [Pamph.]
Eaton (J. H.) *See* Suppt. Studies in Bibl. Theol., 2nd Ser., 32.
Ebert (Manfred) Jakob I. von England (1603-25) als Kirchenpolitiker und Theologe. [Studia Irenica, 12.] 8vo. HILDESHEIM, 1972.

Ebner (Dean) Autobiography in seventeenth-century England: theology and the self. [De Proprietatibus Litterarum, Ser. Practica, 14.] 8vo. THE HAGUE & PARIS, 1971.
Eccles (*Sir* John C.) The human mystery. [Gifford Lects., 1977-78.] 8vo. BERLIN, *etc.*, 1979.
Ecclesiastica. The Axminster Ecclesiastica, 1660-1698. [Attrib. to Matthew Towgood.] (1874.) Ed. with annotations and appendixes by K. W. H. Howard. 8vo. SHEFFIELD, 1976.
—— *See* Wigfield (W. M.)
Ecclesiastical History Society. *See* Suppt.
Eckardt (A. Roy) The theologian at work: a common search for understanding. [Forum Books.] 8vo. LOND., 1968.
Eckhart (Johannes) *Meister. See* Schürmann (R.)
Ecumenical Review. *See* Suppt.
Eddington Memorial Lectures. *See* Suppt. Arthur Stanley Eddington Memorial Lectures.
Edel (Abraham) Ethical judgment: the use of science in ethics. (1955.) repr. 8vo. NEW YORK & LOND., 1964.
Edmunds (Edwyn) John Myles and the Ilston Baptists. (1927.) repr. 8vo. [ABERDARE.] 1949. [Pamph.]
Education Act, 1902-1903. The American appeal to the Primate [Randall T. Davidson]. The Primate's reply, together with letters from Dr. Clifford, *etc.* 8vo. TUNBRIDGE WELLS, [1905]. [Pamph.]
Edward, *the Black Prince. See* Gollancz (*Sir* I.)
Edwards (David L.) F. J. Shirley: an extraordinary headmster. 8vo. LOND., 1969.
—— The British churches turn to the future: one man's view of the Church Leaders' Conference, Birmingham, 1972. 8vo. LOND., 1973.
Edwards (Francis) 'The Gunpowder Plot'. [Royal Stuart Papers, 2.] 8vo. ILFORD, 1972. [Pamph.]
Edwards (Jonathan) 1703-58. [Two or more works.] Treatise on grace, and other posthumously published writings [on the Trinity]. Ed. with an introd. by Paul Helm. 8vo. CAMB. & LOND., 1971.
—— —— Scientific and philosophical writings:—The "spider" papers—Natural philosophy—The mind—Short scientific and philosophical papers. Ed. Wallace E. Anderson. [Works of Jonathan Edwards, 6.] 8vo. NEW HAVEN & LOND., 1980.
—— [Notebooks.] The philosophy of Jonathan Edwards from his private notebooks. Ed. Harvey G. Townsend. [Univ. of Oregon Monographs, Studies in Philos., 2.] (1955.) repr. 8vo. WESTPORT (Conn.), 1974.
—— *See* Cherry (C.)
[**Edwards** (L. D.) and **Jones** (A. D.]) North Finchley Baptist Church, 1868-1968: a short history to commemorate our centenary. 8vo. LOND., 1968. [Pamph.]
Edwards (*Sir* Owen Morgan) *See* Davies (*Sir* A. T.) *ed.;* Jones (G. A.)
Edwards (Richard A.) *See* Suppt. Studies in Bibl. Theol., 2nd Ser., 18.
Edwards (Rowland A.) Church and chapel: a study of the problem of reunion in the light of history. 8vo. LOND., 1952.
Edwards (William) 1848-1929, *Principal of S. Wales Baptist Coll.* A handbook of Protestant Nonconformity. (1901.) 2nd ed. 8vo. SWANSEA, 1905.
Edwards (William) *fl.*1915-41, *M.A.* Redland Park Congregational Church, Bristol: a chapter in Congregational history. 8vo. BRISTOL, 1941.
Eekhof (A.) De zinspreuk, In necessariis unitas, in non necessariis libertas, in utrisque caritas. . .Oorsprong, beteekenis en verbreidging. 8vo. LEIDEN, 1931.
Egri (Lukács) *See* Kathona (G.)
Egypt Exploration Society. *See* Suppt.
Ehrenpreis (Irvin) Jonathan Swift. [Annual Lect. on a Master Mind, Brit. Acad., 1968.] 8vo. LOND., [1970]. [Pamph.]
Eichhorn (Werner) Das Heilige und das Königsheil. 4to. BERN, 1970.
Eichrodt (Walther) Ezekiel: a commentary. [Trans. Coslett Quin from Das A. T. Deutsch, 22.] [Old Test. Lib.] 8vo. LOND., 1970.
—— *See* Suppt. Studies in Bibl. Theol., 2nd Ser., 30.
Einstein (Albert) *See* Wickham (H.)
Eissfeldt (Otto) Kleine Schriften. Hrsg. Rudolf Sellheim und Fritz Maass. 8vo. TÜBINGEN, 1962-
5. 1973.

Elder (Ellen R.) *ed.* A guide to Cistercian scholarship. 8vo. KALAMAZOO (Mich.), 1974. [Pamph.]

Elders (E. A.) The kirk on the green: the story of Richmond's Presbyterian congregation, 1876-1976. 8vo. RICHMOND, [1976.]. [Pamph.]

Elenchus Bibliographicus Biblicus. *See* Suppt. Biblica.

Elert (Werner) Der christliche Glaube: Grundlinien der lutherischen Dogmatik. (1940.) 3te. Aufl. 8vo. HAMBURG, 1956.

Eliade (Mircea) A history of religious ideas. Trans. from the French by Willard R. Trask. 8vo. LOND., 1979-
 1. From the Stone Age to the Eleusinian Mysteries. 1979.
 No more yet published, 1980.

Elim Foursquare Gospel Alliance. Duties of local church officers (except secretaries and treasurers). (Section A.) 8vo. LOND., 1929. [Pamph.]
—— Rules for churches with local government under a recognised minister or leader. (Section B.) 8vo. LOND., 1932. [Pamph.]
—— Constitution and general rules. 8vo. LOND., [1934]. [Pamph.]
—— Rules for ministers. (Direct government under the Council.) 8vo. LOND., 1934. [Pamph.]
—— Rules for local church government. 8vo. LOND., 1935. [Pamph.]
—— *See* Jeffreys (G.); Suppt.

Elim Pentecostal Church. Elim Pentecostal Churches diamond jubilee [1915-75]. [Ed. Percy S. Brewster.] 4to. [CHELTENHAM, 1974.] [Pamph.]
—— The constitution of the Elim Pentecostal Church (Elim Foursquare Gospel Alliance). 2pts. 8vo. CHELTENHAM, 1975. [Pamphs.]
—— *See* Liturgies. *Pentecostal;* Suppt.

Eliot (Frederick May) An anthology. Selected and ed. by Alfred P. Stiernotte. With a memorial address by Wallace W. Robbins. 8vo. BOSTON (Mass.), 1959.

Eliot (George) *pseud.* Letters. Ed. Gordon S. Haight. [Yale Edition.] (7 vols., 1954-56.) 2 suppt. vols. [8 & 9]. 8vo. NEW HAVEN & LOND., 1978.
—— *See* Catalogues. *Dr. Williams's Lib.;* Levitt (R.)

Eliot (Samuel Atkins) *See* McGiffert (A. C.)

Eliot (T. S.) The classics and the man of letters. Presidential Address to the Classical Association, 15 Apr. 1942. (1942.) repr. 8vo. LOND., *etc.*, 1943. [Pamph.]
—— Milton. [Annual Lect. on a Master Mind, Brit. Acad., 1947.] 8vo. LOND., [1948]. [Pamph.]
—— Notes towards a definition of culture. 8vo. LOND., 1948.
—— George Herbert. [Writers and their work, 152.] 8vo. LOND., 1962. [Pamph.]

Elkins (W. R.) A new English primer: an introd. to linguistic concepts and systems. 8vo. LOND. & BASINGSTOKE, 1974.

Ellens (G. S. F.) The Ranters ranting: reflections on a ranting counter culture. 8vo. [CHICAGO,] 1971. [Pamph.]

Elliger (Karl) *See* Bible. O.T. Commentaries. Handbuch zum A.T., I, 4.

Elliot (Thomas) Leaves from a lay preacher's ministry. A selection from sermons preached at Highgate Hill Unitarian Christian Church. 8vo. LOND., 1902.

Elliott (J. K.) *See* Suppt. Novum Testamentum. Suppts., 44.

[Elliott (W. S.)] Richmond Baptist Church, Breck Road, Liverpool 5, 1865-1965: centenary brochure. 8vo. [LIVERPOOL, 1965.] [Pamph.]

Ellis (W. H.) The Eignbrook story: an account of the Congregational Church at Hereford, 1662-1962. 8vo. LOND., 1962.

Ellison (S. K.) *comp. See* Catalogues. *House of Lords Record Office.*

Ellul (Jacques) The ethics of freedom. Trans. and ed. Geoffrey W. Bromiley. 8vo. LOND., 1976.

Elmslie (W. A. L.) Westminster College, Cambridge: an account of its history, 1899-1949. 8vo. LOND., [1949]. [Pamph.]

Eltester (Walther) *See* Suppt. Zeitschr. für N.T. Wiss. Beihefte, 40.

Eltham. *Congregational Church.* The first 125 years, 1846-1971: souvenir year book. 8vo. LOND., 1971. [Pamph.]

Elton (G. R.) Policy and police: the enforcement of the Reformation in the age of Thomas Cromwell. 8vo. CAMB., 1972.
—— Reform and renewal: Thomas Cromwell and the common weal. [Wiles Lects., 1972] 8vo. CAMB., 1973.

Emberton (Wilfrid) *See* Young (P.) and Emberton (W.)

Emden (A. B.) A biographical register of the University of Oxford, A.D. 1501 to 1540. 8vo. OXF., 1974.

Emden (P. H.) Quakers in commerce: a record of business achievement. 8vo. LOND., [1939].

Emerton (J. A.) *See* Suppt. Vetus Testamentum. Suppts.,30.

—— *ed. See* Suppt. Zeitschr. für A. T. Wiss. Beihefte, 150.

Emmison (F. G.) *ed.* Early Essex Town Meetings: Braintree, 1619-1636; Finchingfield, 1626-1634. 8vo. LOND. & CHICHESTER, 1970.

Endy (M. B.) William Penn and early Quakerism. 8vo. PRINCETON, 1973.

Engemann (Josef) *See* Suppt. Jahrbuch für Antike u. Christentum. Erg.Bd. 2.

[England (H. S.)] Ferme Park retrospect: 75th church anniversary, 1889-1964. 8vo. [LOND., 1964.] [Pamph.]

English Association. *See* Suppt.

English Historical Review. *See* Suppt.

English Place-Name Society. *See* Suppt.

English Revolution (The) I. Fast Sermons to Parliament. [1640-1653.] Reproductions in facsimile with notes by Robin Jeffs. 34 vols. 8vo. LOND., 1970-71. [*No more published.*]

Enslin (Morton S.) *See* Bible. Apocrypha. Judith.

Ephraim, *Syrus, Saint.* [Misc.] XVIe centenaire de Saint Ephrem (373-1973), célébré à l'Université Saint-Esprit de Kaslik, 15-21 octobre 1973. [Parole de l'Orient, IV, 1-2, 1973.] 8vo. KASLIK (Liban), [1974.]

—— *See* Kronholm (T.); Suppt. Corpus Script. Christ. Orient., Syri, 134-135, 138-141, 148-149, 159-160, 181-182; Subsid., 55; Patrologia Orientalis, XXXVII, 2-3.

Epicurus. *See* Rist (J. M.)

Epiphany Philosophers. *See* Suppt. Theoria to Theory.

Epworth Review. *See* Suppt.

Erasmus (Desiderius) Correspondence. Trans. R. A. B. Mynors and D. F. S. Thomson. [Collected Works of Erasmus, 1 +.] 4to. TORONTO & BUFFALO, 1974-
1. 1974.
2. 1975.
3. 1976.
4. 1977.
5. 1979.
No more yet published, 1980.

—— Inquistitio de fide. A colloquy. (1524.) Ed. with introd. and commentary by Craig R. Thompson. (1950.) 2nd ed. Introd. by Roland H. Bainton. Bibliog. by Craig R. Thompson. 8vo. HAMDEN (Conn.), 1975.

—— *See* Allen (H. M.); Bainton (R. H.); Catalogues. *Leeds Univ. Brotherton Lib.;* DeMolen (R. L.) *ed.;* Dolet (E.); Pineau (J.-B.); Tracy (J. D.); Treu (E.); Winkler (G. B.)

Erskine (*Lady* Horatia) *See* Porter (M.) *and others.*

Esper (M. N.) Allegorie und Analogie bei Gregor von Nyssa. [Habelts Dissertationsdrucke. Reihe klassische Philologie, 30.] 8vo. BONN, 1979.

Essays and Reviews. (1860.) facsim. repr. 8vo. FARNBOROUGH, 1970.

Essex Education Committee. History of Christianity in the Essex region. obl. 8vo. [CHELMSFORD,] 1964. [Pamph.]

Essex Hall Lectures. *Se* Suppt.

Essex Hall Yearbook. *See* Suppt. General Assembly of Unitarian and Free Christian Churches.

Estcourt (E. E.) and **Payne** (J. O.) *ed.* The English Catholic Nonjurors of 1715: being a summary of the register of their estates, with genealogical and other notes, and an appendix of unpublished documents in the Public Record Office. (1885.) facsim. repr. 8vo. FARNBOROUGH, 1969.

Estcourt (*Sir* William) *See* Smallwood (F. T.)

Esterson (Aaron) *See* Laing (R. D.) and Esterson (A.)

Estienne (Robert) *See* Armstrong (A. E.)

Esze (Tamás) A magyar református egyház útja a reformációtól napjainkig. 8vo. BUDAPEST, 1960. [Pamph.]

Etheria, *abbess.* Egeria's travels, newly trans. with supporting documents and notes by John Wilkinson. 8vo. LOND., 1971.

Ethics. *See* Suppt.
Études Bergsoniennes. *See* Suppt.
Eugyppius, *Africanus. See* Suppt. Corpus Script. Eccles. Lat., 87.
Eusebius, *Bp. of Caesarea. See* Chesnut (G. F.); Drake (H. A.)
Eusebius, *Bp. of Emesa. See* Lehmann (H. J.)
Evagrius, *Scholasticus. See* Chesnut (G. F.)
Evans (Caleb) *See* Moon (N. S.)
Evans (Christopher F.) The beginning of the Gospel. Four lectures on St. Mark's Gospel. 8vo. LOND., 1968.
—— "Speeches" in Acts. 8vo. [GEMBLOUX (Belg.), 1970.] [Pamph.]
—— Explorations in theology, 2. 8vo. LOND., 1977.
—— Romans 12.1-2: the true worship. 8vo. ROME, 1979. [Pamph.]
—— [Misc.] What about the New Testament? Essays in honour of Christopher Evans. Ed. Morna Hooker and Colin Hickling. 8vo. LOND., 1975.
Evans (David Tyssil) The life and ministry of the Rev. Caleb Morris, who was minister of the Tabernacle, Narberth, and of Fetter Lane Chapel, London. 8vo. LOND., 1902.
Evans (Eifion) When he is come: an account of the 1858-60 revival in Wales. 8vo. BALA, 1959.
—— The Welsh revival of 1904. Foreword by D. Martyn Lloyd-Jones. 8vo. GLAMORGAN, 1969.
Evans (Evan Herber) *See* Lewis (H. E.)
Evans (Gillian R.) Anselm and a new generation. 8vo. OXF., 1980.
Evans (John) 1830-1917, *Calv. Meth. minister.* Hanes Methodistiaeth rhan ddeheuol Sir Aberteifi, o ddechreuad y "Ddiwygiad Methodistaidd" yn 1735 hyd 1900. 8vo. DOLGELLAU, 1904.
Evans (Walker) *See* Agee (J.) and Evans (W.)
Evennett (H. O.) The Catholic schools of England and Wales. [Current Problems, 22.] 8vo. CAMB., 1944.
Everitt (Alan) Change in the provinces: the seventeenth century. [Dept. of English Local Hist. Occasional Papers, 2nd Ser., 1.] 4to. LEICESTER, 1969. [Pamph.]
—— Nonconformity in country parishes. 4to. [READING,] 1970. [Pamph.]
—— The pattern of rural dissent: the nineteenth century. [Dept. of English Local Hist. Occasional Papers, 2nd Ser., 4.] 4to. LEICESTER, 1972.
Evershed (J. J.) Free Christian Church, Billingshurst: 200th anniversary of the building of the chapel, 18th July 1954. 8vo. *Duplicated.* MAIDSTONE, [1954]. [Pamph.]
Everson (F. H.) The Manchester round [1747-1947]. 8vo. MANCHESTER, [1947]. [Pamph.]
Every (George) The Mass. 4to. DUBLIN, 1978.
Everyman. *See* Suppt.
Ewing (A. C.) Value and reality: the philosophical case for theism. [Muirhead Lib. of Philos.] 8vo. LOND., 1973.
Exeter. *St. Thomas Baptist Church.* A history of St. Thomas Baptist Church (Bartholomew Memorial Church), Exeter: terjubilee, 1817-1967. 8vo. [EXETER, 1967.] [Pamph.]
Explorations in theology, 2. *See* Evans (C. F.)
Expositio totius mundi et gentium. [Ed. and annot. with appendices by A. P. Sainton.] 8vo. [LOND., 1972.]
Expository Times. *See* Suppt.

Faber (Heije) Pastoral care in the modern hospital. [Trans. from the Dutch by Hugo de Waal.] 8vo. LOND., 1971.
Fairweather (E. R.) Episcopacy re-asserted: a rejoinder to 'The Historic Episcopate' [ed. K. M. Carey]. 8vo. LOND., 1955.
Fairweather (E. R.) and **Hettlinger** (R. F.) Episcopacy and reunion. (1952.) Foreword by the Bishop of Durham [A. M. Ramsey]. 8vo. LOND., 1953.
Faith and Freedom. *See* Suppt.
Falconer (*Sir* Robert A.) The idea of immortality and Western civilisation. [Ingersoll Lect., 1930.] 8vo. CAMB. (Mass.), 1930.
Fancutt (Walter) The Southern Baptist Association and its churches: in the Western Association, c.1653-1823; as the Southern Association, 1824-1974. 8vo. ANDOVER, [1974]. [Pamph.]
—— *See* White (B. R.) and Fancutt (W.)

Farmer (D. H.) *See* Dictionaries. Biography.
Farmer (W. R.) The Synoptic problem: a critical analysis. (1964.) repr. 8vo.
DILSBORO (N.C.), 1976.
—— The last twelve verses of Mark. [Soc. for N.T. Studies, Monograph Ser., 25.]
8vo. CAMB., 1974.
Farrer (Augustine J. D.) Rickmansworth Baptist Church, 1843-1943: a centenary
review. 8vo. [RICKMANSWORTH, 1943.] [Pamph.]
Farrer (Austin M.) Reflective faith: essays in philosophical theology. Ed. Charles C.
Conti. 8vo. LOND., 1972.
—— The end of man. 8vo. LOND., 1973.
Fast (Heinold) *ed.* Der linke Flügel der Reformation: Glaubenszeugnisse der Täufer,
Spiritualisten, Schwärmer und Antitrinitarier. [Klassiker des Protestantismus, 4.]
8vo. BREMEN, 1962.
Fawcett (Thomas) Hebrew myth and Christian gospel. 8vo. LOND., 1973.
Fawcett (Timothy J.) *See* Suppt. Alcuin Club. Collections, 54.
Fawkes (F. A.) The riddle of life after death. Introd. by A. A. David. 8vo. LOND.,
1923.
Fawkes (Guy) *See* Suppt. London University. Inst. of Hist. Research. Bulletin.
Special Suppts., 9.
Fechner (Hilde) Die politische Tätigkeit des Abtes Bernhard von Clairvaux, in seinen
Briefen. 8vo. BONN & KÖLN, 1931.
Felixstowe. *Maidstone Road Baptist Church.* Ter-jubilee, 1808-1958. 8vo. [FELIX-
STOWE, 1958.] [Pamph.]
Fell (John) *Bp. of Oxford.* *See* Catalogues. *Oxford Univ. Press;* Suppt. Oxfordshire
Record Soc., N.S., 52.
Fellowship of St. Alban and St. Sergius. *See* Suppt. Sobornost.
Felltham (Owen) 1604?-1668. Poems. Ed. with an introd. and notes by Ted-Larry
Pebworth and Claude J. Summers. [SCN Editions and Studies, 1.] 8vo. UNI-
VERSITY PARK (Pa.), 1973.
Fenlon (Dermot) Heresy and obedience in Tridentine Italy: Cardinal Pole and the
Counter Reformation. 8vo. CAMB., 1972.
Fenn (W. W.) Theism: the implication of experience. Ed. D. H. Fenn. 8vo.
PETERBOROUGH (N.H.), 1969.
[**Fenter** (Margaret)] Erdington (Six Ways) Baptist Church, Birmingham, 1878-1978.
8vo. [BIRMINGHAM, 1978.] [Pamph.]
Ferencz (József) A short account of the Unitarian Church of Hungary. 8vo.
BUDAPEST, 1907.
Ferguson (Fergus) *See* Leckie (J. H.)
Ferguson (Frederic S.) *See* Suppt. Bibliographical Soc. Publs., 1973-75.
Ferguson (James P.) The philosophy of Dr. Samuel Clarke and its critics. 8vo.
NEW YORK, *etc.*, 1974.
Ferguson (John) Christ, community and peace. [Alex Wood Memorial Lect., 1971.]
8vo. NEW MALDEN, 1971. [Pamph.]
—— Some Nigerian church founders. 12mo. IBADAN, 1971. [Pamph.]
—— Aristotle. [Twayne's World Authors Ser., 211.] 8vo. NEW YORK, 1972.
—— The place of suffering. 8vo. CAMB. & LOND., 1972.
—— Sermons of a layman. 8vo. LOND., 1972.
—— The politics of love: the New Testament and non-violent revolution. 8vo.
CAMB. & NEW MALDEN, [1973].
—— Clement of Alexandria. [Twayne's World Authors Ser., 289.] 8vo. NEW
YORK, 1974.
War and peace in the world's religions. 8vo. LOND., 1977.
—— Greek and Roman religion: a source book [Noyes Classical Studies.] 8vo.
PARK RIDGE (N.J.), 1980.
—— *See* Dictionaries. Religion.
Ferguson (Robert) Some reminiscences and studies. 8vo. LOND., 1961.
Ferguson (William Everett) Early Christians speak. 8vo. AUSTIN (Tex.), 1971.
Fernley (- **Hartley**) **Lectures.** *See* Suppt.
Festugière (André-Jean) *See* Suppt. Analecta Bollandiana. Subsid. Hagiog., 48, 53.
Feuillet (André) Le mystère de l'amour divin dans la théologie johannique. [Études
Bibliques.] 8vo. PARIS, 1972.
—— *See* Dictionaries. Biblical.

[Fewkes (Anne V.)] Eye Baptist Church, 1810-1960. 8vo. [EYE, 1960.] [Pamph.]
Fichte (Johann Gottlieb) Attempt at a critique of all revelation. Trans. with an introd.
by Garrett Green. 8vo. CAMB., 1978.
—— *See* Hartmann (N.)
Field (G. C.) The philosophy of Plato. (1949.) 2nd ed. with an appendix by R. C.
Cross. 8vo. LOND., *etc.*, 1969.
Fiey (Jean-Maurice) *See* Suppt. Corpus Script. Christ. Orient., Subsid., 36, 44, 54.
Fifoot (C. H. S.) Pollock and Maitland. [David Murray Lects., 31, 1970.] [Glas-
gow Univ. Publs.] 8vo. GLASGOW, 1971. [Pamph.]
Finch (J. S.) Sir Thomas Browne: a doctor's life of science and faith. [Life of
Science Lib.] 8vo. NEW YORK, 1950.
Findlay (J. Arthur) The rock of truth: or, Spiritualism, the coming world religion.
(1933.) repr. 8vo. LOND., 1933.
Findlay (J. N.) Values and intentions: a study in value-theory and philosophy of
mind. [Muirhead Lib. of Philos.] 8vo. LOND., 1961.
Findlow (Bruce) Religion in people: a broadcast sermon and six signposts. 8vo.
LOND., 1966. [Pamph.]
—— I believe. [Essex Hall Lect., 1974.] 8vo. LOND., 1974. [Pamph.]
Findon Valley. *Free Church (Baptist).* History, year book and blotter, 1959-1960.
8vo. [FINDON VALLEY, 1959.] [Pamph.]
Finlayson (A. R. M.) Life of Canon Fleming, Vicar of St. Michael's, Chester Square,
Canon of York, Chaplain in Ordinary to the King. 8vo. LOND., 1909.
Fiore (Il) *See* Took (J. F.)
Firth (Katharine R.) The apocalyptic tradition in Reformation Britain, 1530-1645.
[Oxford Historical Monographs.] 8vo. OXF., 1979.
Fischer (Karl M.) *See* Suppt. Forschungen zur Religion u. Lit., 111.
Fischer (Kuno) Hegels Leben, Werke und Lehre. [Gesch. der neuern Philosophie,
8, i.] (1901.) 2te. Aufl. (1911.) repr. 2 vols. 8vo. DARMSTADT, 1963.
Fischer (R. H.) *ed.* Franklin Clark Fry: a palette for a portrait. [Suppt. no. of The
Lutheran Quarterly, vol. 24, 1972.] 8vo. [SPRINGFIELD (Ohio),] 1972.
Fischer (Ulrich) *See* Suppt. Zeitschr. für N. T. Wiss. Beihefte, 44.
Fish (Stanley E.) *ed.* Seventeenth-century prose: modern essays in criticism. 8vo.
NEW YORK, 1971.
Fisher (Geoffrey Francis) *Abp. of Canterbury.* The scheme for church union in South
India: a statement made in the Full Synod of the Convocation of Canterbury on 15th
May, 1945. 8vo. LOND., 1945. [Pamph.]
Fisher (J. S.) People of the Meeting House: tales of a church in Luton. 8vo. [LUTON,
1975.] [Pamph.]
Fisher (John) 1459-1535, *Saint, Bp. of Rochester.* Opera, quae hactenus inueniri
potuerunt omnia. (1597.) facsim. repr. fol. FARNBOROUGH, 1967.
—— *See* Rouschausse (J.)
Fisher (John D. C.) *See* Suppt. Alcuin Club. Collections, 60; Misc. Publs., 1975, 1979.
Fitzmyer (J. A.) Essays on the Semitic background of the New Testament. 8vo.
LOND., 1971.
—— A wandering Aramean: collected Aramaic essays. [Soc. of Biblical Lit. Mono-
graph Ser., 25.] 8vo. MISSOULA, 1979.
Fitzpatrick (M. H.) *ed. See* Suppt. Price-Priestley Newsletter.
Flavell (John) *See* Russell (P.)
Flegg (J. E.) Ebenezer: a centenary review of the history of the church at 'Ebenezer',
Richmond Street, Brighton. 8vo. LOND. [printed], [1924]. [Pamph.]
Fleming (James) *See* Finlayson (A. R. M.)
Flesseman-Van Leer (Ellen) Grace abounding: a comparison of Frederick Denison
Maurice and Karl Barth. [F. D. Maurice Lects., King's Coll., Lond, 1968.] 8vo.
LOND., [1968]. [Pamph.]
Fletcher (Anthony) A county community in peace and war: Sussex, 1600-1660.
8vo. LOND., 1975.
Fletcher (J. F.) *See* Miller (S.) and Fletcher (J. F.)
Fletcher (Lionel B.) Mighty moments. 8vo. LOND., [1931].
—— The pathway to the stars. 8vo. LOND., [1933].
—— *See* Malcolm (C. W.)
Flew (Antony G. N.) Evolutionary ethics. [New Studies in Ethics.] (1967.) repr.
8vo. LOND., 1970.

Flew (Antony G. N.)—*continued*
—— The presumption of atheism, and other philosophical essays on God, freedom and immortality. 8vo. LOND., 1976.
Florovsky (G. V.) Vostochnye Ottsy IV-go veka. Eastern Fathers of the IVth century. Based on lects. given at the Orthodox Theological Institute in Paris. (1931.) facsim. repr. Introd. by the author. 8vo. FARNBOROUGH, 1972.
—— Vizantiiski Ottsy V-VIII (vv.). Byzantine Fathers of the V-VIII (centuries). Based on lects. given at the Orthodox Theological Institute in Paris. (1933.) facsim. repr. Introd. by the author. 8vo. FARNBOROUGH, 1972.
Flower (R. E. W.) The Irish tradition. (1947.) repr. 8vo. OXF., 1948.
Floyd (W. E. Gregory) Clement of Alexandria's treatment of the problem of evil. [Oxford Theological Monographs.] 8vo. LOND., 1971.
Fogle (F. R.) and **Trevor-Roper** (H. R.) Milton and Clarendon. Two papers on 17th century English historiography. [Clark Lib. Seminar Papers.] 8vo. LOS ANGELES, 1965. [Pamph.]
Fohrer (Georg) Introduction to the Old Testament. [10th ed. (1965) of Ernst Sellin's Einleitung in das A. T., first publ. 1910.] Trans. David Green. (1968.) Brit. ed. (1970.) repr. 8vo. LOND., 1974.
—— History of Israelite religion. Trans. David E. Green. 8vo. LOND., 1973.
—— [Misc.] *See* Suppt. Zeitschr. für A. T. Wiss. Beihefte, 150.
Foley, *family of. See* Palfrey (H. E.)
Foot (Philippa R.) *ed.* Theories of ethics. [Oxford Readings in Philos.] (1967.) repr. 8vo. OXF., 1977.
Foote (Arthur) *See* Suppt. Hymn Soc. of America. Papers, 26.
Foote (H. W.) Mr. George Phillips, first minister of Watertown. 8vo. BOSTON (Mass.), 1930. [Pamph.]
—— *See* Suppt. Hymn Soc. of America. Papers, 26.
Forbes (Alexander Penrose) *See* Allchin (A. M.)
Forbes (Duncan) Hume's philosophical politics. 8vo. CAMB., 1975.
Ford (Jack) In the steps of John Wesley: the Church of the Nazarene in Britain. 8vo. KANSAS CITY, 1968.
Ford (R. C.) Twenty-five years of Baptist life in Yorkshire, 1912-1937. 8vo. LEEDS & LOND., [1937].
Ford Lectures. *See* Suppt.
Forman (R. S.) *ed.* Great Christians. 8vo. LOND., 1933.
Fornberg (Tord) An early church in a pluralistic society: a study of 2 Peter. [Trans. Jean Gray.] [Coniectanea Biblica, N.T. Ser., 9.] 6vo. LUND, 1977.
Forrest (H. E.) The old houses of Shrewsbury: their history and associations. (1911.) 4th ed. 8vo. SHREWSBURY, 1935.
—— The old churches of Shrewsbury: their history, architecture, and associations. 8vo. SHREWSBURY, 1922.
Forschungen zur Religion und Literatur des Alten und Neuen Testaments. *See* Suppt.
Forster (E. M.) Pharos and Pharillon. 8vo. RICHMOND, 1923.
—— A letter to Madan Blanchard. [Hogarth Letters, 1.] 8vo. LOND., 1931.
—— What I believe. [Hogarth Sixpenny Pamphs., 1.] 8vo. LOND., 1939.
—— Virginia Woolf. [Rede Lect., 1941.] (1942.) repr. 8vo. CAMB., 1942.
Forster (Johann Reinhold) *See* Hoare (M. E.)
Forsyth (P. T.) [Selections.] Peter Taylor Forsyth (1848-1921), director of souls: selections from his practical writings. compiled and ed. by Harry Escott. 8vo. LOND., 1948.
—— Socialism, the Church, and the poor. 8vo. LOND., 1908.
—— Marriage: its ethic and religion. 8vo. LOND., [1912].
—— The Christian ethic of war. 8vo. LOND., 1916.
—— Congregationalism and reunion. Two lectures. (1918.) repr. 8vo. LOND., 1952.
—— The roots of a world-commonwealth. 8vo. LOND., 1918. [Pamph.]
—— *See* Bradley (W. L.)
Fortman (E. J.) The triune God: a historical study of the doctrine of the Trinity. [Theological Resources.] 8vo. LOND. & PHILADELPHIA, 1972.
Foscolo (Niccolo Ugo) *See* Lindon (J. M. A.)
Foster (Kenelm) The two Dantes, and other studies. 8vo. LOND., 1977.

Fountain (D. G.) Isaac Watts remembered. (1974.) 2nd ed. 8vo. HARPENDEN, 1978.

Fox (Charles James) *See* Mitchell (L. G.)

Fox (George) Narrative papers, unpublished or uncollected. Ed. from the MSS. with introds. and notes by Henry J. Cadbury. 8vo. RICHMOND (Ind.), 1972.

—— [Misc.] Annual catalogue of George Fox's papers compiled in 1694-1697. Ed. (with ommissions and additions) by Henry J. Cadbury. 4to. PHILADELPHIA & LOND., 1939.

Fox (H. J.) Pilgrimage. . .Copnor Baptist Church, 1802-1952. 8vo. [PORTSMOUTH, 1952.] [Pamph.]

Foxe (John) *martyrologist.* *See* Olsen (V. N.); Williams (N. J.)

Fränkel (Hermann) Dichtung und Philosophie des frühen Griechentums: eine Geschichte der greichischen Epik, Lyrik und Prosa bis zur Mitte des fünften Jahrhunderts. (1951.) 2te. Aufl. 8vo. MÜNCHEN, 1962.

Francis, *Saint, of Assisi.* *See* Adderley (J. G.); Bonaventura, *St.*; Thode (H.)

[**Francis** (Alan)] Mount Pleasant Baptist Church, Kingsway, Swansea, 1825-1975. 8vo. [SWANSEA, 1975.] [Pamph.]

Francis (L. R.) Christ incognito and the Church myth: the way towards Christian unity in the United Kingdom. 8vo. GERARDS CROSS, 1971.

[**Francis** (Richard)] The Presbyterian Church of Wales, Oakley Park: a history of the church on the centenary of the present chapel, 1826-1876-1976. 8vo. [LLANIDLOES, 1976.] [Pamph.]

Franck (F. S.) Days with Albert Schweitzer: a Lambaréné landscape. (1959.) repr. 8vo. LOND., 1959.

Franck (Sebastian) *See* Weigelt (H.)

Frank (K. Suso) *ed.* *See* Suppt. Jahrbuch für Antike u. Christentum. Erg. Bd. 8.

Franklin, *family of.* *See* Franklin (A. E.)

Franklin (A. E.) *comp.* Records of the Franklin family and collaterals.(1915.) 2nd ed. 4to. LOND., 1935.

Franklin (Benjamin) *See* Buxbaum (M. H.)

[**Franklin** (Bernard G.) *comp.*] A century and a half—and more—at High Street Methodist Church, Leagrave, Luton. 8vo. [LUTON, 1974.] [Pamph.]

Franklin (J. H.) John Locke and the theory of sovereignty: mixed monarchy and the right of resistance in the political thought of the English Revolution. [Cambridge Studies in the Hist. and Theory of Politics.] 8vo. CAMB., 1978.

Franks (E. W.) The Revolution and the Revival. A textbook for the examination conducted by the Young People's Department of the Congregational Union. 8vo. LOND., [1914].

Franks (R. S.) *See* Pringle (A.) *ed.*

Franz Joseph Dölger-Institut. *See* Suppt. Jahrbuch für Antike u. Christentum.

[**Fraser** (David)] Pellon Baptist Sunday School centenary, 1875-1975. 8vo. *Duplicated.* [HALIFAX,] 1975. [Pamph.]

Frede (H. J.) *ed.* *See* Bible. *Latin.* [Old Latin.]

Free Church Federal Council. The Free Churches and the state. The report of the Commission on Church and State appointed Mar. 1950. 8vo. LOND., 1953. [Pamph.]

Free Church of England. Year Book. 8vo. [LOND.,] 1916/17. [*No more in Library.*]

—— The Free Church of England: what is it? 16mo. LOND., n.d. [Pamph.]

Free Presbyterian Church of Scotland. History of the Free Presbyterian Church of Scotland (1893-1933). Compiled by a committee appointed by the Synod of the Free Presbyterian Church. (1933.) repr. with suppt. 8vo. [GLASGOW,] 1965.

—— —— [Rev. ed.] (1893-1970) 8vo. [GLASGOW,] 1970.

Freedman (D. Noel) *ed.* *See* Bible. Commentaries. Anchor Bible; N.T. Misc. John, Epistles of.

Freeman (P.) *See* Moulam (G. E.) and Freeman (P.)

Frege (F. L. G.) [Selections. *English.*] Translations from the philosophical writings of Gottlob Frege. Ed. Peter Geach and Max Black. (1952.) 2nd ed. (1960.) repr. 8vo. OXF., 1977.

Frei (H. W.) The eclipse of biblical narrative: a study in eighteenth and nineteenth century hermeneutics. 8vo. NEW HAVEN & LOND., 1974.

Freiburger Rundbrief. *See* Suppt.

French (Allen) Charles I and the Puritan upheaval: a study of the causes of the Great Migration. 8vo. LOND., 1955.

French (P. J.) John Dee: the world of an Elizabethan magus. 8vo. LOND., 1972.

Frend (William) *See* Knight (F. F. E.)

Frere (W. H.) *See* Liturgies. *Latin Rite.* [Graduals.]

Freund (Michael) Die Idee der Toleranz im England der grossen Revolution. [Deutsche Viertelj.schr. für Literaturwiss. u. Geistesgesch., Buchreihe, 12.] 8vo. HALLE A.D.S., 1927.

Friedlander (A. H.) Leo Baeck, teacher of Theresienstadt. [Littman Lib. of Jewish Civilization.] 8vo. LOND., 1973.

Friedman (Jerome) Michael Servetus: a case study in total heresy. [Travaux d'Humanisme et Renaissance, 163.] 4to. GENÈVE, 1978.

Friends' Historical Society. *See* Suppt.

Friends of Dr. Williams's Library. *See* Suppt.

Fries (Heinrich) *ed. See* Dictionaries. Christianity.

Frith (Rowley) *and others.* First Baptist Church, Ottawa, 1857-1957. 8vo. OTTAWA 1957. [Pamph.]

Frothingham (Octavius Brooks) *See* Caruthers (J. W.)

Froude (Hurrell) *See* Guiney (L. I.)

Fry (Franklin Clark) *See* Fischer (R. H.) *ed.*

Fürst (Walther) *ed.* "Dialektische Theologie" in Scheidung und Bewährung, 1933-1936. Aufsätze, Gutachten und Erklärungen. [Theologische Bücherei, 34.] 8vo. MÜNCHEN, 1966.

Fuidge (W. Clayton) The Countess of Huntingdon's Connexion: what it was! what it is! what it might become! 8vo. WORTHING, [193-]. [Pamph.]

Fuller (Andrew) *See* Kirkby (A. H.)

Fuller (F. W. T.) The Baptists of Stratton Green: a brief survey of the history of the church. 8vo. [STRATTON ST. MARGARET, 1950.] [Pamph.]

Fuller (R. H.) The formation of the resurrection narratives. 8vo. LOND., 1972.

Fullerton (W. Y.) Thomas Spurgeon: a biography. 8vo. LOND., 1919.

—— *See* Baptist Union of G.B. and Ireland.

Fundamentals (The) A testimony to the truth. [A series of tracts by 64 authors. Vols. 1-5 ed. by A. C. Dixon, 6-10 by Louis Meyer, and 11-12 by R. A. Torrey.] 12 vols. in 2. CHICAGO, [1910-15].

Fursdon (H. W.) A history of the Baptist Church, Earl Shilton. 8vo. LEICESTER, 1931.

Fuss (Werner) *See* Suppt. Zeitschr. für A. T. Wiss. Beihefte, 126.

Future life (The) A symposium. [Broadcast talks by various thinkers.] 8vo. LOND., 1933.

G. (R.) A copy of a letter from an officer of the army in Ireland, to his highness the Lord Protector, concerning his changing of the government. [Attrib. to Richard Goodgroom.] (1656.) facsim. repr. 8vo. EXETER, 1974. [Pamph.]

Gabb (Arthur) A history of South Street Baptist Church, Exeter. 8vo. [EXETER, 195-.] [Pamph.]

Gäbler (Ulrich) and **Zsindely** (Endre) *ed.* Bullinger-Tagung 1975. Vorträge, gehalten aus Anlass von Heinrich Bullingers 400. Todestag. Im Auftrag des Instituts für Schweiz. Reformationsgesch. 8vo. ZÜRICH, 1977.

Gaffney (Patricia H.) *ed.* Goldwin Smith papers at Cornell University, 1844-1915. 8vo. ITHACA (N.Y.), 1971. [Pamph.]

—— Goldwin Smith bibliography, 1845-1913. 8vo. ITHACA (N.Y.), 1972. [Pamph.]

Gaiffier (Baudouin de) *See* Suppt. Analecta Bollandiana. Subsid. Hagiog., 52, 61.

Gál (Kelemen) A Kolozsvári Unitárius Kollégium története (1568-1900). 2 vols. 8vo. [KOLOZSVÁR,] 1935.

Galavaris (George) Bread and the liturgy: the symbolism of early Christian and Byzantine bread stamps. 8vo. MADISON (Wis.), *etc.*, 1970.

Galilei (Galileo) *See* Koyré (A.)

Gallenga (Antonio) *See* Cerutti (T.)

Galling (Kurt) *See* Bible. O.T. Commentaries. Handbuch zum A.T., I, 18.

Gallus (Thomas) d.1246, *Abbot of Vercelli.* Le commentaire du Cantique des Cantiques "Deiformis animae gemitus". Étude d'authenticité et éd. critique par Jeanne Barbet. [Publs. de la Sorbonne, Sér. "Documents", 21.] 8vo. PARIS & LOUVAIN, 1972.

Gammie (Alexander) Dr. George H. Morrison: his life and work. [Great Church-men Ser.] (1928.) 2nd ed. 8vo. LOND., [1928].
—— Rev. John McNeill: his life and work. 8vo. LOND., [1933.]
[**Gamston** (B. W.) *comp.*] Lichfield Street Baptist Church, Willenhall, Staffordshire. 1862-1962. 8vo. [WILLENHALL, 1962.] [Pamph.]
Gannat Bussame. *See* Corpus Script. Christ. Orient., Subsid., 57.
Garbett (Cyril F.) *Abp. of York.* In the heart of South London. 8vo. LOND., 1931.
—— The Church of England to-day. 8vo. LOND., 1953.
Gardiner (G. G.) Ellesmere and Frankton [Congregational churches]. 4to. SHREWSBURY, 1960. [Pamph.]
Gardiner (Samuel R.) *See* Tyacke (N. R. N.)
Gardner (Helen L.) A reading of Paradise Lost. [Alexander Lects., Univ. of Toronto, 1962.] (1965.) repr. 8vo. OXF., 1978.
Garesché (E. F.) Communion with the spirit world: a book for Catholics and non-Catholics. 8vo. LOND., 1925.
Garforth (F. W.) Educative democracy: John Stuart Mill on education in society. [Univ. of Hull Publs.] 8vo. OXF., 1980.
Garland (David E.) *See* Suppt. Novum Testamentum. Suppts., 52.
Garlick (K. B.) *comp.* Mr. Wesley's preachers: an alphabetical arrangement of Wes-leyan Methodist preachers and missionaries, and the stations to which they were appointed, 1739-1818. 8vo. LOND., 1977. [Pamph.]
Garner (A. A.) Boston and the great Civil War, 1642-1651. [Hist. of Boston Ser., 7.] 8vo. BOSTON (Lincs.), 1972. [Pamph.]
—— Boston, politics, and the sea, 1652-1674. [Hist. of Boston Ser., 13.] 8vo. BOSTON (Lincs.), 1975. [Pamph.]
Garrett (Clarke) Joesph Priestley, the millennium, and the French Revolution. 4to. [LANCASTER (Pa.),] 1973. [Pamph.]
—— Respectable folly: millenarians and the French Revolution in France and England. 8vo. BALTIMORE & LOND., 1975.
—— The spiritual odyssey of Jacob Duché. 8vo. PHILADELPHIA, 1975. [Pamph.]
[**Garside** (Arnold)] Fifty-years at Steep Lane, 1874-1924: jubilee of the opening of the present Sunday School, and the laying of the foundation stones of the present sanc-tuary. 8vo. [SOWERBY, 1924.] [Pamph.]
Garston, *Lancs. Island Road Methodist Church.* 100th anniversary, 1872-1972. obl. 8vo. [GARSTON, 1972.] [Pamph.]
Gartner (L. P.) The Jewish immigrant in England, 1870-1914. 8vo. DETROIT, 1960.
Garvie (A. E.) The Holy Catholic Church from the Congregational point of view, namely, the one Church in the many churches. 8vo. LOND., 1920.
—— Memories and meanings of my life. 8vo. LOND., [1938].
Garvie (A. E.) *and others.* Our dead: where are they? By A. E. Garvie, Charles Brown, R. F. Horton, J. W. Ewing, Frederick Hastings, J. Golder Burns. 8vo. LOND., [1934.].
Gaskell (E. C., Mrs.) *See* Payne (G. A.)
Gaskin (J. C. A.) Hume's philosophy of religion. [Lib. of Philos. and Relig.] 8vo. LOND., 1978.
Gasque (W. Ward) and Martin (R. P.) *ed.* *See* Bruce (F. F.) [Misc.]
Gasquet (F. A.) *Cardinal.* Cardinal Pole and his early friends. [Letters from Leonicus, trans. with an introd.] 8vo. LOND., 1927.
Gastaldi (Ugo) Storia dell'anabattismo, dalle origini a Münster (1525-1535). [Studi Storici.] 8vo. TORINO, 1972.
Gathorne-Hardy (Robert) Recollections of Logan Pearsall Smith: the story of a friendship. 8vo. LOND., 1949.
Gauger (Joseph) *ed.* Gotthard-Briefe. 138-145 (Mai-Dezember 1934). Chronik der Kirchenwirren. Von Joachim Gauger in Elberfeld. I. Vom Aufkommen der "Deut-schen Christen" 1932 bis zur Bekenntnis-Reichssynode im Mai 1934. 4to. [ELBER-FELD, 1934.] [Photocopy.] [*No more in Library.*]
Gaussen (Alice C. C.) Percy: prelate and poet. Preface by Sir George Douglas. 8vo. LOND., 1908.
Gaustad (E. S.) George Berkeley in America. 8vo. NEW HAVEN & LOND., 1979.
Gauthier (R. A.) *See* Suppt. Corpus Philos. Medii Aevi. Aristoteles Latinus. Opera, XXVI.

Gautrey (Thomas) "Lux mihi laus": School Board memories. With an introd. chapter by P. B. Ballard. 8vo. LOND., [1937].

Gavrilović (Z. A.) The humiliation of Leo VI the Wise (The mosaic of the Narthex at Saint Sophia, Istanbul). fol. [PARIS,] 1979. [Pamph.]

Gay (C. H.) Three hundred years: the story of Gloucester Street [Congregational Church, Weymouth]. 4to. [WEYMOUTH, 196-.] [Pamph.]

Gay (John D.) The geography of religion in England. 8vo. LOND., 1971.

Geach (P. T.) God and the soul. [Studies in Ethics and the Philos. of Relig.] (1969). repr. 8vo. LOND. & HENLEY, 1978.

—— Truth, love and immortality: an introduction to McTaggart's philosophy. 8vo. LOND., 1979.

Geanakoplos (D. J.) Medieval Western civilization and the Byzantine and Islamic worlds: interaction of three cultures. 8vo. LEXINGTON (Mass.) & TORONTO, 1979.

Gee (Donald) Wind and flame. Incorporating the former book 'The Pentecostal movement' with additional chapters. 8vo. [LOND.,] 1967.

Geldart (E. M.) *See* Downing (A. B.)

General Assembly of Unitarian and Free Christian Churches. *Commission on Unitarian Faith and Action in the Modern World.* Interim reports. 4 pts. 8vo. LOND., 1964. [Pamphs.]
    1. Unitarian theology in 1964.
    2. People and organisations.
    3. The enlightened conscience.
    4. The Unitarian churches in society today.

—— —— Unitarians discuss their faith. . .A statement on the response to the interim reports. 8vo. LOND., 1966. [Pamph.]

—— *Review Commission.* Reports. First and second interim reports dealing with the paid staff at Essex Hall, and the officers, Council and Departmental Committees. 8vo. LOND., 1969. [Pamph.]

—— *Social Service Department.* Men and women in society: a study of the social implications of a free religious faith. 8vo. LOND., [c.1955]. [Pamph.]

—— —— The churches and social service. A report. 8vo. LOND., 1959. [Pamph.]

—— —— Religion in schools: failure or success? A report. 8vo. LOND., 1962. [Pamph.]

—— —— Unitarian social service in the 'sixties. A report. 8vo. LOND., [1963]. [Pamph.]

—— —— Man, woman, and child: a Unitarian study of the family and society. 8vo. LOND., 1964. [Pamph.]

—— —— Prisons, punishment, and people: a Unitarian study. 8vo. LOND., 1966. [Pamph.]

—— —— Church and society: some Unitarian views for discussion. 8vo. LOND., 1969. [Pamph.]

—— *See* Suppt.

General Council of the Congregational Christian Churches of the United States. Digest of minutes of meetings, 1931-1965. 8vo. NEW YORK, 1971.

Geneva. *Compagnie des Pasteurs.* Registres de la Compagnie des Pasteurs de Genève. [Travaux d'Humanisme et Renaissance.] 4to. GENÈVE, 1962-
    4. 1575-1582: O. Labarthe et B. Lescaze. 1974.
    5. 1583-1588: O. Labarthe et M. Tripet. 1976.

—— *See* Stelling-Michaud (S.) *ed.*

George I, *King of Great Britain and Ireland. See* Hatton (R.)

George (David Lloyd) *1st Earl Lloyd George of Dwyfor. See* Owen (F.)

George (W. E.) *comp.* Be comforted: a book of consolation for those in sorrow. An anthology of prose and verse. 8vo. LOND., [1931].

Gerardus (Andreas) *Hyperius. See* Kawerau (P.)

Gerbrandy (P. S.) *P.M. of the Netherlands.* National and international stability: Althusius; Grotius; Van Vollenhoven. [Taylorian Lect., 1944.] 8vo. LOND., 1944. [Pamph.]

Gerish (W. B.) Sir Henry Chauncy, Kt., Serjeant-at-Law and Recorder of Hertford, born 1632, died 1719, author the The historical antiquities of Hertfordshire. [Hertfordshire Historians.] 8vo. LOND., 1907.

Gero (Stephen) *See* Suppt. Corpus Script. Christ. Orient., Subsid., 41, 52.

Gert (Bernard) The moral rules: a new rational foundation for morality. 8vo. NEW YORK, *etc.*, 1970.

Ghali (I. A.) L'orient chrétien et les Juifs. [Histoire et Civilisation Arabe.] 8vo. PARIS, 1970.

[Ghosh (J. C.) and **Withycombe** (Elizabeth G.)] Annals of English literature, 1475-1925: the principal publications of each year together with an alphabetical index of authors and their works. 8vo. OXF., 1935.

Gibb (H. A. R.) *ed.* *See* Dictionaries. Islam.

Gibbon (Edward) *See* Black (J. B.)

Gibbon (*Sir* Gwilym) and **Bell** (R. W.) History of the London County Council, 1889-1939. 8vo. LOND., 1939.

Gibbon (J. M.) Evangelical heterodoxy. 8vo. LOND., 1909.
—— The veil and the vision. Sermons. 8vo. LOND., 1914.
—— *See* Pringle (A.) *ed.*

[Gibbons (John) *comp.*] Concertatio Ecclesiae Catholicae in Anglia adversus Calvinopapistas et Puritanos. (1583.) 2nd ed. (1588.) facsim. repr. With a new introd. by D. M. Rogers. 8vo. FARNBOROUGH, 1970.

Gibbs (J. G.) *See* Suppt. Novum Testamentum. Suppts., 26.

Gibson (Edgar C. S.) John Howard. 8vo. LOND., 1901.

[Gibson (Edmund) *Bp. of London.*] Synodus Anglicana: or, the constitution and proceedings of an English Convocation, shown, from the acts and registers thereof, to be agreeable to the principles of an Episcopal Church. (1702.) facsim. repr. 8vo. FARNBOROUGH, 1967.

Gibson (J. Monro) Protestant principles. [Christian Study Manuals.] (1901.) 2nd ed. 8vo. LOND., 1903.

Gibson (Margaret T.) Lanfranc of Bec. 8vo. OXF., 1978.

Gifford Lectures. *See* Suppt.

Gigon (Olof) Die antike Kultur und das Christentum. 8vo. DARMSTADT, 1967.

Gilbert (A. D.) Religion and society in industrial England: church, chapel and social change, 1740-1914. [Themes in British Social Hist.] 8vo. LOND., 1976.
—— *See* Currie (R.) *and others.*

Gilbourn (Craig A.) The Reverend Samuel Davies in Great Britain. 4to. CHARLOTTESVILLE (Va.), 1973. [Pamph.]

Gilkey (Langdon) Religion and the scientific future: reflections on myth, science and theology. [Deems Lects., 1967.] 8vo. LOND., 1970.
—— Naming the whirlwind: the renewal of God-language. 8vo. INDIANAPOLIS & NEW YORK, 1969.

Gillies (Alexander) John Osborn, F.R.S., and Goethe. 8vo. CAMB., 1971. [Pamph.]

Gillingham (J. B.) *See* Suppt. Historical Assn. Gen. Ser., 77.

Gilmore (G. W.) *See* Scott (R.) and Gilmore (G. W.)

Gilmour (Jane) and **Hurst** (Janet) Congregationalism at Fowlmere: a story from the strays. Monumental inscriptions from Fowlmere Independent Chapel and yard. 8vo. [CAMB., 1979.] [Pamph.]
—— Fowlmere Independent Chapel: the first hundred years. 8vo. [CAMB., 1980.] [Pamph.]

Ginzburg (Carlo) Il Nicodemismo: simulazione e dissimulazione religiosa nell'Europa dell'500. [Biblioteca di Cultura Storica, 107.] 8vo. TORINO, 1970.

Giorgi (Francesco) *See* Yates (F. A.)

Gladstone, *family of.* *See* Checkland (S. G.)

Glasenapp (Helmuth von) Die fünf grossen Religionen. 2 vols. 8vo. DÜSSELDORF, 1952.
  1. Brahmanismus, Buddhismus, Chinesischer Universismus.
  2. Islam und Christentum.

Glasgow. *Cathcart Baptist Church.* Jubilee, 1923-1973. 8vo. [GLASGOW, 1973.] [Pamph.]

Glasgow. *Unitarian Church, St. Vincent Street.* 1856-1956: a brief account of the history of the church during the last 100 years. fol. *Duplicated.* n.p., [1956]. [Pamph.]

Glasson (T. F.) Jesus and the end of the world. 8vo. EDIN., 1980.

Gloël (Elisabeth) Die Frau bei den Quäkern des 17. Jahrhunderts in England. Inaugural-Dissertation. 8vo. WÜRZBURG, 1939.

Glover (Jonathan) Responsibility. [Internat. Lib. of Philos.] 8vo. LOND., 1970.
—— *ed.* The philosophy of mind. [Oxford Readings in Philos.] 8vo. OXF., 1976.
Glover (T. R.) The mind of St. Paul. [Annual Lect. on a Master Mind, Brit. Acad., 1941.] 8vo. LOND., [1942]. [Pamph.]
Goddard (H. E.) *See* Mutimer (G.) and Goddard (H. E.)
[Godfrey (R. A.)] Century chronicle, 1856-1956: historical record of Burlington Baptist Church, Ipswich. 8vo. [IPSWICH, 1956.] [Pamph.]
Godwin (William) *See* Locke (D.)
Goehring (W. R.) The West Parish Church [Meetinghouse] of Barnstable: an historical sketch. 8vo. WEST BARNSTABLE (Mass.), 1959.
Goertz (Hans-Jürgen) *ed.* Umstrittens Täufertum, 1525-1975: neue Forschungen. 8vo. GÖTTINGEN, 1975.
Goethe (J. W. von) *See* Gillies (A.); Gray (R. D.); Wells (G. A.)
Golders Green. *All Souls' Unitarian Church.* Anniversary service, Sun. 12th Oct. 1975. Golders Green Unitarians, 1925-1975. 8vo. *Duplicated.* [LOND.,] 1975. [Pamph.]
—— —— *See* Ross (A. K.)
Goldhawk (N. P.) On hymns and hymnbooks. 8vo. LOND., 1979.
Goldman (Ronald) Readiness for religion: a basis for developmental religious education. 8vo. LOND., 1965.
Gollancz (*Sir* Israel) Ich dene: some observations on a manuscript of the life and feats of arms of Edward Prince of Wales, the Black Prince: a metrical chronicle in French verse by the herald of Sir John Chandos. 8vo. LOND., 1921. [Pamph.]
Gombrich (E. H. J.) Topos and topicality in Renaissance art. [Soc. for Renaissance Studies Annual Lect., 1975.] 8vo. LOND., 1975. [Pamph.]
Gombrich (R. F.) Precept and practice: traditional Buddhism in the rural highlands of Ceylon. 8vo. OXF., 1971.
Gooch (Henry Martyn) William Fuller Gooch: a tribute and a testimony, by his son. Foreword by W. Y. Fullerton. (1929.) 2nd ed. 8vo. LOND., 1929.
Gooch (William Fuller) *See* Gooch (H. M.)
Goodall (E.) The rise and growth of Chester Road Baptist Church during fifty years. 8vo. [SUTTON COLDFIELD, 1955.] [Pamph.]
Goodall (J. A.) East Christian devotion to Our Lady. 8vo. LOND., 1973. [Pamph.]
—— The invocation of the name of Jesus in English XIVth century spiritual writers. 8vo. LOND., 1972. [Pamph.]
Goodall (Norman) *ed.* Der Kongregationalismus. [Die Kirchen der Welt, 11.] 8vo. STUTTGART, 1973.
Goodhart (A. L.) Tolerance and the law. [Robert Waley Cohen Memorial Lect., 1955.] 8vo. LOND., [1955]. [Pamph.]
Gooding (D. W.) Relics of ancient exegesis: a study of the miscellanies in 3 Reigns 2. [Soc. for O.T. Study, Monograph. Ser., 4.] 8vo. CAMB., 1976.
—— Current problems and methods in the textual criticism of the Old Testament. Inaugural lect., Queen's Univ. of Belfast, 10 May 1978. 8vo. BELFAST, 1979. [Pamph.]
—— *See* Walters (P.)
Goodman (A. E.) *ed.* *See* Abramowski (L.) and Goodman (A. E.) *ed.*
Goodwin (Thomas) *See* Routley (E.)
Goodwin (Thomas) *and others.* An apologeticall narration. (1643.) [Facsim. repr. with introd. and notes by] Robert S. Paul. 8vo. PHILADELPHIA & BOSTON (Mass.), 1963.
Goodyear (Hugh) *See* Sprunger (K. La V.)
Goppelt (Leonhard) Typos: die typologische Deutung des Alten Testaments im Neuen. Anhang: Apokalyptik und Typologie bei Paulus. [Beiträge zur Förderung christlicher Theologie, 2. Reihe, 43.] (1939.) repr. 8vo. DARMSTADT, 1966.
—— Christentum und Judentum in ersten und zweiten Jahrhundert: ein Aufriss der Urgeschichte der Kirche. [Beiträge zur Förderung christlicher Theologie, 2. Reihe, 55.] 8vo. GÜTERSLOH, 1954.
Gordis (Robert) The book of Job: commentary, new trans. and special studies. [Moreshet Ser., 2.] 8vo. NEW YORK, 1978.
Gordon (Alexander) Unity Church, Islington: its early history, 1667-1758. An address delivered in the Church, 11 Nov. 1917, in celebration of its 250th anniversary. 8vo LOND., 1918. [Pamph.]

Gordon (Alexander)—*continued*
—— What Manchester owes to Cross Street Chapel. An address delivered in the Chapel, May 20, 1922, on the 250th anniversary of the formation of the congregation. 12mo. MANCHESTER, [1922]. [Pamph.]

Gordon (J. C.)　An adventure almost desperate: the Pilgrim Fathers and their associations with the Netherlands. 8vo. AMSTERDAM, 1970. [Pamph.]

Gore (Charles) *Bp. of Oxford.* The deity of Christ. Four sermons preached during Advent, 1921, in Grosvenor Chapel. 8vo. LOND., 1922.
—— *See* Baker (J. A.)

Goreham (N. J.) Isaac Ambrose, Lancashire Nonconformist. 8vo. PRESTON, 1977. [Pamph.]

Gorges (*Sir* Ferdinando) *See* Burgess (W. H.)

Gorman (George H.)　Essentials of Quakerism. Together with an account of Winchmore Hill Meeting, by Archibald King. 8vo. [LOND.,] 1957. [Pamph.]
—— The amazing fact of Quaker worship. [Swarthmore Lect., 1973.] 8vo. LOND., 1973.

Gosden (John Hervey)　*See* Paul (S. F.)

Gosport. *Brockhurst Baptist Church.* A short history, 1858-1958. 8vo. [GOSPORT, 1958.] [Pamph.]

Gottfried-Wilhelm-Leibniz-Gesellschaft.　*See* Suppt. Mitteilungen der Gottfried-Wilhelm-Leibniz-Gesellschaft.

Gotthard-Briefe.　*See* Gauger (J.) *ed.*

Gough (J. W.)　John Locke's political philosophy: eight studies. (1950.) 2nd ed. 8vo. OXF., 1973.

Gould (Frank J.)　A short history of the Congregational Church, Steeple Bumpstead, Essex: a centenary memorial, 1900 A.D. 8vo. HAVERHILL [printed], [1900].

Gould (Fred J.) and **Day** (John R.)　History of Christ Church, Enfield. 8vo. [ENFIELD,] 1975. [Pamph.]

Goulder (M. D.)　Midrash and lection in Matthew. [Speaker's Lects. in Biblical Studies, 1969-71.] 8vo. LOND., 1974.
—— *ed.* Incarnation and myth: the debate continued. 8vo. LOND., 1979.

Gow (A. S. F.)　A. E. Housman: a sketch, together with a list of his writings and indexes to his classical papers. 8vo. CAMB., 1936.

Gowland (D. A.)　*See* Suppt. Chetham Soc., 3rd Ser., 26.

Grabar (André)　L'empereur dans l'art byzantin. (1936.) [Variorum Reprs.] 8vo. LOND., 1971.
—— Christian iconography: a study of its origins. [A. W. Mellon Lects. in the Fine Arts, 1961, National Gallery of Art, Washington D.C.] [Bollingen Ser., XXXV, 10.] 4to. PRINCETON, 1968.
—— Byzantine painting: historical and critical study. [Trans. Stuart Gilbert.] 4to. LOND., 1979.

Grässer (Enrich)　*See* Suppt. Zeitschr. für N. T. Wiss. Beihefte, 40.

Graffin (François) *ed.*　*See* Suppt. Patrologia Orientalis.

Graham (Eric)　*See* Holtby (R. T.)

Graham (J. J.)　Chronicles of a century of Methodism at King's Cross Wesleyan Church. 8vo. LOND., 1923.

Graham (N. H.) *comp.*　The genealogist's consolidated guide to parish registers in the outer London area, 1538 to 1837. obl. 8vo. ORPINGTON, 1977. [Pamph.]
—— The genealogist's consolidated guide to Nonconformist and foreign registers, copies and indexes in the inner London area. obl. 8vo. BIRCHINGTON, [1980]. [Pamph.]

Grant (George P.)　*See* Schmidt (L.) *ed.*

Grant (Robert M.)　Augustus to Constantine: the thrust of the Christian movement into the Roman world. 8vo. LOND., 1971.

Grass (Hans)　Ostergeschehen und Osterberichte. (1956.) 4te. Aufl. 8vo. GÖTTINGEN, 1970.

Gravatt (Frances M.)　'And we their deeds record': the story of Baptists in Hendon from 1832, and of Hendon Baptist Church, Finchley Lane, 1873-1970. 8vo. LOND., [1970]. [Pamph.]

Gray (A. Herbert)　*See* Papers for War Time, 7, 27.

Gray (R. D.)　Goethe the alchemist: a study of alchemical symbolism in Goethe's literary and scientific works. 8vo. CAMB., 1952.

Gray-Stack (C. M.) "The apple of contention": the Anglican-Roman agreement [in the light] of Vatican II on the Eucharist. 8vo. MÜNCHEN, [197-]. [Pamph.]

Great Ellingham. *Baptist Church.* In touch: the magazine of Great Ellingham Baptist Church. 28oth anniversary issue. 8vo. *Duplicated.* [GREAT ELLINGHAM,] 1979. [Pamph.]

Great Shelford. *Free Church* (*Baptist*). [Centenary booklet.] 8vo. [GREAT SHELFORD, 1956.] [Pamph.]

Greater London Council. Survey of London. See Suppt.

Greaves (Jane) In search of truth: the history of the Unitarian Church, Oldham. 8vo. *Duplicated.* n.p., [1965]. [Pamph.]

Greaves (R. L.) The origins and early development of English covenant thought. 8vo. [ALBUQUERQUE (N.M.),] 1968. [Pamph.]

—— Gerrard Winstanley and educational reform in Puritan England. 8vo. n.p., 1969. [Pamph.]

—— Puritanism and science: the anatomy of a controversy. 8vo. NEW YORK, 1969. [Pamph.]

—— Francis Bampfield (1615-1684): eccentric hebraist and humanitarian. 8vo. LOND., 1971. [Pamph.]

—— William Sprigg and the Cromwellian revolution. 8vo. [SAN MARINO (Calif.),] 1971. [Pamph.]

—— An annotated bibliography of John Bunyan studies. [Bibliographia Tripotamopolitana, 5.]. 4to. *Duplicated.* PITTSBURGH, 1972. [Pamph.]

—— John Knox, the Reformed tradition, and the sacrament of the Lord's Supper. 8vo. GÜTERSLOH, 1975. [Pamph.]

Greeley (D. M.) 25 Beacon Street and other recollections. 8vo. BOSTON (Mass.), 1971.

Green (Bryan S. W.) *See* Cruse (J. H.) and Green (B. S. W.)

Green (David) Queen Anne, 1665-1714. (1970.) repr. 8vo. LOND., 1972.

Green (Ernest) Education for a new society. 8vo. LOND., 1942.

Green (H. C. Benedict) *See* Bible. Commentaries. New Clarendon.

Green (I. M.) The re-establishment of the Church of England, 1660-1663. [Oxford Historical Monographs.] 8vo. OXF., 1978.

Greenslade (S. L.) The work of William Tindale. With an essay on Tindale and the English language by G. D. Bone. 8vo. LOND. & GLASGOW, 1938.

Greenslet (Ferris) The Lowells and their seven worlds. [American Lib.] 8vo. LOND., 1947.

[Greenway (H. W.)] Labourers with God, being a brief account of the activities of the Elim Movement. (1946.) repr. 8vo. LOND., 1946. [Pamph.]

Greenwell (William) Durham Cathedral. (1881.) 9th ed. New preface by R. A. Cordingley. 8vo. DURHAM, [1932].

Greenwood (John) d.1593. *See* Reason (J.)

Greenwood (John Ormerod) Signs of life: art and religious experience. [Swarthmore Lect., 1978.] 8vo. LOND., 1978.

Greg (William Rathbone) The creed of Christendom: its foundations contrasted with its superstructure. (1851.) 3rd ed. Preface by W. R. Washington Sullivan. (1874.) repr. 8vo. LOND., 1905.

Gregg (Edward) Queen Anne. 8vo. LOND., *etc.*, 1980.

Gregory, *Nazianzen, Saint, Patriarch of Constantinople.* *See* Althaus (H.); Spidlik (T.); Suppt. Analecta Bollandiana. Subsid. Hagiog., 58.

Gregory, *Saint, Bp. of Nyssa.* *See* Esper (M. N.); Harl (M.) *ed.*

Gregory I, *Pope, the Great, Saint.* Morales sur Job. Première partie. Livres I et II. (1952.) 2e. éd. Introd. et notes de Robert Gillet. Trad. de André de Gaudemaris. [Sources Chrétiennes, 32.] 8vo. PARIS, 1975.

—— —— Troisième partie. (Livres XI-XVI.) Texte latin, introd. et notes par Aristide Bocognano. [Sources Chrétiennes, 212, 221.] 2 vols. 8vo. PARIS, 1974-75.

—— *See* Dagens (C.); Dando (M.)

Gregory VII, *Pope, Hildebrand.* Epistolae Vagantes. Ed. and trans. H. E. J. Cowdrey. [Oxford Medieval Texts.] 8vo. OXF., 1972.

Gregory (T. E.) Vox populi: popular opinion and violence in the religious controversies of the fifth century A.D. 8vo. COLUMBUS (Ohio), 1979.

Grenkov (Alexander Mikhailovich) *See* Amvrosy, *Staretz, formerly A. M. Grenkov.*

Grey (Edward) *1st Viscount Grey of Fallodon.* *See* Trevelyan (G. M.)
Greisbach (J. J.) *See* Orchard (J. B.) and Longstaff (T. W. R.) *ed.*
Griffin (F. R.) [Selections.] Frederick Robertson Griffin, 1876-1966. [Addresses and prayers, with an appreciation.] n.p. [priv. printed], 1968. [Pamph.]
Griffin (Nicholas) Relative identity. [Clarendon Lib. of Logic and Philos.] 8vo. OXF., 1977.
Griffith (Gwilym O.) John Bunyan. 8vo. LOND., 1927.
Griffith-Jones (Ebenezer) *See* Pringle (A.) *ed.*
Griffiths (Ann) 1776-1805. [Misc.] Homage to Ann Griffiths: a special bicentenary publication. 8vo. PENARTH, 1976. [Pamph.]
Griffiths (David Nigel) The French translations of the English Book of Common Prayer. 8vo. [LOND., 1972.] [Pamph.]
—— Four centuries of the Welsh prayer book. 8vo. [LOND., 1975.] [Pamph.]
Griffiths (David Robert) The New Testament and the Roman state. [Pantyfedwen Trust Lect., 1964.] 8vo. SWANSEA, 1970.
Griffiths (H. J.) Seend Methodist Chapel, 1775 to 1975: bicentenary, March 1975. 8vo. SEEND, 1974. [Pamph.]
Grindal (Edmund) *Abp. of Canterbury.* Visitation, 1575: Comperta et detecta book. [Ed. and introd. by] W. J. Sheils. [Borthwick Texts and Calendars: Records of the Northern Province, 4.] 8vo. YORK, 1977.
—— *See* Collinson (P.)
Groser (W. H.) A hundred years' work for the children; being a sketch of the history and operations of the Sunday School Union, from its formation in 1803 to its centenary in 1903. 8vo. LOND., [1903].
Grosseteste (Robert) *Bp. of Lincoln.* *See* Suppt. Corpus Philos. Medii Aevi. Aristoteles Latinus. Opera, XXVI.
[Groves (Stella)] The family church: New Southgate Baptist Church, 1863-1963. 4to. [LOND., 1963.] [Pamph.]
Gruffydd (R. Geraint) 'In that gentile country . . .' The beginnings of Puritan Nonconformity in Wales. [Annual Lect. of the Evangelical Lib. of Wales, 1975.] 8vo. BRIDGEND (Glam.), 1976. [Pamph.]
Guilday (Peter) The English Catholic refugees on the Continent, 1558-1795. I. The English colleges and convents in the Catholic Low Countries, 1558-1795. (1914.) facsim. repr. 8vo. FARNBOROUGH, 1969. [*No more published.*]
Guildford. *Baptist Church (Millmead Centre).* Changed! [A brochure.] obl. 8vo. [GUILDFORD, 1975.] [Pamph.]
Guillaume (Alfred) Islam. (1954.) 2nd ed. (1956.) repr. 8vo. HARMONDSWORTH, 1961.
Guiney (Louise I.) Hurrell Froude: memoranda and comments. 8vo. LOND., 1904.
Gulik (E. van) and **Vervliet** (H. D. L.) Een gedenksteen voor Plantijn en Van Raphelingen te Leiden. Waarin opgenomen de Catalogvs librorvm residvorvm tabernae Raphelengianae. 8vo. LEIDEN, 1965.
Gumbley (Walter) Obituary notices of the English Dominicans from 1555 to 1952. 8vo. LOND., 1955.
Gundel (H. G.) Weltbild und Astrologie in den greichischen Zauberpapyri. [Münchener Beiträge zur Papyrusforschung u. Antiken Rechtsgesch., 53.] 8vo. MÜNCHEN, 1968.
Gundel (Wilhelm) Dekane und Dekansternbilder: ein Beitrag zur Geschichte der Kulturvölker. Mit einer Untersuchung über die ägyptischen Sternbilder und Gottheiten der Dekane von S. Schott. [Studien der Bibliothek Warburg, 19.] (1936.) 2te. Aufl. Mit einem bibliogr. Anhang von Hans Georg Gundel. 8vo. DARMSTADT, 1969.
—— *See* Boll (Franz) *and others.*
Gundry (R. H.) Sōma in biblical theology, with emphasis on Pauline anthropology. [Soc. for N.T. Studies, Monograph Ser., 29.] 8vo. CAMB., 1976.
Gunkel (Hermann) *ed.* *See* Suppt. Forschungen zur Religion und Lit.
Gunter (P. A. Y.) Henri Bergson: a bibliography. 8vo. BOWLING GREEN (Ohio), 1974.
Gunter-Jones (Roger) Buddhism and the West. [Essex Hall Lect., 1973.] 8vo. LOND., 1973. [Pamph.]
Gunther (J. J.) *See* Suppt. Novum Testamentum. Suppts., 35.

Gunton (C. E.) Becoming and being: the doctrine of God in Charles Hartshorne and Karl Barth. [Oxford Theological Monographs.] 8vo. OXF., 1978.

Gurney (O. R.) Some aspects of Hittite religion. [Schweich Lects., Brit. Acad., 1976.] 8vo. LOND., 1977.

Gusmer (C. W.) *See* Suppt. Alcuin Club. Collections, 56.

Guthrie (W. K. C.) A history of Greek philosophy. 8vo. CAMB., 1962-
3. The fifth-century enlightenment. 1969.
4. Plato, the man and his dialogues: earlier period. 1975.
5. The later Plato and the Academy. 1978.

Gutteridge (R. J. C.) Open thy mouth for the dumb! The German Evangelical Church and the Jews, 1879-1950. [Bampton Lects., 1972.] 8vo. OXF., 1976.

Guy, *Bp. of Amiens.* Carmen de Hastingae Proelio. Ed. [and trans.] Catherine Morton and Hope Muntz. [Oxford Medieval Texts.] 8vo. OXF., 1972.

Gwyn (John) *See* Young (P.) and Tucker (N.) *ed.*

Gwynn (Aubrey) and **Hadcock** (R. N.) Medieval religious houses in Ireland. With an appendix to early sites. Foreword by David Knowles. 8vo. LOND., 1970.

Gysi (Lydia) Platonism and Cartesianism in the philosophy of Ralph Cudworth. (1962.) repr. 8vo. BERN, 1966.

Hadcock (R. N.) *See* Gwynn (A.) and Hadcock (R. N.)

Hadfield (Alice M.) An introduction to Charles Williams. 8vo. LOND., 1959.

Hadot (Pierre) Marius Victorinus: recherches sur sa vie et ses oeuvres. 8vo. PARIS, 1971.

Haec-vir. *See* Hic mulier.

Haenchen (Ernst) The Acts of the Apostles: a commentary. [Trans. from the 14th Ger. ed. (1965) under the supervision of Hugh Anderson and rev. by R. McL. Wilson.] 8vo. OXF., 1971.

Haendler (Klaus) *ed. See* Kinder (E.) and Haendler (K.) *ed.*

Hageman (H. G.) Pulpit and table: some chapters in the history of worship in the Reformed churches. 8vo. LOND., 1962.

Hagner (D. A.) *See* Suppt. Novum Testamentum. Suppts., 34.

Hague (Judy) *and others.* Exploring our heritage. 8vo. [BOSTON (Mass.), 1979.] [Pamph.]

Haig (Charles A.) John Angell James (1785-1859). [Heritage Biographies.] 8vo. LOND., 1961. [Pamph.]

—— John Howe, Cromwell's chaplain. [Heritage Biographies.] 8vo. LOND., 1961. [Pamph.]

Haigh (Christopher) Reformation and resistance in Tudor Lancashire. 8vo. LOND., 1975.

Haile (Martin) Life of Reginald Pole. (1910.) 2nd ed. 8vo. LOND., 1911.

—— An Elizabethan Cardinal: William Allen. 8vo. LOND., *etc.*, 1914.

Halbe (Jörn) *See* Suppt. Forschungen zur Religion u. Lit., 114.

[**Haldane** (Elizabeth Sanderson) *ed.*] Mary Elizabeth Haldane: a record of a hundred years (1825-1925). Ed. by her daughter. 8vo. LOND., 1925.

Haldane (Mary Elizabeth) *See* Haldane (E. S.)

Halecki (Oskar) Un empereur de Byzance à Rome. (1930.) Réimpr. de l'éd. orig. et étude annexe. [Variorum Reprs.] 8vo. LOND., 1972.

Halkin (François) *See* Suppt. Analecta Bollandiana. Subsid. Hagiog., 51, 55, 60.

Hall (Albert C.) Modernism and youth: an attempt at interpretation. [Modernist Pamphs. on Relig., Life and Thought, 2.] 8vo. LOND., 1943. [Pamph.]

Hall (Basil) John à Lasco, 1499-1560: a Pole in Reformation England. [Friends of Dr. Williams's Lib. Lect., 25.] 8vo. LOND., 1971. [Pamph.]

Hall (David D.) The faithful shepherd: a history of the New England ministry in the seventeenth century. 8vo. CHAPEL HILL (N.C.), 1972.

—— *ed.* The Antinomian controversy, 1636-1638: a documentary history. 8vo. MIDDLETOWN (Conn.), 1968.

Hall (Joseph) *Bp. of Norwich. See* Huntley (F. L.)

[**Hall** (Reginald) and **Johns** (S. T. B.)] Boxmoor Baptist Church, 1826-1976. 8vo. [HEMEL HEMPSTEAD, 1976.] [Pamph.]

Hall (Robert) *See* Hughes (G. W.)

Hall (Roland) Fifty years of Hume scholarship: a bibliographical guide. 8vo. EDIN., 1978.
—— *ed.* *See* Suppt. Locke Newsletter.
Hall (Stuart G.) Rome and the churches: the first three centuries. Inaugural lect., Chair of Ecclesiastical Hist., Univ. of London King's Coll , 30th Oct. 1979. 8vo. [LOND., 1980.] [Pamph.]
Haller (Johannes) Über die Aufgaben des Historikers. [Philosophie und Geschichte: eine Sammlung von Vorträgen u. Schriften aus dem Gebiet der Philos. u. Gesch., 53.] 8vo. TÜBINGEN, 1935. [Pamph.]
Halliday (R. J.) John Stuart Mill. [Political Thinkers, 4.] 8vo. LOND., 1976.
Hamer (D. A.) The politics of electoral pressure: a study in the history of Victorian reform agitations. 8vo. HASSOCKS (Sx.) & ATLANTIC HIGHLANDS (N.J.), 1977.
Hamerton-Kelly (R. G.) Pre-existence, Wisdom, and the Son of Man: a study of the idea of pre-existence in the New Testament. [Soc. for N.T. Studies, Monograph Ser., 21.] 8vo. CAMB., 1973.
Hamilton (Bernard) *See* Suppt. Historical Assn. Gen. Ser., 85.
Hamilton (Mary Agnes) Sidney and Beatrice Webb: a study in contemporary biography. 8vo. LOND., [1933].
Hammershaimb (Erling) The Book of Amos: a commentary. Trans. [from the Danish] by John Sturdy. 8vo. OXF., 1970.
Hammond (John) *See* Knight (F. F. E.) *ed.*
[Hammond (Michael) *ed.*] Gidea Park Methodist Church: golden jubilee, 1926-1976. obl. 8vo. [WATFORD, 1976.] [Pamph.]
Hampe (J. C.) *ed.* Die Autorität der Freiheit: gegenwart des Konzils und Zukunft der Kirche im ökumenischen Disput. 3 vols. 8vo. MÜNCHEN, 1967.
Hampshire (Stuart N.) Morality and pessimism. [Leslie Stephen Lect., 1972.] 8vo. CAMB., 1972. [Pamph.]
Hankey (Beatrice) *See* Raven (C. E.) and Heath (R. F.)
Hankey (Donald W. A.) *See* Budd (K. G.)
Hanna (Shenouda) Who are the Copts. 8vo CAIRO [printed], 1958.
Hannay (Alastair) Mental images a defence. [Muirhead Lib. of Philos.] 8vo. LOND. & NEW YORK, 1971.
Hanson (A. T.) Studies in Paul's technique and theology. 8vo. LOND., 1974.
—— Grace and truth: a study in the doctrine of the Incarnation. 8vo. LOND., 1975.
—— The New Testament interpretation of Scripture. 8vo. LOND., 1980.
Hanson (R. P. C.) Christian priesthood examined. [The Cross in the Crucible.] 8vo. GUILDFORD & LOND., 1979.
Hanson (S.) *and others.* Marsh Street congregations: the Congregational Churches and burial ground in Marsh Street, Walthamstow. [Walthamstow Antiquarian Soc. Occ. Publs., 11.] 4to. *Duplicated.* LOND., 1969. [Pamph.]
Hardacre (P. H.) Sir Edward Hyde and the idea of liberty to tender consciences, 1641-1656. 8vo. n.p., 1971. [Pamph.]
—— The genesis of the Declaration of Breda, 1657-1660. 8vo. n.p., 1973. [Pamph.]
[Hardman (David) *ed.*] Enys Street Methodist Church [Pendleton, Salford], 1873-1973. 8vo. SALFORD, [1973]. [Pamph.]
Hardy (*Sir* Alister C.) The biology of God: a scientist's study of man the religious animal. 8vo. LOND., 1975.
—— The spiritual nature of man: a study of contemporary religious experience. 8vo. OXF., 1979.
Hardy (Henry Ernest) *Father Andrew, S.D.C.* Life and letters. Ed. and comp. Kathleen E. Burne. 8vo. LOND., 1948.
[Hargrove (Charles) *ed.*] The Unitarian chapels of Yorkshire. obl. 8vo. LEEDS, [190-].
Harl (Marguerite) *ed.* Écriture et culture philosophique dans la pensée de Grégoire de Nysse. Actes de Colloque de Chevetogne (22-26 sept. 1969) organisé par le Centre de Recherche sur l'Hellénisme Tardif de la Sorbonne. 8vo. LEIDEN, 1971.
Harleian Society. *See* Suppt.
[Harley (M. J.)] East Finchley Baptist Church, 1877-1977. 8vo. *Duplicated.* [LOND.,] 1977. [Pamph.]
Harley (Robert) *1st Earl of Oxford.* *See* Downie (J. A.)

Harman (L. W.)   The history of Christianity in Reading. With addit. material by Keith R. Brymer. 8vo. READING, 1952.

Harnisch (Wolfgang)   *See* Suppt. Forschungen zur Religion u. Lit., 110.

Harper (Joyce)   *See* Suppt. Christian Brethren Research Fellowship, Occ. Papers, 5.

Harries (John)   G. Campbell Morgan: the man and his ministry. 8vo. NEW YORK, *etc.*, 1930.

Harris (Brian E.)   *See* Suppt. Record Soc. of Lancs. and Chesh., 118.

Harris (Donald B.)   *See* Pare (P. N.) and Harris (D. B.)

Harris (Errol E.)   Hypothesis and perception: the roots of scientific method.   [Muirhead Lib. of Philos.]   8vo.   LOND. & NEW YORK, 1970.

Harris (Frederick W. P.)   Philip Doddridge: eighteenth century ecumenist.   8vo.   NEW YORK, 1971.   [Pamph.]

Harris (Henry Wilson)   J. A. Spender. 8vo. LOND., 1946.

Harris (Horton)   David Friedrich Strauss and his theology. 8vo. CAMB., 1973.

—— The Tübingen school. 8vo. OXF., 1975.

Harris (Howel!)   *See* Jones (M. H.)

Harris (J. Carlyon)   Man's essential immortality proved by his supreme experience. With a preparatory synopsis of scriptural and deductive evidence. 8vo. SYDNEY, 1920.

Harris (James Rendel)   *See* Pickard (I.); Wilson (W. E.)

Harris (John Charles)   Couriers of Christ: pioneers of the London Missionary Society. 8vo. LOND., 1931.

Harris (Richard Reader)   *See* Hooker (M. R.) *née Harris.*

Harris (Ronald Walter)   Reason and nature in the eighteenth century, 1714-1780. 8vo. LOND., 1968.

Harris (William Melville)   The struggle for religious liberty. (The story of 1662.) A textbook for young people. 8vo. LOND., [1910].

—— The dawn of Christianity in the Empire. A textbook for the exam. conducted by the Young People's Dept. of the Congregational Union. 8vo. LOND., [c. 1911].

—— Richard Baxter: the making of a Nonconformist. 8vo. LOND., [1912].

Harrison (F. M. W.)   The Eastwood Baptist Church, 1876-1976. 8vo. [EASTWOOD, 1976.] [Pamph.]

Harrison (John F. C.)   The second coming: popular millenarianism, 1780-1850. 8vo. LOND. & HENLEY, 1979.

Harrison (Jonathan)   Our knowledge of right and wrong. [Muirhead Lib. of Philos.] 8vo. LOND. & NEW YORK, 1971.

Harrison (Joshua C.) [Misc.]   Joshua Clarkson Harrison: a memoir by one who knew him. Preface by R. F. Horton. 8vo. LOND., 1900.

Harrison (R. K.)   Introduction to the Old Testament. 8vo. LOND., 1970.

[Harrod (J.) and **Tomkins** (M.)]   Church and chapel. [Wheathampstead and Harpenden, 3.] 8vo. HARPENDEN & ST. ALBANS, 1975. [Pamph.]

Harrop (Sylvia A.) and **Rose** (E. A.) *ed.* Victorian Ashton. 8vo. [ASHTON-UNDER-LYNE,] 1974. [Pamph.]

Harte (Negley B.) and **North** (John A.)   The world of University College, London, 1828-1978. Introd. by Lord. Annan. 4to. [LOND., 1978.]

Hartill (Isaac)   History of Orange Street Chapel, Leicester Square. W.C. 8vo. LOND., [1919?]. [Pamph.]

Hartley (A. J.)   The novels of Charles Kingsley: a Christian social interpretation. 8vo. FOLKESTONE, 1977.

Hartmann (Nicolai)   Grundzüge einer Metaphysik der Erkenntnis. (1921.) 2te. Aufl. 8vo. BERLIN & LEIPZIG, 1925.

—— Ethik. 8vo. BERLIN & LEIPZIG, 1926.

—— Die Philosophie des deutschen Idealismus. I. Fichte, Schelling und die Romantik. (1923.) II. Hegel. (1929.) 2te. Aufl. 2 vols. in 1. 8vo. BERLIN, 1960.

—— Das Problem des geistigen Seins: Untersuchungen zur Grundlegung der Geschichtsphilosophie und der Geisteswissenschaften. 8vo. BERLIN & LEIPZIG, 1933.

Hartshorne (Charles)   *See* Gunton (C. E.)

Harvard Theological Review.   *See* Suppt.

Harvey (John H.)   Henry Yevele reconsidered. 8vo. LOND., 1952. [Pamph.]

—— Sources for the history of houses. [British Records Assoc., Archives and the User, 3.] 8vo. LOND., 1974. [Pamph.]

Harvey (P. D. A.) *ed.* *See* Suppt. Hist. MSS. Comm. Joint Publs., 23; Oxfordshire Record Soc., 50.

Haselmayer (L. A.) The Church of South India: its relationship to the Anglican Communion. 8vo. NEW YORK, 1948. [Pamph.]

Haselmere. *Hope Baptist Chapel.* A brief memorial of the goodness of the Lord during one hundred years to the church and congregation now worshipping at "Hope" Baptist Chapel, Haselmere. 8vo. HASELMERE, [1948]. [Pamph.]

Hassan (*Sir* J. A.) *See* Suppt. Jewish Hist. Soc. Publs., 1970.

Hastings (Adrian) A history of African Christianity, 1950-1975. [African Studies Ser., 26.] 8vo. CAMB., 1979.

Haswell (J. H. W.) An introduction to the Holy Land, based on modern tour routes. 8vo. LOND., 1969.

Hathaway (W. G.) A sound from heaven. 8vo. LOND., 1947.
—— Sealed with the Holy Spirit of promise. 8vo. LOND., 1965. [Pamph.]
—— A consideration of modern Pentecostal phenomena. 8vo. CROYDON, 1967. [Pamph.]

Hatton (Ragnhild) George I, Elector and King. 8vo. LOND., 1978.

Haussig (H.-W.) A history of Byzantine civilization. Trans. J. M. Hussey. 4to. LOND., 1971.

Hawes (Stephen) *See* Suppt. Early Eng. Text Soc., O.S., 271.

Hawker (R. S.) *See* Brendon (P.)

[Hawkin (Richard)] Crawshawbooth Meeting House. 8vo. *Duplicated.* n.p., [196-]. [Pamph.]

Hawkins (E. J. W.) *See* Suppt. Dumbarton Oaks. Studies, 14.

Hawkins (F. H.) The Presbytery of Durham. 8vo. SOUTH SHIELDS [printed], [1975].

Hawksworth (G. F. B.) The Central Congregational Church in Sheffield. 8vo. [SHEFFIELD, 1971.] [Pamph.]

Haworth (Elizabeth A.) *See* Horner (I. B.) and Haworth (E. A.)

Hay (A. M.) Charles Inwood: his ministry and its secret. 8vo. LOND., [1929].

Hay (Denys) The church in Italy in the fifteenth century. [Birkbeck Lects., 1971.] 8vo. CAMB., 1977.

Hayden (Roger) *ed.* *See* Bristol. *Broadmead Church.*

Hayes (Alan J.) Edinburgh Methodism, 1761-1975: the mother churches. 8vo. EDIN, 1976.

[Hayes (E. H.)] Three hundred years witness for Christ: Devonshire Square Baptist Church, 1638-1938. 4to. [LOND., 1938.] [Pamph.]

Hayes (John H.) and **Miller** (J. Maxwell) *ed.* Israelite and Judaean history. [Old Test. Lib.] 8vo. LOND., 1977.

Hayes (Will) *comp.* The stamper of the skies: a Bible for animal lovers. (1933.) repr. 4to. LOND., 1938.
—— *See* Bible. N.T. Gospels. *English.*

Haym (Rudolf) Herder. (1877-85.) repr. 2 vols. 8vo. BERLIN, 1958.

Hazelhurst (Cameron) *See* Suppt. Royal Hist. Soc. Guides and Handbooks. Suppt. Ser., 1.

Hazlitt (William) Letters. Ed. Herschel Moreland Sikes, asstd. by Willard Hallam Bonner and Gerald Lahey. 8vo. LOND., 1980.

Head (Constance) Justinian II of Byzantium. 8vo. MADISON (Wis.), *etc.*, 1972.

Heal (Felicity) *ed.* *See* O'Day (R.) and Heal (F.) *ed.*

Heal (Felicity) and **O'Day** (Rosemary) *ed.* Church and society in England: Henry VIII to James I. [Problems in Focus.] 8vo. LOND., 1977.

Healey (William) [Misc.] Alderman William Healey, J.P., C.C., 1852-1913. 8vo. ROCHDALE [printed], [1913].

Hearn (Lafcadio) Shadowings. 8vo. LOND., 1900.

Hearnshaw (F. J. C.) The centenary history of King's College, London, 1828-1928. 8vo. LOND., *etc.*, 1929.

Heath (Rachel F.) *See* Raven (C. E.) and Heath (R. F.)

Heath-Agnew (E.) Roundhead to Royalist: a biography of Colonel John Birch, 1615-1691. Foreword by Margaret Toynbee. 8vo. HEREFORD, 1977.

Hebburn-on-Tyne. *St. Andrew's Presbyterian Church.* [A brief history,] 1873-1913. 12mo. HEBBURN, [1913]. [Pamph.]

Hebly (J. A.) *ed.* Lowland highlands: Church and oecumene in the Netherlands. 8vo. KAMPEN, 1972.

Hebraica. *See* Suppt. Journal of Near E. Studies.

Hederich (Michael) Um die Freheit der Kirche: Geschichte der Evangelischen Kirche von Kurhessen-Waldeck. [Monographia Hassiae, 1.] 2te. Aufl. 8vo. KASSEL, 1977.

Heeney (Brian) Mission to the middle classes: the Woodard schools, 1848-1891. [Church Historical Soc.] 8vo. LOND., 1969.

Heering (G. J.) and **Sirks** (G. J.) Het Seminarium der Remonstranten driehonderd jaar, 1634-1934. 8vo. AMSTERDAM, 1934.

Hegel (G. W. F.) Hegel's Philosophy of mind: being part three of the Encyclopaedia of the Philosophical Sciences (1830), trans. William Wallace. (1894.) Together with the Zusätze in Boumann's text (1845), trans. A. V. Miller. Foreword by J. N. Findlay. 8vo. OXF., 1971.

—— Hegel's Introduction to Aesthetics: being the introd. to the Berlin aesthetics lects. of the 1820s. Trans. T. M. Knox. With an interpretative essay by Charles Karelis. 8vo. OXF., 1979.

—— *See* Fischer (K.); Hartmann (N.); Reardon (B. M. G.); Schmitt (G.)

Heidegger (Martin) Sein und Zeit. Erste Hälfte. (1927.) 3te. Aufl. 8vo. HALLE A.D.S., 1931.

—— Die Frage nach dem Ding: zu Kants Lehre von den transzendentalen Grundsätzen. (1962.) 2te. Aufl. 8vo. TÜBINGEN, 1975.

—— *See* Biemel (W.); Schmitt (G.)

Hein (Lorenz) Italienische Protestanten und ihr Einfluss auf die Reformation in Polen während der beiden Jahrzehnte vor dem Sandomirer Konsens (1570). 8vo. LEIDEN, 1974.

Heinemann (Margot) Puritanism and theatre: Thomas Middleton and opposition drama under the early Stuarts. [Past and Present Publs.] 8vo. CAMB., 1980.

Heinz (Bernard) Center Church on-the-Green [New Haven, Connecticut]. 8vo. NEW HAVEN, 1976. [Pamph.]

Heisenberg (August) Quellen und Studien zur spätbyzantinischen Geschichte. Gesammelte Arbeiten ausgewählt von Hans-George Beck. [Variorum Reprs.] 8vo. LOND., 1973.

Heiwik (Hans) Er liebte seine Kirche: in memoriam D. Hans Meiser. Biographie und Gestaltung. 8vo. MÜNCHEN, 1956.

Helm (Paul) The varieties of belief. [Muirhead Lib. of Philos.] 8vo. LOND., 1973.

Hemmens (H. L.) The lighted path: Baptist witness in Harrow: its origins and history. 8vo. LOND., 1951.

Henderson (Ian) Scotland: Kirk and people. 8vo. EDIN., 1969.

Hendry (G. S.) The Holy Spirit in Christian theology. [Thomas White Currie Lects., Austin Presbyterian Theol. Seminary, Texas, 1955.] 8vo. LOND., 1955.

Hengel (Martin) Judentum und Hellenismus: Studien zu ihrer Begegnung unter besonderer Berücksichtigung Palästinas bis zur Mitte des 2. Jh.s v. Chr. [Wissenschaftl. Untersuch. zum N.T., 10.] (1969.) 2te. Aufl. 8vo. TÜBINGEN, 1973.

—— —— Judaism and Hellenism: studies in their encounter in Palestine during the early Hellenistic period. [Trans. John Bowden.] 2 vols. 8vo. LOND., 1974.

—— The Son of God: the origin of Christology and the history of Jewish-Hellenistic religion. [Trans. John Bowden.] 8vo. LOND., 1976.

Hennell (M. M.) Sons of the prophets: Evangelical leaders of the Victorian Church. 8vo. LOND., 1979.

Hennig (Martin) Quellenbuch zur Geschichte der Inneren Mission. 8vo. HAMBURG, 1912.

Henry VII, *King of England.* *See* Chrimes (S. B.)

Henry (Marie-Louise) Glaubenskrise und Glaubensbewährung in den Dichtungen der Jesajaapokalypse. [Beiträge zur Wiss. vom A. u. N.T., 5te. Folg., 6.] 8vo. STUTTGART, 1967.

Henry Bradshaw Society. *See* Suppt.

Herbert (Edward) *1st Baron Herbert of Cherbury.* Life, written by himself. Ed. with an introd. by J. M. Shuttleworth. [Oxford English Memoirs and Travels.] 8vo. OXF., 1976.

—— *See* Bedford (R. D.)

Herbert (George) English poems. Ed. C. A. Patrides. [Everyman's Univ. Lib.] 8vo. LOND., 1974.
—— Poems from the Temple. With an introd. [by Amy M. Charles]. 8vo. SEWANEE (Tenn.), 1976. [Pamph.]
—— The Williams manuscript of George Herbert's poems. A facsim. repr. with an introd. by Amy M. Charles. 8vo. DELMAR (N.Y.), 1977.
—— *See* Charles (A. M.); Eliot (T. S.); Lewalski (B. K.) and Sabol (A. J.) *ed.*
Herde (Peter) Dante als Florentiner Politiker. [Frankfurter Historische Vorträge, 3.] 8vo. WIESBADEN, 1976. [Pamph.]
Herder (J. G. von) *See* Dobbek (W.); Haym (R.); Richter (J. P. F.)
Herford (Brooke) The main lines of religion as held by Unitarians. [Tracts for the Times, 20.] 8vo. LOND., 1902. [Pamph.]
—— *See* Cuckson (J.)
Herford (Catharine Tayler) Sunday's child. 8vo. [LOND.,] 1979.
Hergenröther (J. A. G.) *ed.* Monumenta Graeca ad Photium ejusque historiam pertinentia. (1869.) facsim. repr. With a new introd. by J. M. Hussey. 8vo. FARNBOROUGH, 1969.
Héring (Jean) The Epistle to the Hebrews. Trans from the first French ed. by A. W. Heathcote and P. J. Allcock. 8vo. LOND., 1970.
Herman (Stewart W.) It's your souls we want. 8vo. LOND., 1943.
Hermas. *See* Suppt. Novum Testamentum Suppts., 37.
Herod Antipas. *See* Hoehner (H. W.)
Herodian, *of Syria.* [History of the Roman Empire. *Greek and English.*] Trans. C. R. Whittaker. [Loeb Classical Lib.] 2 vols. 8vo. LOND. & CAMB. (Mass.), 1969-70.
Herrick (Robert) *See* Lewalski (B. K.) and Sabol (A. J.) *ed.*
Herrmann (Siegfried) A history of Israel in Old Testament times. [Trans. John Bowden.] 8vo. LOND., 1975.
—— *See* Suppt. Studies in Bibl. Theol., 2nd Ser., 27.
Hesiod. [Works. *Greek.*] Theogonia.—Opera et Dies.—Scutum. Ed. Friedrich Solmsen. Fragmenta selecta. Ed. R. Merkelbach et M. L. West. [Oxford Classical Texts.] 8vo. OXF., 1970.
Hesychius, *Saint, of Jerusalem.* *See* Aubineau (M.) *ed.*; Suppt. Analecta Bollandiana. Subsid. Hagiog., 59.
Hetherington (Ralph) The sense of glory: a psychological study of peak experiences. [Swarthmore Lect., 1975.] 8vo. LOND., 1975.
Hettlinger (R. F.) *See* Fairweather (E. R.) and Hettlinger (R. F.)
Hewett (A. Phillip B.) Racovia: the Unitarian search for community in sixteenth-century Poland. [Minns Lects., 1972.] 4to. *Duplicated.* n.p., [1973].
—— Unitarians in Canada. 8vo. TORONTO, *etc.*, 1978.
[Hewett (Sylvia R.)] The story of Eltham Park Baptist Church, 1903-1953. 8vo. [ELTHAM, 1953.] [Pamph.]
[Hewinson (J.)] A brief history of Prestbury Congregational Church, 1866-1966. 8vo. [PRESTBURY, 1966.] [Pamph.]
Heylin (Peter) Aërius redivivus: or the history of the Presbyterians. (1670.) 2nd ed. (1672.) facsim. repr. fol. FARNBOROUGH, 1969.
Heythrop Journal *See* Suppt.
Heywood (Oliver) *See* Millson (F. E.); Notestein (W.)
Heywood (Robert) *See* Brown (W. E.)
Hic mulier: or, the man-woman (1620.), and Haec-vir, or the womanish man. (1620.). facsim. reprs. 2 pts. in 1. 8vo. EXETER, 1973. [Pamph.]
Hick (John H.) Arguments for the existence of God. [Philos. of Relig. Ser.] 8vo. LOND , 1970.
—— Biology and the soul. [Arthur Stanley Eddington Memorial Lect., 25.] 8vo. CAMB., 1972. [Pamph.]
—— God and the universe of faiths: essays in the philosophy of religion. 8vo. LOND., 1973.
—— Death and eternal life. 8vo. LOND., 1976.
—— *ed.* The myth of God Incarnate. 8vo. LOND., 1977.
Hickling (Colin J. A.) *ed.* *See* Evans (C. F.) [Misc.]
Higham (Florence M. G.) Faith of our fathers: the men and movements of the seventeenth century. 8vo. LOND., 1939.

Hildebrandt (Franz)   I offered Christ: a Protestant study of the Mass.   8vo.   LOND., 1967.
[**Hilditch** (E. L.)]   Little Neston Methodist Church: centenary history, 1872-1972. 8vo.   BIRKENHEAD [printed], [1971].   [Pamph.]
[**Hill** (A. J.)]   Fifty years at Cranbrook, 1899-1949: Cranbrook Road Baptist Church, Ilford.   8vo.   [ILFORD, 1949.]   [Pamph.]
Hill (Andrew M.)   What do Unitarians believe? (1973.)   repr.   8vo.   LOND., 1974. [Pamph.]
Hill (Christopher)   Antichrist in seventeenth-century England.   [Riddell Memorial Lects., 41, 1969.]   8vo.   LOND., etc., 1971.
—— The world turned upside down: radical ideas during the English Revolution. 8vo.   LOND., 1972.
—— Milton and the English Revolution.   8vo.   LOND., 1977.
—— The religion of Gerrard Winstanley.   [Past and Present Suppt. 5.]   8vo. [OXF.,] 1978.   [Pamph.]
—— [Misc.]   Puritans and revolutionaries: essays in seventeenth-century history presented to Christopher Hill.   Ed. Donald Pennington and Keith Thomas.   8vo. OXF., 1978.
—— See Bunyan (John) [Misc.]
Hill (David)   New Testament prophecy.   [Marshalls Theol. Lib.]   8vo.   LOND., 1979.
—— See Bible. Commentaries. New Century Bible.
Hill (John Arthur)   From agnosticism to belief: an account of further evidence for survival.   8vo.   LOND., 1924.
Hill (Michael)   The religious order: a study of virtuoso religion and its legitimation in the nineteenth-century Church of England.   8vo.   LOND., 1973.
—— ed.   See Suppt. Sociological Yearbook of Religion in Britain.
Hill (Rosalind M. T.)   Unfashionable history. Inaugural lect., Westfield Coll., 26th Oct. 1972.   8vo.   [LOND., 1972.]   [Pamph.]
—— [Misc.]   See Suppt. Ecclesiastical Hist. Soc. Studies in Church Hist. Subsid., 1.
Hill (W. S.) ed.   Studies in Richard Hooker. Essays preliminary to an edition of his works.   8vo.   CLEVELAND (Ohio) & LOND., 1972.
Hillerbrand (H. J.)   The Reformation in its own words.   [Selected sources in Eng. trans. with introds. and notes.]   8vo.   LOND., 1964.
—— The world of the Reformation.   8vo.   NEW YORK, 1973.
Hillgarth (J. N.)   Ramon Lull and Lullism in fourteenth-century France.   [Oxford-Warburg Studies.]   8vo.   OXF., 1971.
Hillier, family of.   See Horton-Smith (L. G. H.)
Hilton (Denbigh)   The Unitarian Free Christian Church, South Terrace, Hastings: centenary, 1867-1967.   8vo.   [ST. LEONARDS-ON-SEA, printed, 1967.]   [Pamph.]
Hinckley. Great Meeting Unitarian Chapel.   300 years, 1672-1972.   8vo.   HINCKLEY, 1972.   [Pamph.]
[**Hind** (T.)]   New Basford Methodist Church, Rawson Street, Nottingham: jubilee, 1895-1945.   8vo.   [NOTTINGHAM, 1945.]   [Pamph.]
Hindle (G. B.)   See Suppt. Chetham Soc., 3rd Ser., 22.
Hippolytus, Saint, Bp. of Rome.   Contra Noetum. Text introd., ed. and trans. by Robert Butterworth.   [Heythrop Monographs, 2.]   8vo.   LOND., 1977.
Hirsch (Emanuel)   See Tillich (P. J.)
Hirshson (S. P.)   The lion of the Lord: a biography of the Mormon leader, Brigham Young.   8vo.   LOND., 1971.
[**Hirst** (Stuart)]   A brief story of Mill Hill and its two centuries of tradition, 1674-1950. [Leeds Church Ser., 1.]   8vo.   LEEDS, [1950].   [Pamph.]
Historia Monachorum.   See Suppt. Analecta Bollandiana. Subsid. Hagiog., 53.
Historical Association.   See Suppt.
Historical Manuscripts Commission.   See Suppt.
Historical Monuments Commission.   See Suppt.
History.   See Suppt.
Hoare (M. E.)   The tactless philosopher: Johann Reinhold Forster (1729-98).   8vo. MELBOURNE, 1976.
Hobbes (Thomas)   See Collins (A.); Nicastro (O.); Wolin (S. S.)
[**Hobbs** (J. G.)]   Westgate Baptist Church, Carlisle Road, Bradford: souvenir of the bi-centenary, Nov. 1953.   8vo.   [BRADFORD, 1953.]   [Pamph.]

Hobley (William) Hanes Methodistiaeth Arfon. [Vol. 6.] Dosbarth Bangor (o'r deehre hyd ddiwedd y flwyddyn 1900). 8vo. [CAERNARVON,] 1924.
Hockey (S. F.) Quarr Abbey and its lands, 1132-1631. 8vo. LEICESTER, 1970.
Hocking, *family of.* See Thorne (R. F. S.) *comp.*
Hocking (Joseph) See Horton (R. F.) and Hocking (J.)
Hocking (Silas Kitto) My book of memory: a string of reminiscences and reflections. 8vo. LOND., 1923.
Hodge (Charles) See Huh (S. G.)
Hodges (Frank) My adventures as a labour leader. 8vo. LOND., [1925].
Hodgkin (George Lloyd) 1880-1918. [Life, by his sister, Lucy Violet Hodgkin.— Life, from his own letters and diaries.—Short papers and fragments.] 8vo. [EDIN., priv. printed,] 1921.
Hodgkin (Lucy Violet) Gulielma, wife of William Penn. 8vo. LOND., *etc.*, 1947.
—— See Hodgkin (G.Ll.)
Hodgkins (J. R.) The history of Cliff Town Congregational Church, Southend-on-Sea, 1799-1972. 4to. SOUTHEND-ON-SEA, 1974.
Hodgson (Leonard) Anglicanism and South India. 8vo. CAMB., 1943. [Pamph.]
Hodnett (Edward) See Suppt. Bibliographical Soc. Illus. Monographs, 22/22a.
Hoehner (H. W.) Herod Antipas. [Soc. for N.T. Studies, Monograph Ser., 17.] 8vo. CAMB., 1972.
Hoenderdaal (G. J.) Geloven in de heilige Geest. [Cahiers bij het Nederlands Theol. Tijdschr., 2.] 8vo. WAGENINGEN, 1968.
—— Daders des woords: theorie en pratijk bij de verkondiging van het evangelie. Afscheids-college te Leiden, 24 Feb. 1978. 8vo. [LEIDEN, 1978.] [Pamph.]
Hoffmann (Hans W.) See Suppt. Zeitschr. für A. T. Wiss. Beihefte, 136.
Hoffmann (Heinrich) Die Humanitätsidee in der Geschichte des Abendlandes. 8vo. BERN, 1951.
Hoffmann (Melchior) See Kawerau (P.)
Hofmeyr (J. W.) Johannes Hoornbeeck als polemikus. Proefschrift. 8vo. KAMPEN, 1975.
Hogg (A. G.) See Papers for War Time, 15.
Holifield (E. B.) The covenant sealed: the development of Puritan sacramental theology in Old and New England, 1570-1720. 8vo. NEW HAVEN & LOND., 1974.
Holland, *family of.* Some records of the Holland family. (The Hollands of Barton-under-Needwood, Staffordshire, and the Hollands in history.) 8vo. LOND., 1929.
Holland (Bernard G.) See Suppt. Wesley Hist. Soc. Occ. Publs., N.S., 1.
Holland (Henry Scott) Fibres of faith. 8vo. LOND., [1910].
—— Facts of the faith: being a collection of sermons not hitherto publ. in book form. Ed. with a preface by Christopher Cheshire. 8vo. LOND., 1919.
—— See Lyttelton (E.)
Hollenweger (W. J.) The Pentecostals. [Trans. R. A. Wilson.] 8vo. LOND., 1972.
Holmes (Clive) The Eastern Association in the English Civil War. 8vo. LOND., 1974.
Holmes (G. S.) See Suppt. Historical Assn. Gen. Ser., 86.
Holmes (John) Selected poems. Introd. by John Ciardi. 8vo. BOSTON (Mass.), [1963].
Holstein (Henri) See Dumeige (G.) *ed.*
Holt (P. M.) A seventeenth-century defender of Islam: Henry Stubbe (1632-76) and his book. [Friends of Dr. Williams's Lib. Lect., 26.] 8vo. LOND., 1972. [Pamph.]
Holt (R. V.) Progress and Christianity. [Religion: its Modern Needs and Problems, 1.] 8vo. LOND., 1931.
Holtby (R. T.) Eric Graham, 1888-1964: Dean of Oriel, Principal of Cuddesdon, Bishop of Brechin. 8vo. LOND., 1967.
Holtrop (P. N.) Tussen Piëtisme en réveil: het "Deutsche Christentumsgesellschaft" in Nederland, 1784-1833. Academisch proefschrift. 8vo. AMSTERDAM, 1975.
Holyoake (G. J.) See Clifford (J.)
Homélies Pascales. See Aubineau (M.) *ed.*
Honderich (Ted) *ed.* Essays on freedom of action. 8vo. LOND., 1973.
Hood (Henry G.) The public career of John Archdale, 1642-1717. 8vo. GREENSBORO (N.C.), 1976. [Pamph.]

Hooker (Mary Reader) *née Harris*. Adventures of an agnostic: life and letters of Reader Harris, Q.C. 8vo. LOND., 1959.

Hooker (Morna D.) and **Hickling** (C.) *ed. See* Evans (C. F.) [Misc.]

Hooker (Richard) *See* Hill (W. S.) *ed.*

Hooker (Thomas) Writings in England and Holland, 1626-1633. Ed. with introd. essays by George H. Williams, Norman Pettit, Winifred Herget, and Sargent Bush. [Harvard Theol. Studies, 28.] 8vo. CAMB. (Mass.), 1975.

—— *See* Sprunger (K. La. V.)

[Hooper (H. C.) *ed.*] The 250th anniversary of Centenary Baptist Church, March, 1700-1950. 8vo. [MARCH, 1950.] [Pamph.]

Hooper (John) c. 1495-1555, *Bp. of Gloucester & Worcester. See* West (W. M. S.)

Hooper (Thomas) The story of English Congregationalism. Introd. by Rev. John Brown. 8vo. LOND., 1907.

Hoornbeeck (Johannes) *See* Hofmeyr (J. W.)

Hopkins (Hugh Evan) Charles Simeon of Cambridge. 8vo. LOND., 1977.

Horn (Pamela L. R.) Joseph Arch (1826-1919), the farm workers' leader. 8vo. KINETON (Warw.), 1971.

—— *ed. See* Suppt. Oxfordshire Record Soc., 48.

Horne (C. Silvester) The ministry of the modern Church. Lects. to the students of Regent's Park Baptist Coll. 8vo. LOND., [1907].

—— Pulpit, platform and Parliament. 8vo. LOND., 1913.

Horne (John) *d.* 1676, *of Lynn. See* Nuttall (G. F.)

Horner (Isaline B.) and **Haworth** (Elizabeth A.) Alice M. Cooke: a memoir. 8vo. MANCHESTER, 1940.

Hornus (J.-M.) Introduction aux églises orientales. [Cahier d'Études Chrétiennes Orientales, 12.] [Foi et Vie, 73, 1, Jan. 1974.] 8vo. PARIS, 1974.

—— Cent cinquante ans de présence évangélique au Proche-Orient (1808-1958). [Cahier d'Études Chrétiennes Orientales, 13.] [Foi et Vie, 78, 2, Mar. 1979.] 8vo. PARIS, 1979.

Horr (G. E.) The Christian faith and eternal life. [Ingersoll Lect., 1923.] 8vo. CAMB. (Mass.), 1923.

Horsfield (T. W.) [Misc.] Thomas Walker Horsfield, F.S.A., historian of Sussex and Lewes: the order of service at the unveiling of a tablet to his memory in Westgate Chapel, Lewes, Mar. 23rd, 1927, and addresses by J. M. Connell, J. H. Every, and Lord Monkbretton. 8vo. LEWES, 1927. [Pamph.]

Horsley (C. D.) *Bp. of Colombo.* Some problems connected with the proposed scheme of church union in South India. 8vo. LOND., [1942.] [Pamph.]

Horsley (Lee) *See* Currie (R.) *and others.*

Horst (Irvin B.) The radical brethren: Anabaptism and the English Reformation to 1558. [Bibliotheca Humanistica et Reformatorica, 2.] 8vo. NIEUWKOOP, 1972.

Horton (Douglas) Let us not forget the mighty William Ames. 8vo. [NEW YORK, *c.* 1960.] [Pamph.]

—— *See* Peel (A.) and Horton (D.)

Horton (E. A.) Scenes in the life of Jesus: thirty-six lessons. (1905.) repr. 8vo. BOSTON (Mass.), 1909.

Horton (F. L.) The Melchizedek tradition: a critical examination of the sources to the fifth century A.D. and in the Epistle to the Hebrews. [Soc. for N.T. Studies, Monograph Ser., 30.] 8vo. CAMB., 1976.

Horton (Josephine Padman) *née Bellamy. See* Drew (K.)

Horton (R. F.) Alfred Tennyson: a saintly life. [Saintly Lives.] 8vo. LOND. & NEW YORK, 1900.

—— The Bible: a missionary book. 8vo. EDIN. & LOND., 1904.

—— —— 2nd ed. 8vo. EDIN. & LOND., 1908.

—— St. John: a poem 8vo. LOND., 1904.

—— Does the cross save? 8vo. LOND., 1905.

—— The law of spiritual power, being addresses delivered at the Hampstead convention for the deepening of spiritual life. 8vo. LOND., 1906.

—— The Holy Spirit. 12mo. LOND., 1907.

—— My belief: answers to certain religious difficulties. 8vo. LOND., 1908.

—— The triumph of the cross: brief counsels on faith and duty. 8vo. LOND., 1909.

—— The Hero of heroes: a life of Christ for young people. 8vo. LOND., [1911].

Horton (R. F.)—*continued*
—— Three months in India. 8vo. LOND., *etc.*, 1913.
—— The mystical quest of Christ. 8vo. LOND., 1923.
—— *See* Pringle (A.) *ed.*
Horton (R. F.) and **Hocking** (Joseph) Shall Rome reconquer England? 8vo.
LOND., [1910].
Horton (W. H.) *ed.* The glossolalia phenomenon. 8vo. CLEVELAND (Tenn.), 1966.
Horton (William D.) The story of Methodism in Sevenoaks from 1746. Lecture,
23rd Mar. 1979. fol. *Duplicated.* n.p., [1979]. [Pamph.]
Horton-Smith (L. Graham H.) The Hillier family of Cirencester from 1635, together
with the family of Parry, and a suppt. on the families of Dix Roberts and Smith.
(1944.) repr. 8vo. GLOUCESTER, 1945. [Pamph.]
Horwitz (Henry G.) Comprehension in the later seventeenth century: a postscript.
8vo. [CHICAGO,] 1965. [Pamph.]
—— Parliament, policy and politics in the reign of William III. 8vo. MANCHESTER,
1977.
Hosford (David H.) Nottingham, nobles, and the north: aspects of the Revolution
of 1688. [Studies in British Hist. and Culture, 4.] 8vo. HAMDEN (Conn.), 1976.
Hostler (John) Leibniz's moral philosophy. 8vo. LOND., 1975.
Houghton (Thomas) Liberal Evangelicalism criticised. Foreword by F. J. Hamilton.
8vo. LOND., 1924.
Houlbrooke (R. A.) Church courts and the people during the English Reformation,
1520-1570. [Oxford Historical Monographs.] 8vo. OXF., 1979.
Houlden (J. Leslie) *See* Bible. N.T. Commentaries. Black's.
Housman (A. E.) The name and nature of poetry. [Leslie Stephen Lect., 1933.]
(1933.) repr. 8vo. CAMB., 1933.
—— *See* Gow (A. S. F.)
Howard (Elizabeth Fox) Upstream: a family scrapbook. 8vo. LOND., 1944.
Howard (George) Paul: crisis in Galatia. A study in early Christian theology. [Soc.
for N.T. Studies, Monograph Ser., 35.] 8vo. CAMB., 1979.
Howard (George Broadley) The Christians of St. Thomas and their liturgies . . .
trans. from Syriac MSS. obtained in Travancore. (1864.) facsim. repr. 8vo.
FARNBOROUGH, 1969.
Howard (John) *See* Gibson (E. C. S.)
Howard (K. W. H.) *comp.* A comprehensive textual index of the published sermons
and pulpit expositions of Joseph Charles Philpot (1802-1869). fol. *Duplicated.*
n.p., 1972. [Pamph.]
—— *See* Suppt. Baptist Hist. Soc. Publs.
—— *ed. See* Ecclesiastica.
Howe (D. W.) The Unitarian conscience: Harvard moral philosophy, 1805-1861.
8vo. CAMB. (Mass.), 1970.
Howe (John) *See* Haig (C. A.)
Hoyles (John) The waning of the Renaissance, 1640-1740: studies in the thought
and poetry of Henry More, John Norris and Isaac Watts. [Internat. Archives of the
Hist. of Ideas, 39.] 8vo. THE HAGUE, 1971.
—— The edges of Augustanism: the aesthetics of spirituality in Thomas Ken, John
Byrom and William Law. [Internat. Archives of the Hist. of Ideas, 53.] 8vo.
THE HAGUE, 1972.
Hubbard (Irene M.) The present religious situation: a review of the series. [Reli-
gion: its Modern Needs and Problems, 22.] 8vo. LOND., 1937.
Huber (Friedrich) *See* Suppt. Zeitschr. für A. T. Wiss. Beihefte, 137.
Hudson (A. O.) Future probation in Christian belief. 8vo. HOUNSLOW, 1975.
[Pamph.]
Hudson (Anne) *ed.* Selections from English Wycliffite writings. With an introd.,
notes and glossary. 8vo. CAMB., 1978.
Hudson (William D.) A philosophical approach to religion. 8vo. LOND., 1974.
—— Wittgenstein and religious belief. [New Studies in the Philos. of Relig.] 8vo.
LOND., 1975.
Hudson (Winthrop S.) and **Trinterud** (Leonard J.) Theology in sixteenth- and
seventeenth-century England. [Clark Lib. Seminar Papers.] 8vo. LOS ANGELES,
1971. [Pamph.]
Hübner (Hans) *See* Suppt. Forschungen zur Religion u. Lit., 119.

Hügel (Friedrich, *Baron* von) The life of prayer. (1927.) repr. 8vo. LOND., 1928.
Huelin (Gordon) King's College, London, 1828-1978. 8vo. LOND., 1978.
Hughes (F. C.) and **Mottram** (W.) *ed.* The alchohol question: a new appeal to the Christian Church. A booklet for Temperance Sunday, Nov. 11, 1917. 8vo. LOND., 1977. [Pamph.]
Hughes (G. E.) and **Cresswell** (M. J.) An introduction to modal logic. (1968.) repr. 8vo. LOND., 1974.
Hughes (Graham) Hebrews and hermeneutics: the Epistle to the Hebrews as a New Testament example of biblical interpretation. [Soc. for N.T. Studies, Monograph Ser., 36.] 8vo. CAMB., 1979.
Hughes (Graham Werden) Robert Hall (1764-1831). [Heritage Biographies.] 8vo. LOND., 1961. [Pamph.]
Hughes (Hugh Price) *See* Mantle (J. G.)
Hughes (Katherine Price) The story of my life. 8vo. LOND., 1945.
[**Hughes** (*Mrs.* Margaret)] A charge to keep: Tiviot Dale Methodist Church, Stockport, 1826-1976. 8vo. [STOCKPORT, 1976.] [Pamph.]
Hughes (Thomas Hywel) The atonement: modern theories of the doctrine. 8vo. LOND., 1949.
Huguenot Society of London. *See* Suppt.
Huh (Soon Gil) Presbyter in volle rechten: het debat tussen Charles Hodge en James H. Thornwell over het ambt van ouderling. Academisch proefschrift. 8vo. GRONINGEN, 1972.
Hull (J. M.) *See* Suppt. Studies in Bibl. Theol., 2nd Ser., 28.
Hulsean Lectures. *See* Suppt.
Hulton (Henry) *See* Brown (Wallace)
Humber (Robert D.) Heversham: the story of a Westmorland school and village. 8vo. KENDAL [printed], [1969?].
Hume (David) *See* Black (J. B.); Forbes (D.); Gaskin (J. C. A.); Hall (Roland); Hurlbutt (R. H.); Noxon (J.); Weinberg (J. R.)
Humphrey (David C.) Colonial colleges and English dissenting academies: a study in Transatlantic culture. 8vo. [PITTSBURGH, 1972.] [Pamph.]
Humphrey (W. G.) The Christian and education. 8vo. LOND., 1940.
Hunger (Herbert) Byzantinistische Grundlagenforschung. Gesammelte Aufsaetze. [Variorum Reprs.] 8vo. LOND., 1973.
—— *ed.* Das byzantinische Herrscherbild. [Wege der Forschung, 341.] 8vo. DARMSTADT, 1975.
Hunt (A. R.) *See* Rowberry (D. E.) and Hunt (A. R.)
Hunt (E. W.) Portrait of Paul. 8vo. LOND., 1968.
Hunt (Noreen) *ed.* Cluniac monasticism in the central Middle Ages. [Readings in European Hist.] 8vo. LOND., 1971.
Hunter (A. M.) Introducing New Testament theology. (1957.) 5th imp. 8vo. LOND., 1973.
Hunter (William Bridges) *and others.* Bright essence: studies in Milton's theology: [W. B.] Hunter, [C. A.] Patrides, [J. H.] Adamson. 8vo. SALT LAKE CITY, 1971.
Huntingdon (Selina Hastings, *Countess of*) *See* Welch (C. E.)
Huntley (F. L.) Bishop Joseph Hall, 1574-1656: a biographical and critical study. 8vo. CAMB., 1979.
Hurlbutt (R. H.) Hume, Newton, and the design argument. 8vo. LINCOLN (Neb.), 1965.
Hurley (Michael) *ed.* Irish Anglicanism, 1869-1969. Essays on the role of Anglicanism in Irish life presented to the Church of Ireland on the occasion of the centenary of its Disestablishment. By a group of Methodist, Presbyterian, Quaker and Roman Catholic scholars. 4to. DUBLIN, 1970.
Hurst (Janet) *See* Gilmour (J.) and Hurst (J.)
Hurstfield (Joel) *ed.* The Reformation crisis. 8vo. LOND., 1965.
—— [Misc.] The English Commonwealth, 1547-1640. Essays in politics and society presented to Joel Hurstfield. Ed. Peter Clark, Alan G. R. Smith and Nicholas Tyacke. 8vo. LEICESTER, 1979.
Hus (John) Letters. Trans. from the Latin and Czech by Matthew Spinka. 8vo. MANCHESTER, 1972.
—— *See* De Vooght (P.); Zinzendorf (N. L. von) [Misc.]

Husserl (Edmund) Logische Untersuchungen. (1900.) 2 vols. in 3. 8vo. HALLE A.D.S.
 1. Prolegomena zur reinen Logik. 4te. Aufl. 1928.
 2. i Untersuchungen zur Phänomenologie und Theorie der Erkenntnis. 4te. Aufl. 1928.
 2. ii. Elemente einer phänomenologischen Aufklärung der Erkenntnis. 3te. Aufl. 1922.
—— Ideen zu einer reinen Phänomenologie und phänomenologischen Philosophie. Erstes Buch. Allgemeine Einführung in die reine Phänomenologie. (1913.) repr. 8vo. HALLE A.D.S., 1928.
Hutchinson (Anne) *See* Battis (E.)
Hutchinson (F. E.) Milton and the English mind. [Teach Yourself Hist. Lib.] 8vo. LOND., 1946.
Hutchinson (John) 1615-64, *Colonel*. *See* Hutchinson (Lucy)
Hutchinson (Lucy) Memoirs of the life of Colonel Hutchinson, Governor of Nottingham, by his widow Lucy. Ed. from the original MS. by the Rev. Julius Hutchinson (1806.) Rev. with addit. notes by C. H. Firth. [London Lib.] 8vo. LOND. & NEW YORK, 1906.
Hutchison (W. R.) The Transcendentalist ministers: Church reform in the New England renaissance. (1959.) repr. 8vo. HAMDEN (Conn.), 1972.
Huth (Hans) *See* Rupp (E. G.)
Hutton (R. H.) *See* Tener (R. H.)
Huxley (Aldous) T. H. Huxley as a man of letters. [Huxley Memorial Lect., Imperial Coll. of Science and Technol., 1932.] 8vo. LOND., [1932]. [Pamph.]
Huxley (Leonard) Progress and the unfit. [Conway Memorial Lect., 1926.] 8vo. LOND., 1926.
Huxley (T. H.) *See* Huxley (A.)
Hyatt (J. Philip) *See* Bible. Commentaries. New Century Bible.
Hyde (Edward) *1st Earl of Clarendon*. Calendar of the Clarendon State Papers preserved in the Bodleian Library. 5 vols. 8vo. OXF., 1869-1970
 5. 1660-1726. With index to vols. 4 and 5. 1970.
—— *See* Fogle (F. R.) and Trevor-Roper (H. R.); Hardacre (P. H.)
Hylkema (C. B.) Reformateurs: geschiedkundige studiën over de godsdienstige bewegingen uit de nadagen onzer gouden eeuw. 2 vols. 8vo. HAARLEM, 1900-02.
Hyman (Louis) *See* Suppt. Jewish Hist. Soc. Publs., 1972.
Hymn. *See* Suppt.
Hymns. Cantate Domino. World's Student Christian Federation hymnal. 8vo. GENEVA, [1924].
—— Hymns of universal praise. Ed. by the Union Hymnal Committee. [With tunes.] 8vo. SHANGHAI, 1936.
—— We sing of life: songs for children, young people, adults. Vincent Silliman, editor; Irving Lowens, music editor. [With tunes.] 8vo. BOSTON (Mass.), 1955.
—— Again I say rejoice: hymns and verse. By Albert F. Bayly. (1967.) [With suppt. 'Rejoice always: hymns and verse' (1971).] 8vo. THAXTED [the author], 1971.
—— Rejoice in God: hymns and verse. By Albert F. Bayly. 8vo. CHELMSFORD [the author], 1977. [Pamph.]
—— Hymns of the higher life, with canticles and aspirations. Arranged by O. A. Shrubsole. 8vo. READING, n.d.
—— *See* Christian Endeavour.
—— [Misc.] *See* Suppt. Alcuin Club. Misc. Publs., 1980; Hymn Soc. of America; Hymn Soc. of G.B. and Ireland; Methodist Sacramental Fellowship. M.S.F. Booklets. Wesley Reprs., 1.
Hymn Society of America. *See* Suppt.
Hymn Society of Great Britain and Ireland. *See* Suppt.

Ignatius Yacoub III, *Patriarch of Antioch*. The Syrian Orthodox Church of Antioch. [In English and Arabic.] 8vo. ATCHANE (Lebanon), 1974. [Pamph.]
Ijsewijn (Jozef) Companion to Neo-Latin studies. 8vo. AMSTERDAM, *etc*, 1977.
Ikeda (Daisaku) *See* Toynbee (A. J.) and Ikeda (D.)
Ilford. *Cranbrook Road Baptist Church*. Diamond jubilee, 1899-1959. 8vo. [ILFORD, 1959.] [Pamph.]
Ingham (Benjamin) *See* Thompson (R. W.)

Ingram (Kenneth) Christianity and sexual morality: a modernist view. [Modernist Pamphs. on Relig., Life and Thought, 3.] 8vo. LOND., 1944. [Pamph.]

Ingrey (Mabel) *and others.* 'The sacred flame': a record of Methodism in Shillington. High Road Methodist Church, Shillington, Beds.: centenary, 1872-1972. 8vo. [SHILLINGTON, 1972.] [Pamph.]

Injunctions. 1538. A photographic reproduction [with transcript] of the original royal Injunctions issued under the authority of King Henry VIII by his vicegerent [*sic*] Thomas (Lord) Cromwell, ordering that the Bible in English be set up in every parish church. Dated Sept. 5th, 1538. 8vo. LOND., 1938. [Pamph.]

Inquirer. *See* Suppt.

Institut International de Philosophie. *See* Suppt. Bibliographie de la Philosophie.

Institute of Historical Research. *See* Suppt. London University. Institute of Historical Research.

Intellectual Repository and New Jerusalem Magazine. *See* Suppt.

International Association for the History of Religions. *See* Suppt. Numen.

International Bibliography of the History of Religions. *See* Suppt. Numen.

International Conference on Patristic Studies. *See* Suppt. Texte u. Untersuchungen, 5te. Reihe, 108, 115-117.

International Congregational Council. Proceedings of the 3rd Council, Edinburgh, Jun. 30-Jul. 9, 1908. Ed. John Brown. 8vo. LOND., 1908.

International Congress of Byzantine Studies. 11. Berichte zum XI. Internationalen Byzantinisten-Kongress, München, 1958. 7pts. 8vo. MÜNCHEN, 1958. [*Incomplete.*]

—— [Misc.] Chalikes: Festgabe für die Teilnehmer an XI. Internationalen Byzantinistenkongress, München, 1958. 8vo. FREISING, 1958.

—— 13. Thirteenth International Congress of Byzantine Studies, Oxford, 1966. Supplementary papers.—Summaries. 8vo. [LOND.,] 1966.

International Congress of Papyrologists. *See* Suppt. Egypt Exploration Soc. Graeco-Rom. Memoirs, 61.

International Congress on New Testament Studies. *See* Suppt. Texte u. Untersuchungen, 5te. Reihe, 103, 112.

International Journal of Ethics. *See* Suppt. Ethics.

International Library of Philosophy and Scientific Method. *See* Suppt.

International Organization for the Study of the Old Testament. *See* Suppt. Vetus Testamentum.

International Review of Biblical Studies. *See* Suppt. Internationale Zeitschriftenschau für Bibelwissenschaft und Grenzgebiete.

International Review of Missions. *See* Suppt.

Internationale Zeitschriftenschau für Bibelwissenschaft und Grenzgebiete. *See* Suppt.

Interpretation. *See* Suppt.

Inwood (Charles) *See* Hay (A. M.)

Irenaeus, *Saint, Bp. of Lyons.* Contre les hérésies: mise en lumière et réfutation de la prétendue 'Connaissance'. Éd. critique. [Sources Chrétiennes.] 8vo. PARIS, 1952—
    Livre 3. (1952.) new ed. i-ii. Introd., notes, tables; texte et trad.: Adelin Rousseau et Louis Doutreleau. 2 vols. 1974.

—— *See* Suppt. Patrologia Orientalis, XXXIX. 1.

Ireton (Henry) *Lord Deputy of Ireland. See* Ramsey (R. W.)

Irish Mission. *See* Suppt. Christian Irishman.

Irving (Edward) *See* Strachan (C. G.)

Isaac, *Sebastocrator.* "Peri tes ton kakon hypostaseos" (De malorum subsistentia). [Ed. with an introd. by] James John Rizzo. [Beiträge zur klass. Philol., 42.] 8vo. MEISENHEIM AM G., 1971.

Isaias, *abbas, Saint, Abbot of Egypt. See* Suppt. Corpus Script. Christ. Orient., Syri, 144-145, 150-151.

Ishida (Tomoo) *See* Suppt. Zeitschr. für A. T. Wiss. Beihefte, 142.

Ishò'dad, *of Merv, Bp. of Hadatha. See* Suppt. Corpus Script. Christ. Orient., Syri, 146-147.

[Iskender (Yervant H.)] Citizens of the world. 8vo. PITLOCHRY, [1914]. [Pamph.]

Isleham. *High Street Baptist Church.* Ter-jubilee celebrations. Souvenir programme. 8vo. [ISLEHAM, 1962.] [Pamph.]

Ivánka (Endre von)   Rhomäerreich und Gottesvolk: das Glaubens-, Staats- und Volksbewusstsein der Byzantiner und seine Auswirkung auf die ostkirchlich-osteuropäische Geisteshaltung.   8vo.   FREIBURG & MÜNCHEN, 1968.

Ivory (D. J.)   Stokes Croft endowed school and almshouse, Bristol, 1722-1940.   8vo. BRISTOL, 1979.   [Pamph.]

Ivory (L. S.)   Long Buckby Congregational Church, 1707-1957: a brief historical sketch.   8vo.   NORTHAMPTON, 1957.   [Pamph.]

[Izod (Lionel)]   Guildford Baptist Church, 1824-1974: a historical sketch.   4to. *Duplicated.* n.p., [1974].   [Pamph.]

Jackson (Arthur)   Brearley Baptist Church centenary, 1875-1975: a short history of the church.   8vo.   *Duplicated.* n.p., 1974.   [Pamph.]

Jackson (Douglas)   Bideford Baptist Church: a short history to commemorate the opening of the new chapel, Oct. 1964.   8vo.   [BIDEFORD, 1964.]   [Pamph.]

Jackson (W. A.)   *See* Suppt. Bibliographical Soc. Publs., 1973-75.

Jacob.   *See also* James.

Jacob, *the Patriarch.*   *See* Suppt. Corpus Script. Christ. Orient., Aethiop., 73-74.

Jacob (Margaret C.)   The Newtonians and the English Revolution, 1689-1720. 8vo.   ITHACA (N.Y.), 1976.

Jagger (Peter J.)   *See* Suppt. Alcuin Club. Misc. Publs., 1975.

[Jagger (T. I.) *and others.*]   Lyndhurst Road Church, Hampstead: a thanksgiving for its life and work, 1880-1978.   8vo.   LOND., [1978].   [Pamph.]

Jahrbuch für Antike und Christentum.   *See* Suppt.

James, *Bp. of Batnan in Sĕrūgh.*   *See* Chesnut (R. C.); Suppt. Corpus Script. Christ. Orient., Subsid., 39-40; Patrologia Orientalis, XXXVIII. 1.

James I, *King of Great Britain and Ireland.*   *See* Ebert (M.)

James, *of Venice, fl.*1143.   *See* Suppt. Corpus Philos. Medii Aevi. Aristoteles Latinus. Opera, VI.

James, *family of.*   *See* Stonebridge (E. R.) and Stonebridge (L. M.)

James (Brian Lloyd) *ed.*   *See* Catalogues. *St. David's Univ. Coll., Lampeter.*

James (Edwin O.)   The beginnings of religion: an introductory and scientific study. [Hutchinson's Univ. Lib.]   8vo.   LOND., [1948].

James (Eric A.)   *See* Bunyan (John) [Misc.]

James (John Angell 1785-1859.   *See* Haig (C. A.)

James (Patricia)   Population Malthus: his life and times.   8vo.   LOND., *etc.*, 1979.

James (Philip) 1664-1748, *Welsh Baptist minister.*   *See* Nuttall (G. F.); Stonebridge (E. R.) and Stonebridge (L. M.)

James (R. Edwards)   *See* Jenkins (J. A.) and James (R. E.)

James (Ralph E.) *ed.*   *See* Brown (Delwin) *and others, ed.*

James (Thomas T.)   The work and administration of a Congregational Church. 8vo.   LOND., 1925.

James (William)   *See* Wickham (H.)

Janelle (Pierre)   Robert Southwell the writer: a study in religious inspiration.   8vo. LOND., 1935.

Janssens (Uta)   Matthieu Maty and the Journal Britannique, 1750-1755: a French view of English literature in the middle of the eighteenth century.   8vo.   AMSTER-DAM, 1975.

Janzen (Waldemar)   *See* Suppt. Zeitschr. für A. T. Wiss. Beihefte, 125.

Jaspers (Karl)   Die massgebenden Menschen: Sokrates, Buddha, Konfuzius, Jesus. [New ed. of part of Die grossen Philosophen, Bd.I (1957).]   [Piper Paperback.] (1964.) repr.   8vo.   MÜNCHEN, 1965.

—— Drei Gründer des Philosophierens: Plato, Augustin, Kant.   [Repr. from Die grossen Philosophen, Bd.I (1957).]   [Piper Paperback.]   8vo.   MÜNCHEN, 1966.

—— Aus dem Ursprung denkende Metaphysiker: Anaximander, Heraklit, Parmenides, Plotin, Anselm, Spinoza, Laotse, Nagarjuna.   [Repr. from Die grossen Philosophen, Bd.I (1957).]   [Piper Paperback.]   8vo.   MÜNCHEN, [1967?]

—— *See* Samay (S.)

Jedin (Hubert)   Kardinal Contarini: als Kontroverstheologe.   [Katholisches Leben u. Kämpfen im Zeitalter der Glaubensspaltung, 9.]   8vo.   MÜNSTER IN W., 1949.

—— Der Abschluss des Trienter Konzils, 1562/63: ein Rückblick nach vier Jahrhunderten.   [Katholisches Leben u. Kämpfen im Zeitalter der Glaubensspaltung, 21.]   (1963.)   2te. Aufl.   8vo.   MÜNSTER IN W., 1964.

Jedin (Hubert) and **Dolan** (John) *ed.* Handbook of church history. vols. 1, 3, 4. 8vo. LOND., *etc.*, 1965-70.
    4. From the high Middle Ages to the eve of the Reformation: Hans-Georg Beck, *etc.* 1970.
    [*No more published under this title.*]
Jeffrey (Francis) *See* Lindon (J. M. A.)
Jeffreys (Edward) Stephen Jeffreys, the beloved evangelist. 8vo. LOND., 1946.
Jeffreys (George) Healing rays. 8vo. LOND., 1932.
—— Pentecostal rays: the baptism and gifts of the Holy Spirit. 8vo. LOND., 1933.
—— Elim Foursquare Gospel Alliance deed poll. 4to. LOND., 1934. [Pamph.]
Jeffreys (Stephen) *See* Jeffreys (E.)
Jeffs (Harry) "J. B.": J. Brierley: his life and work. 8vo. LOND., [1915].
Jenkins (Daniel T.) The Christian belief in God. 8vo. LOND., 1964.
Jenkins (E. T.) *and others.* Calvary English Baptist Church, Treforest: historical outline, 1849-1949. 8vo. LOND., 1949. [Pamph.]
Jenkins (Geraint Huw) Literature, religion and society in Wales, 1660-1730. [Studies in Welsh Hist., 2.] 8vo. CARDIFF, 1978.
Jenkins (James Ewart) History of Unitarianism in Padiham, 1806-1906: a centenary volume. Together with some reminiscences contributed by past ministers. 8vo. ACCRINGTON, 1906.
Jenkins (John Austin) and **James** (R. Edwards) The history of Nonconformity in Cardiff. 8vo. CARDIFF & LOND., 1901.
Jenkins (Robert T.) Gruffydd Jones, Llanddowror, 1683-1761. 8vo. CAERDYDD, 1930.
—— *See* Jones (M. H.); Llewelyn-Williams (A.); Nuttall (G. F.)
Jenkins (Romilly J. H.) Studies on Byzantine history of the 9th and 10th centuries. [Variorum Reprs.] 8vo. LOND., 1970.
Jenkins (Roy H.) Mr. Balfour's poodle: an account of the struggle between the House of Lords and the Government of Mr. Asquith. 8vo. LOND., 1954.
Jeremias (Christian) *See* Suppt. Forschungen zur Religion u. Lit., 117.
Jeremias (Joachim) New Testament theology. [Trans. John Bowden.] [New Test. Lib.] 8vo. LOND.
    1. 1971.
    No more yet published, 1980.
Jerome, *Saint. See* Kelly (J. N. D.); Rousseau (P.)
Jervell (Jacob) Luke and the people of God: a new look at Luke-Acts. 8vo. MINNEAPOLIS (Minn.), 1972.
Jessop (T. E.) Reason and religion: a plea for a rational faith. [Modernist Pamphs. on Relig., Life and Thought, 4.] 8vo. LOND., 1945. [Pamph.]
Jewish Annual. *See* Suppt.
Jewish Historical Society of England. *See* Suppt.
Jewish Quarterly Review. *See* Suppt.
Jewson (C. B.) The Jacobin city: a portrait of Norwich in its relation to the French Revolution, 1788-1802. 8vo. GLASGOW & LOND., 1975.
—— Simon Wilkin of Norwich. 8vo. NORWICH, 1979.
[**Jewson** (C. B.) *and others.*] St. Mary's in four centuries, 1669-1969. 8vo. [NOR-WICH, 1969.] [Pamph.]
Joachim, *of Flora. See* Reeves (M. E.)
Joachim (H. H.) Immediate experience and mediation. Inaugural lect., Univ. of Oxford, 20 Nov. 1919. 8vo. OXF., 1919. [Pamph.]
Joannes, *Saba, monk of Daliatha. See* Suppt. Patrologia Orientalis, XXXIX. 3.
Joannou (Theophilos) Mnemeia hagiologica nyn proton ekdidomena. (1884.) Volumen phototypice edendum praefatione instruxit Jürgen Dummer. [Subsidia Byzantina, 8.] 8vo. LEIPZIG, 1973.
Johansen (J. H.) *See* Suppt. Hymn Soc. of America. Papers, 20.
John, *Bp. of Beirut. See* Aubineau (M.) *ed.*
John, *Saint, of the Cross. See* Morales (J. L.)
John *Saint of Damascus.* [Works. *Greek.*] Schriften. Hrsg. Byzantinisches Institut der Abtei Scheyern. Besorgt von Bonifatius Kotter. [Patristische Texte u. Studien.] 8vo. BERLIN, 1969-
    2. Ekdosis akribes tes orthodoxou pisteos: expositio fidei. 1973.
    3. Contra imaginum calumniatores orationes tres. 1975.

John, *Metropolitan of Dara.   See* Suppt. Corpus Script. Christ. Orient., Syri, 132-133.
John V or **VI,** *Palaeologus, Emperor of the East.   See* Halecki (O.)
John XXIII, *Pope.   See* Trevor (M.)
John, *of Salisbury, Bp. of Chartres.*   Letters.   [Text and trans.]   [Oxford Medieval
  Texts.]   2 vols.   8vo.   LOND., *etc.*, 1955-79.
  2.   The later letters (1163-1180).   Ed. W. J. Millor and C. N. L. Brooke.   1979.
John (Glymor)   Congregationalism in the early continental reform.   [Congregational
  Studies, 1.]   4to.   *Duplicated.*   4to.   LOND., [1964].   [Pamph.]
John (J. Mansel) *ed.*   Welsh Baptist studies.   [Contributors: Glanmor Williams, B. R.
  White, R. Tudur Jones, B. G. Owens.]   8vo.   [CARDIFF,] 1976.
John Rylands Library, *Manchester.   See* Suppt. Bulletin of the John Rylands (Uni-
  versity) Library.
Johnson (Agnes)   Glimpses of ancient Leicester, in six periods. (1891.)   2nd ed.
  8vo.   LEICESTER, 1906.
Johnson (Aubrey R.)   The cultic prophet and Israel's psalmody.   8vo.   CARDIFF,
  1979.
Johnson (Clive) *ed.*   Vedanta: an anthology of Hindu scripture, commentary and
  poetry. Ed. under the supervision of Swami Prabhavananda.   8vo.   NEW YORK, *etc.*,
  1971.
Johnson (Harriet E.)   Handbook of the Arlington Street Church.   8vo.   [BOSTON
  (Mass.),] 1929.   [Pamph.]
Johnson (Henry H.)   A short life of Jesus.   [Religion: its Modern Needs and Pro-
  blems, 15.]   8vo.   LOND., 1933.
Johnson (Joseph) 1738-1809, *bookseller.   See* Tyson (G. P.)
Johnson (Joseph) 1848-1926, *Congreg. minister.*   George MacDonald: a biographical
  and critical appreciation.   8vo.   LOND., 1906.
Johnson (Samuel)   *See* Bate (W. J.)
Johnson (William Charles)   Encounter in London: the story of the London Baptist
  Association, 1856-1965.   8vo.   LOND., 1965.
Johnston (William)   Christian Zen.   8vo.   NEW YORK, *etc.*, 1971.
Johnstone (Henry F. V.)   A short history of Skinner Street United Reformed Church,
  Poole, 1777-1977.   4to.   *Duplicated.*   [POOLE, 1977.]   [Pamph.]
Johnstone (Henry W.)   *See* Anderson (J. M.) and Johnstone (H. W.)
Johnstone (Hilda)   Oliver Cromwell and his times.   [People's Books.]   12mo.
  LOND., [1912].
**Joint Committee for Negotiations between Churches of Christ and the United
  Reformed Church.**   Proposals for unification. With the proposed Parliamentary
  Bill and supporting information.   8vo.   BIRMINGHAM [printed], 1976.   [Pamph.]
Jolly (C. A.)   The spreading flame: the coming of Methodism to Norfolk, 1751-1811.
  8vo.   [GRESSENHALL, 1973.]
Jones (Alan D.)   *See* Edwards (L. D.) and Jones (A. D.)
Jones (Cheslyn P. M.) *and others, ed.*   The study of liturgy.   Ed. Cheslyn Jones,
  Geoffrey Wainwright, Edward Yarnold, S. J.   8vo.   LOND., 1978.
[Jones (Clive) *comp.*]   1925-1975 jubilee: the first 50 years.   [New Malden Evangelical
  Free Church.]   8vo.   [NEW MALDEN, 1975.]   [Pamph.]
Jones (D. J. Odwyn)   Daniel Rowland, Llangeitho (1713-1790).   8vo.   LLANDYSUL,
  1938.
Jones (David)   Life and times of Griffith Jones, sometime Rector of Llanddowror.
  8vo.   LOND. & BANGOR, 1902.
Jones (David M.)   *See* Suppt. Methodist Sacramental Fellowship. M.S.F. Booklets.
  N.S., 3.
Jones (Edmund) 1702-93.   *See* Catalogues. *Edmund Jones Lib.*
Jones (Emyr Gwynne)   Cymru a'r hen ffydd.   8vo.   CAERDYDD, 1951.
Jones (Francis)   The holy wells of Wales.   8vo.   CARDIFF, 1954.
Jones (George Randall)   Christian experience.   [Religion: its Modern Needs and
  Problems, 21.]   8vo.   LOND., 1935.
Jones (Glynne R.)   David Daniel Davis, M.D., F.R.C.P. (1777-1841).   4to.   [CAR-
  MARTHEN, 1972.]   [Pamph.]
—— David Daniel Davis, physician, and his son Edward Davis, sculptor: a supple-
  mentary note.   4to.   [CARMARTHEN, 1973.]   [Pamph.]
Jones (Griffith)   *See* Cavenagh (F. A.); Jenkins (R. T.); Jones (D.)

Jones (Gwilym Arthur) Bywyd a gwaith Owen Morgan Edwards, 1858-1920. 8vo ABERYSTWYTH, 1958.

[**Jones** (H. A.)] Priory Street Baptist Church, York, 1862-1962: centenary brochure. 8vo. [YORK, 1962.] [Pamph.]

[**Jones** (Herbert H. C.)] The Unitarian Church, Skene Street, Aberdeen: centenary souvenir, 1833-1933. 8vo. [ABERDEEN, 1933.] [Pamph.]

Jones (Hubert Cunliffe-) See Cunliffe-Jones (H.)

Jones (Ieuan Gwynedd) and **Williams** (David) ed. The religious census of 1851: a calendar of the returns relating to Wales. [Univ. of Wales Board of Celtic Studies, Hist. and Law Ser., 30- .] 8vo. CARDIFF.
 1. South Wales. 1976.
 2. Not yet published, 1980.

Jones (James W.) The shattered synthesis: New England Puritanism before the Great Awakening. 8vo. NEW HAVEN & LOND., 1973.

Jones (John) d. 1785, Vicar of Dovercourt. See Suppt. Wesley Hist. Soc. Publs., 7.

Jones (John Daniel) Congreg. minister of Bournemouth. The way into the Kingdom, or Thoughts on the Beatitudes. 8vo. LOND., [1900].

—— Reasons why for Free Churchmen. 8vo. BOURNEMOUTH & LOND., 1904.

Jones (Sir John Morris) See Parry (T.)

Jones (John Robert) See Davies (W. T. P.)

Jones (John Viriamu) See Jones (K. V.)

Jones (Katharine Viriamu) Life of John Viriamu Jones. 8vo. LOND., 1915.

Jones (Marc Edmund) Occult philosophy: an introduction, the major concepts, and a glossary. (1948.) repr. 8vo. STANWOOD (Wash.) & BOULDER (Colo.), 1977.

Jones (Margaret P.) A short history of Maldon Baptist Church, 1872-1972. 8vo. Duplicated. [MALDON, 1972.] [Pamph.]

Jones (Morgan Hugh) The Trevecka letters, or the unpublished MSS. correspondence of Howell Harris and his contemporaries: an inventory of the letters with a digest of their contents. [Davies Lect., 1922.] Prepared for publ. by R. T. Jenkins. 8vo. CAERNARVON, 1932.

Jones (Owain William) and **Walker** (David G.) ed. Links with the past: Swansea and Brecon historical essays. 8vo. LLANDYBIE, 1974.

Jones (Owen Roger) ed. The private language argument. [Controversies in Philos.] 8vo. LOND. & BASINGSTOKE, 1971.

Jones (Peter M. S.) The Diocese of St. David's in the nineteenth century: a comment based on the life and career of the Rev. W. Seaton. 8vo. [CARDIFF, 1979.] [Pamph.] [Photocopy.]

Jones (Robert Tudur) J. R., Conwy. 8vo. [ABERYSTWYTH, 1960.] [Pamph.]

—— Religion in post-Restoration Brecknockshire, 1660-1688. 4to. [BRECON,] 1962.

—— See John (J. M.) ed.

Jones (Sally) Allen Raine. [Writers of Wales.] 8vo. [CARDIFF,] 1979.

Jones (Tom) Henry Tate, 1819-1899: a biographical sketch. (1952.) rev. ed. 8vo. LOND., 1960.

Jonson (Ben) See Lewalski (B. K.) and Sabol (A. J.) ed.

Jordan (W. K.) Social institutions in Kent, 1480-1660: a study of the changing pattern of social aspirations. [Archaeologia Cantiana, 75.] 8vo. ASHFORD, 1961.

Joseph (Barnett) The festival of Succot. 8vo. LOND., 1971. [Pamph.]

—— History of the Hackney Synagogue, Brenthouse Road E.9, and order of service to commemorate the 75th anniversary (1897-1972). 8vo. [LOND., 1972.] [Pamph.]

Josselin (Ralph) See Macfarlane (A.)

Journal of . . . See Suppt.

Joutard (Philippe) comp. Les Camisards. 8vo. [PARIS,] 1976.

Jowett (J. H.) The Epistles of St. Peter. [Devotional and Practical Commentary.] 8vo. LOND., 1905.

—— The high calling: meditations on S. Paul's letter to the Philippians. (1909.) 2nd imp. 8vo. LOND., 1909.

—— Things that matter most: short devotional readings. (1913.) 4th imp. 8vo. LOND., [19--].

Joyce (James Wayland) England's sacred synods: a constitutional history of the Convocations of the clergy. (1855.) facsim. repr. 8vo. FARNBOROUGH, 1967.

Julian, the Apostate, Emperor of Rome. Briefe. Eingeleitet, übersetzt und erläutert von Lisette Goessler. [Bibliothek der Alten Welt.] 8vo. ZÜRICH & STUTTGART, 1971.

Julian, *the Apostate, Emperor of Rome—continued*
—— *See* Bowersock (G. W.); Browning (R.)
Juliana, *of Norwich.* Showings. Trans. with an introd. by Edmund Colledge and James Walsh. Preface by Jean Leclercq. [Classics of Western Spirituality.] 8vo. NEW YORK, *etc.,* 1978.
Julianos, *Saba. See* Suppt. Corpus Script. Christ. Orient., Syri, 140-141.
Jurieu (Pierre) *See* Le Brun (J.)
Jurriaanse (M. W.) The founding of Leyden University. 8vo. LEIDEN, 1965. [Pamph.]
Justinian I, *Emperor of the East.* [Two or more works. *Greek and Latin.*] Drei dogmatische Schriften Iustinians. Von Eduard Schwartz. (1939.) 2a. ed., a cura di Mario Amelotti, Rossangela Albertella e Livia Migliardi. [Florentina Studiorum Universitas, Legum Iustiniani Imperatoris Vocabularium, Subsidia, 2.] 4to. MILANO, 1973.
—— *See* Browning (R.); Chrysos (E. K.)
Justinian II, *Emperor of the East. See* Head (C.)

Käsemann (Ernst) Perspectives on Paul. [Trans. Margaret Kohl.] [New Test. Lib.] 8vo. LOND., 1971.
Kaiser (Otto) Isaiah 1-12: a commentary. [Trans. R. A. Wilson from Das A. T. Deutsch, 17.] [Old Test. Lib.] 8vo. LOND., 1972.
—— Isaiah 13-39: a commentary. [Trans. R. A. Wilson from Das A. T. Deutsch, 18.] [Old Test. Lib.] 8vo. LOND., 1974.
—— Introduction to the Old Testament: a presentation of its results and problems. Trans. John Sturdy. 8vo. OXF., 1975.
—— *See* Bible. O.T. Commentaries. Das A. T. Deutsch.
Kant (Immanuel) Critique of pure reason. Trans. Norman Kemp Smith. (1929.) repr. 8vo. LOND., 1961.
—— *See* Aune (B.); Heidegger (M.): Jaspers (K.); Walsh (W. H.); Ward (K.); Wolff (R. P.) *ed.*
Karelis (Charles) *See* Hegel (G. W. F.)
Karlstadt (Andreas Bodenstein von) *See* Sider (R. J.)
Karpozilos (A. D.) The ecclesiastical controversy between the kingdom of Nicaea and the principality of Epiros (1217-1233). [Byzantine Texts and Studies, 7.] 8vo. [THESSALONIKI,] 1973.
Kathona (Géza) Egri Lukács antitrinitárius-anabaptista nézetei. [Reneszánsz-füzetek, 12.] 8vo. BUDAPEST, 1971. [Pamph.]
Katz (Peter) *See* Walters (Peter) *formerly Katz.*
Kauffmann (C. M.) *See* Catalogues. *Brussels. Royal Lib.*
Kaufman (Helen A.) Conscientious cavalier: Colonel Bullen Reymes, M.P., F.R.S., 1613-1672: the man and his times. 8vo. LOND., 1962.
Kaufmann (W. A.) Tragedy and philosophy. (1968.) repr. 8vo. PRINCETON, 1979.
Kawecka-Gryczowa (Alodia) Les imprimeurs des antitrinitaires polonais Rodecki et Sternacki: histoire et bibliographie. [In Polish and French.] 8vo. WROCLAW, *etc.,* 1974.
Kawerau (Peter) Melchior Hoffman als religiöser Denker. 8vo. HAARLEM, 1954.
—— Die jakobitische Kirche im Zeitalter der syrischen Renaissance: Idee und Wirklichkeit. [Deutsche Akad. der Wissensch. zu Berlin, Berliner byzant. Arbeiten, 3.] 8vo. BERLIN, 1955.
—— Die nestorianischen Patriarchate in der neuern Zeit. 8vo. [GOTHA, *etc.,* 1956.] [Pamph.]
—— Johann Adam Steinmetz als Vermittler zwischen dem deutschen und amerikanischen Pietismus im 18. Jahrhundert. 8vo. [GOTHA, *etc.,* 1959.] [Pamph.]
—— Zur Kirchengeschichte Asiens. 8vo. BERLIN, 1959. [Pamph.]
—— Die Homiletik des Andreas Hyperius. 8vo. [GOTHA, *etc.,* 1960.] [Pamph.]
—— Das Christentum des Ostens. [Religionen der Menschheit, 30.] 8vo. STUTTGART, 1972.
—— *See* Suppt. Corpus Script. Christ. Orient., Subsid., 46, 50, 53.
Kay, *family of. See* Ramsden (G. M.)
Kaye (John) *Bp. of Lincoln. See* Varley (J.)
Keach (Benjamin) *See* Martin (H.)

Keats (John)   *See* Brown (C. A.); Murry (J. M.)

Kee (Howard Clark)   Community of the new age: studies in Mark's Gospel. [New Test. Lib.] 8vo. LOND., 1977.

Keel (Othmar)   *See* Suppt. Forschungen zur Religion u. Lit., 121.

Keen (Sam)   Apology for wonder. 8vo. NEW YORK, *etc.*, 1969.

Keep (David J.)   Dissent in Woodbury and Lympstone. fol. *Duplicated.* [EXMOUTH, 1976.] [Pamph.]

Kellaway (R. A.)   The trying out: personal reflections on the universal adventure. 8vo. BOSTON (Mass.), 1967. [Pamph.]

Keller (Werner)   The Bible as history: archaeology confirms the bcok of books. Trans. William Neil. (1956.) Rev. with a postscript by Joachim Rehork. New material trans. B. H. Rasmussen. 8vo. LOND., *etc.*, 1980.

Kelly (J. N. D.)   Early Christian doctrines. (1958.) 5th ed. 8vo. LOND., 1977.
—— Jerome: his life, writings, and controversies. 8vo. LOND., 1975

Kelvedon. *Congregational Church.* Year Book, 1917. 8vo. [KELVEDON, 1917.] [Pamph.]

Kemmler (D. W.)   *See* Suppt. Novum Testamentum. Suppts., 40.

Kemp (Eric W.)   *See* Suppt. Alcuin Club. Misc. Publs., 1977.

Kemp (John) 1850-1932. [Misc.]   Memoir of John Kemp, first pastor of "Ebenezer" Strict Baptist Chapel, Bounds Cross, Biddenden, Kent. Incl. autobiog., extracts from letters, meditations, verses, and sermons. Foreword by his son, J. Kemp. Publ. by his widow. 8vo. LOND., 1933.

Kempis (Thomas à)   *See* Suppt. Methodist Sacramental Fellowship. M.S.F. Booklets. Wesley Reprs., 4.

Ken (Thomas) *Bp. of Bath and Wells.*   *See* Hoyles (J.)

Kendall (E. E.)   Doing and daring: the story of Melbourne Hall Evangelical Free Church, Leicester, founded by F. B. Meyer, and constituted Sep. 23rd, 1878. 8vo. RUSHDEN, [1955].

Kendall (H. B.)   History of the Primitive Methodist Church. (189-.) rev. ed. 8vo. LOND., 1919.

Kendall (R. T.)   Calvin and English Calvinism to 1649. [Oxford Theological Monographs.] 8vo. OXF., 1979.

Kennedy (Howard Angus)   *See* Kennedy (John)

Kennedy (John) 1813-1900.   Old Highland days: the reminiscences of Dr. John Kennedy. With a sketch of his later life by his son, Howard Angus Kennedy. 8vo. LOND., [1901].

Kenny (Anthony J. P.)   The five ways: St. Thomas Aquinas' proofs of God's existence. [Studies in Ethics and the Philos. of Relig.] (1969.) repr. 8vo. LOND., 1972.
—— The Aristotelian Ethics: a study of the relationship between the Eudemian and Nichomachean Ethics of Aristotle. 8vo. OXF., 1978.
—— Aristotle's theory of the will. 8vo. LOND., 1979.

Kenny (Anthony J. P.) *and others.*   [The phenomenon of mind:] A. J. P. Kenny, H. C. Longuet-Higgins, J. R. Lucas, C. H. Waddington. [Gifford Lects., 1971-72 and 1972-73.] 2 vols. 8vo. EDIN., 1972-73.
   [1.]   The nature of mind.   1972.
   [2.]   The development of mind.   1973.

Kenrick, *family of.*   *See* Church (R. A.)

Kent (J. H. S.)   Holding the fort: studies in Victorian revivalism. 8vo. LOND., 1978.

Kenworthy (Fred)   From authority to freedom in church life: the Act of Uniformity and Unitarian Dissent. 8vo. [LOND., 1962.] [Pamph.]
—— Cross Street Chapel in the life of Manchester. 8vo. n.p., [1973]. [Pamph.]

Kenyon (J. P.)   Revolution principles: the politics of party, 1689-1720. [Ford Lects., 1975-76.] [Cambridge Studies in the Hist. and Theory of Politics.] 8vo. CAMB., 1977.

Kepler (Johannes)   *See* Breitsohl-Klepser (R.)

Ker (N. R.)   *See* Catalogues. *Lambeth Palace Lib.*

Kerridge (Eric)   *See* Suppt. Chetham Soc., 3rd Ser., 21.

Kerschensteiner (Josef)   *See* Suppt. Corpus Script. Christ. Orient., Subsid., 37.

Kestenbaum (Victor)   The phenomenological sense of John Dewey: habit and meaning. 8vo. ATLANTIC HIGHLANDS (N.J.), 1977.

Ketton-Cremer (R. W.)   Norfolk assembly. 8vo. LOND., 1957.

Kevan (E. F.)   The grace of law: a study in Puritan theology. 8vo. LOND., 1964.

Keynes, *family of.* *See* Keynes (F. A.)
Keynes (Florence A.) Gathering up the threads: a study in family biography. 8vo. CAMB., 1950.
Khomiakoff (A.-S.) L'Église latine et le Protestantisme au point de vue de l'Église d'Orient. (1872.) facsim. repr. 8vo. FARNBOROUGH, 1969.
—— *See* Berdyaev (N.)
Khoury (Adel-Théodore) Les théologiens byzantins et l'Islam: textes et auteurs (VIIIe-XIIIe s.). 8vo. LOUVAIN & PARIS, 1969.
Kibre (Pearl) Scholarly privileges in the Middle Ages: the rights, privileges, and immunities, of scholars and universities at Bologna, Padua, Paris, and Oxford. [Mediaeval Acad. of America, Publ. 72.] 8vo. LOND., 1961.
Kierkegaard (S. A.) Crisis in the life of an actress, and other essays on drama. Trans. with an introd. and notes by Stephen Crites. 8vo. LOND., 1967.
—— *See* Diem (H.); Lowrie (W.)
Killingback (Sam) Corsham Methodist Church, 1878-1978: centenary. 8vo. [CORSHAM,] 1978. [Pamph.]
Kilpatrick (G. D.) [Misc.] *See* Suppt. Novum Testamentum. Suppts., 44.
Kilwardby (Robert) *Abp. of Canterbury.* Merton College: injunctions of Archbishop Kilwardby, 1276. [Introd. by H. W. Garrod.] 4to. OXF., 1929. [Pamph.]
[Kinder (A. G.)] One hundred years of Trinity. [Trinity Methodist Chapel, Sale, 1875-1975.] 8vo. [WILMSLOW, 1975.] [Pamph.]
Kinder (Ernst) and **Haendler** (Klaus) *ed.* Gesetz und Evangelium: Beiträge zur gegenwärtigen theologischen Diskussion. [Wege der Forschung, 142.] 8vo. DARMSTADT, 1968.
King (Archibald) *See* Gorman (G. H.)
King (C. Seymour) The centenary history of Chipperfield Baptist Church. 8vo. [LOND., 1920.] [Pamph.] [Photocopy.]
King (D. W.) Ralph Margery, Cromwell's plain russet coated captain. 8vo. n.p., [1980]. [Pamph.] [Photocopy.]
King (Edward) *Bp. of Lincoln.* *See* Newton (J. A.)
King (William) *Abp. of Dublin.* *See* Collins (A.)
Kingdon (Robert M.) Démocratie et l'église: aspects de la querelle disciplinaire chez les Calvinistes au XVI siècle. 8vo. n.p., [1966]. [Pamph.]
Kingsbury (J. D.) Matthew: structure, Christology, kingdom. 8vo. LOND., 1976.
Kingsford (H. E.) *See* Pettman (K.) and Kingsford (H. E.)
King's Langley. *Christ Church Baptist.* We have been here for 100 years. obl. 8vo. [KING'S LANGLEY, 1975.] [Pamph.]
Kingsley (Charles) *See* Hartley (A. J.)
King's Weigh House Monthly. *See* Suppt.
Kingswood School. Register [1748-1910], with which is incorporated the Register of the Old Woodhouse Grove School, together with a list of masters and other lists. (1898.) 2nd ed. 8vo. KINGSWOOD, 1910.
Kinloch (T. F.) Religious education in provided schools. [Handbooks of Relig. Educ.] 8vo. LOND., 1938.
Kippenberg (H. G.) Garizim und Synagoge: traditionsgeschichtliche Unter-suchungen zur samaritanischen Religion der aramäischen Periode. [Religionsgesch. Versuche u. Vorarbeiten, 30.] 8vo. BERLIN, 1971.
—— Religion und Klassenbildung im antiken Judäa: eine religionssoziologische Studie zum Verhältnis von Tradition und gesellschaftlicher Entwicklung. 8vo. GÖTTINGEN, 1978.
Kirk (*Sir* John) *See* Williamson (D.)
Kirk (K. E.) *ed.* The apostolic ministry. *See* Neill (S. C.) *ed.*
Kirkby (A. H.) Andrew Fuller (1754-1815). [Heritage Biographies.] 8vo. LOND., 1961. [Pamph.]
Kirkpatrick (Robin) Dante's Paradiso and the limitations of modern criticism: a study of style and poetic theory. 8vo. CAMB., 1978.
Kirsten (Hans) Warum heute lutherische Freikirche? 8vo. FRANKFURT AM M., 1949. [Pamph.]
Kishlansky (M. A.) The rise of the New Model Army. 8vo. CAMB., 1979.
Kitchen (K. A.) The Bible in its world: the Bible and archaeology today. 8vo. EXETER, 1977.
Kittel (Gerhard) *ed.* *See* Dictionaries. Languages. *Greek.*

Kittelson (J. M.) Wolfgang Capito: from humanist to reformer. [Studies in Medieval and Reformation Thought, 17.] 8vo. LEIDEN, 1975.

Kitzinger (Ernst) Byzantine art in the making: main lines of stylistic development in Mediterranean art, 3rd-7th century. 4to. LOND., 1977.

Klaiber (A. J.) *ed.* The Upper Holloway Messenger: organ of Upper Holloway Baptist Church and Rupert Road Mission. May 1938 [70th anniversary]. 4to. [LOND.,] 1938. [Pamph.]

Klauser (Theodor) *See* Suppt. Jahrbuch für Antike u. Christentum. Erg.Bde., 3, 5, 7.

Klein (Charlotte) Anti-Judaism in Christian theology. Trans. Edward Quinn. 8vo. LOND., 1978.

Klein (K. H.) Positivism and Christianity: a study of theism and verifiability. 8vo. THE HAGUE, 1974.

Klijn (A. F. J.) *See* Suppt. Novum Testamentum. Suppts., 36, 46, 47-48.

Kneller (*Sir* Godfrey) *See* National Portrait Gallery.

Knight (Frideswide F. E.) University rebel: the life of William Frend (1757-1841). 8vo. LOND., 1971.

—— *ed.* Letters to William Frend from the Reynolds family of Little Paxton and John Hammond of Fenstanton, 1793-1814. [Cambridge Antiquarian Records. Soc., 1, 1972.] 8vo. CAMB., 1974.

Knight (G. W.) The Nonconformist churches of Enfield. [Edmonton Hundred Hist. Soc. Occ. Paper, N.S., 24.] 4to. [EDMONTON,] 1973. [Pamph.]

Knight (Marcus) Spiritualism, reincarnation, and immortality. [Colet Lib., 6.] 8vo. LOND., 1950.

Knight of the Tower. *See* Suppt. Early Eng. Text Soc. Suppt. Texts, 2.

[Knighton (G. L.)] "Three hundred years of religious freedom", 1662-1962. [Maidstone Unitarian Church.] 8vo. *Duplicated.* n.p., [1962]. [Pamph.]

Knights (Ben) The idea of the clerisy in the nineteenth century. 8vo. CAMB., 1978.

Knollys (Hanserd) *See* White (B. R.)

Knopp (B. B.) In season, out of season: the story of Cavendish Place Chapel, Eastbourne. 8vo. EASTBOURNE, 1979. [Pamph.]

Knott (J. R.) Bunyan's Gospel day: a reading of the Pilgrim's Progress. 8vo. n.p., 1973. [Pamph.]

Knowles (David) Saint Bernard of Clairvaux, 1090-1153. 8vo. [LOND., 1953.] [Pamph.]

—— Lord Macaulay, 1800-1859. 8vo. CAMB., 1960. [Pamph.]

—— Thomas Becket. [Leaders of Relig.] 8vo. LOND., 1970.

—— *See* Morey (A.); Stacpoole (A.)

Knox (John) *See* Greaves (R. L.); Simpson (M. A.)

Knox (R. Buick) Wales and "Y Goleuad" (1869-1879): a survey to mark the centenary of the foundation of Y Goleuad in 1869. 8vo. CAERNARVON, [1969].

—— Little Baddow United Reformed Church: a history. fol. *Duplicated.* n.p., 1976. [Pamph.]

—— Westminster College, Cambridge: its background and history. 8vo. CAMB. [& LOND.], [1978]. [Pamph.]

—— The links between Irish and English Presbyterianism between 1840 and 1976. [Bull. of the Presb. Hist. Soc. of Ireland, 9, 1979.] 8vo. BELFAST, 1979. [Pamph.]

—— St. Columba's Church, Cambridge, 1879-1979: a centenary survey. 8vo. OXF. [printed], [1979]. [Pamph.]

—— *ed. See* Nuttall (G. F.) [Misc.]

Knox (Ronald A.) Let dons delight, being variations on a theme in an Oxford common-room. (1939.) 2nd imp. 8vo. LOND., 1939.

Koch (Dietrich-Alex) *See* Suppt. Zeitschr. für N.T. Wiss. Beihefte, 42.

Koch (Georg) Die bäuerliche Seele: eine Einführung in die religiöse Volkeskunde. 8vo. BERLIN, 1935.

Koch (Günter) Strukturen und Geschichte des Heils in der Theologie des Theodoret von Kyros: eine dogmen- und theologiegeschichtliche Untersuchung. [Frankfurter Theol. Studien, 17.] 8vo. FRANKFURT AM M., 1974.

Koch (Klaus) *See* Suppt. Studies in Bibl. Theol., 2nd Ser., 22.

Koester (Helmut) *See* Robinson (J. M.) and Koester (H.)

Köstlin (Julius) Luthers Theologie in ihrer geschichtlichen Entwicklung und ihrem unneren Zusammenhange dargestellt. (1863.) 2te. Aufl. (1901.) repr. 2 vols. 8vo. DARMSTADT, 1968.

Kötting (Bernhard) [Misc.] *See* Suppt. Jahrbuch für Antike u. Christentum. Erg. Bd. 8.
Kötzsche-Breitenbruch (Lieselotte) *See* Suppt. Jahrbuch für Antike u. Christentum. Erg. Bd. 4.
Kohls (Ernst-Wilhelm) Die theologische Lebensaufgabe des Erasmus und die oberrheinischen Reformatoren: zur Durchdringung von Humanismus und Reformation. [Arbeiten zur Theologie, 1. Reihe, 39.] 8vo. STUTTGART, 1969. [Pamph.]
Kolakowski (Leszek) Chrétiens sans église: la conscience religieuse et le lien confessionel au XVIIe siècle. Trad. du polonais par Anna Posner. [Bibliothèque de Philosophie.] 8vo. PARIS, 1969.
Kon (Abraham) Prayer. Trans. by the author from his book Sí'ah Tefillah. 8vo. LOND., *etc.*, 1971.
Korner (Stephan) Abstraction in science and morals. [Arthur Stanley Eddington Memorial Lect., 24.] 8vo. CAMB., 1971. [Pamph.]
Koss (S. E.) Nonconformity in modern British politics. 8vo. LOND., 1975.
Kossman (E. H.) and **Mellink** (A. F.) *ed.* Texts concerning the Revolt of the Netherlands. [Cambridge Studies in the Hist. and Theory of Politics.] 8vo. LOND., 1974.
Kostof (Spiro) Caves of God: the monastic environment of Byzantine Cappadocia. 4to. CAMB. (Mass.) & LOND., 1972.
Kowalski (Jan Maria Michal) *See* Peterkiewicz (J.)
Koyré (Alexandre) Galileo studies. Trans. from the French by John Mepham. [European Philos. and the Human Sciences.] 8vo. HASSOCKS (Sx.), 1978.
Kraeling (E. G. H.) The book of the ways of God. [A study of Job.] 8vo. LOND., 1938.
Kraft (Heinrich) *comp.* Clavis Patrum Apostolicorum: catalogum vocum in libris Patrum qui dicuntur Apostolici non raro occurrentium. Adiuvante Ursula Früchtel, congessit contulit conscripsit Henricus Kraft. 8vo. DARMSTADT, 1963.
Krahn (Cornelius) Dutch Anabaptism: origin, spread, life and thought, 1450-1600. 8vo. THE HAGUE, 1968.
Kraus (Hans-Joachim) Prophetie und Politik. [Theologische Existenz Heute.] 8vo. MÜNCHEN, 1952.
—— Psalmen. [Biblischer Kommentar, A.T., 15.] (1961.) 4te. Aufl. 2 vols. NEUKIRCHEN-VLUYN, 1972.
—— Prophetie in der Krisis: Studien zu Texten aus dem Buch Jeremia. [Biblische Studien, 43.] 8vo. NEUKIRCHEN-VLUYN, 1964.
—— Predigt aus Vollmacht. 8vo. [NEUKIRCHEN-VLUYN, 1966.]
Krause (J. H.) Die Byzantiner des Mittelalters in ihrem Staats-, Hof- und Privatleben, insbesondere vom Ende des zehnten bis gegen Ende des vierzehnten Jahrhunderts nach den byzantinischen Quellen. (1869.) facsim. repr. 8vo. LEIPZIG, 1974.
Kreider (A. F.) English chantries: the road to dissolution. [Harvard Historical Studies, 97.] 8vo. CAMB. (Mass.) & LOND., 1979.
Kretschmar (Georg) *See* Dörries (H.) and Kretschmar (G.)
Kretschmar (Georg) and **Lohse** (Bernhard) *ed.* Ecclesia und Res Publica. [Kurt Dietrich Schmidt zum 65. Geburtstag.] 8vo. GÖTTINGEN, 1961.
Kretzmann (Norman) Elements of formal logic. 8vo. INDIANAPOLIS, *etc.*, 1965.
Krishnamurti (Jiddu) The awakening of intelligence. 8vo. LOND., 1973.
Kronholm (Tryggve) Motifs from Genesis 1-11 in the genuine hymns of Ephrem the Syrian, with particular reference to the influence of Jewish exegetical tradition. [Coniectanea Biblica, O.T. Ser., 11.] 8vo. LUND, 1978.
Krummel (D. W.) *See* Suppt. Bibliographical Soc. Publs., 1971.
Kümmel (W. G.) Kirchenbegriff und Geschichtsbewusstsein in der Urgemeinde und bei Jesus. (1943.) 2te. Aufl. 8vo. GÖTTINGEN, 1968.
—— The New Testament: the history of the investigation of its problems. [Trans. S. McLean Gilmour and Howard C. Kee.] [New Test. Lib.] 8vo. LOND., 1973.
—— The theology of the New Testament according to its major witnesses: Jesus, Paul, John. [Trans. John E. Steely.] [New Test. Lib.] 8vo. LOND., 1974.
Küng (Hans) Infallible? An enquiry. Trans. Eric Mosbacher. 8vo. LOND., 1971.
—— On being a Christian. Trans. Edward Quinn. 8vo. LOND., 1977.
Künneth (Walter) Antwort aus den Mythus: die Entscheidung zwischen dem nordischen Mythus und dem biblischen Christus. (1935.) 3te. Aufl. 8vo. BERLIN, 1935.

Kupperman (J. J.) Ethical knowledge. [Muirhead Lib. of Philos.] 8vo. LOND. & NEW YORK, 1970.
Kutsch (Ernst) *See* Suppt. Zeitschr. für A. T. Wiss. Beihefte, 131.
Kutter (Hermann) Reden an die deutsche Nation. 8vo. JENA, 1916.
Kysar (Robert) The fourth Evangelist and his Gospel: an examination of contemporary scholarship. 8vo. MINNEAPOLIS (Minn.), 1975.

Laboucheix (Henri) Richard Price: théoricien de la Révolution américaine; le philosophe et le sociologue; le pamphlétaire et l'orateur. [Études Anglaises, 37.] 8vo. PARIS, etc., 1970.
Labrousse (Elisabeth) L'entrée de Saturne au Lion [l'éclipse de soleil du 12 août 1654). [Internat. Archives of the Hist. of Ideas, Ser. Minor, 14.] 8vo. LA HAYE, 1974.
Lactantius (Lucius Coelius Firmianus) *See* Ogilvie (R. M.)
Lacy (Edmund) *Bp. of Exeter. See* Suppt. Canterbury and York Soc., 63, 66.
Lacy-McIntyre (H.) Grange Park United Reformed Church: links with the distant past. 8vo. *Duplicated.* LEYTON, 1973. [Pamph.]
Laing (R. D.) and **Esterson** (Aaron) Sanity, madness, and the family: families of schizophrenics. (1964.) repr. 8vo. HARMONDSWORTH, 1972.
Laiou (Angeliki E.) Constantinople and the Latins: the foreign policy of Andronicus II, 1282-1328. [Harvard Historical Studies, 88.] 8vo. CAMB. (Mass.), 1972.
Lamb (Charles) *See* Suppt. Charles Lamb Bulletin.
Lamb (Charles) and **Lamb** (Mary) Letters. Ed. Edwin W. Marrs. 8vo. ITHACA (N.Y.) & LOND., 1975-
    1. Letters of Charles Lamb, 1796-1801. 1975.
    2. 1801-1809. 1976.
    3. 1809-1817. 1978.
    No more yet published, 1980.
Lamb (Mary) *See* Lamb (Charles) and Lamb (Mary)
Lambert (Henri) *See* Papers for War Time, 29.
Lambert (John) 1619-83, *General. See* Dawson (W. H.)
Lambert (M. D.) Medieval heresy: popular movements from Bogomil to Hus. 8vo. LOND., 1977.
Lambert (W. G.) The background of Jewish apocalyptic. [Ethel M. Wood Lect., 1977.] 8vo. LOND., 1978. [Pamph.]
Lamond (John) Kathleen. A study of the supernormal. 8vo. LOND., [1925].
Lamont (W. M.) Puritanism as history and historiography: some further thoughts. 8vo. OXF., 1969. [Pamph.]
—— Richard Baxter, the Apocalypse and the Mad Major. 8vo. OXF., 1972. [Pamph.]
—— Richard Baxter and the millennium: Protestant imperialism and the English Revolution. [Croom Helm Social Hist. Ser.] 8vo. LOND. & TOTOWA (N.J.), 1979.
Lampe (G. W. H.) God as Spirit. [Bampton Lects., 1976.] 8vo. OXF., 1977.
Lancashire. *See* Suppt. Record Society of Lancashire and Cheshire.
Lander (T. J.) The history of Southgate Congregational Church, Gloucester, 1660-1972. 8vo. GLOUCESTER, [1976]. [Pamph.]
Lane (L. J.) The Vernon story: to commemorate the centenary, 1861-1961. 8vo. [LOND., 1961.] [Pamph.]
Lanfranc, *Abp. of Canterbury.* Letters. Ed. and trans. by the late Helen Clover and Margaret Gibson. [Oxford Medieval Texts.] 8vo. OXF., 1979.
—— *See* Gibson (M. T.)
Lang (D. M.) Armenia: cradle of civilization. 4to. LOND., 1970.
—— The Bulgarians from pagan times to the Ottoman conquest. [Ancient Peoples and Places, 84.] 8vo. LOND., 1976.
Langer (Susanne K.) Philosophical sketches. (1962.) repr. 8vo. NEW YORK, 1964.
—— Mind: an essay on human feeling. 2 vols. 8vo. BALTIMORE & LOND., 1967-72.
    2. 1972.
Laporte-Payne (R. M.) St. Mary Abchurch, E.C.4. (1946.) rev. ed. 8vo. LOND., 1949.

Laredo (Bernadino de) The ascent of Mount Sion, being the third book of the treatise of that name. Trans. with an introd. and notes by E. Allison Peers. [Classics of the Contemplative Life.] 8vo. LOND., 1952.

[**Large** (H. T.) and **Fitch** (W. K.) Thetford Baptist Church: a short history, 1859-1959. 8vo. [THETFORD, 1959.] [Pamph.]

Laski (Jan) *See* A Lasco (John)

Laski (Marghanita) *See* Bloom (A.)

Latham (R. E.) *See* Dictionaries. Languages. *Latin, Medieval.*

Lauer (Rosemary Z.) The mind of Voltaire: a study in his "constructive Deism". 8vo. WESTMINSTER (Md.), 1961.

Law (William) [Selections.] William Law. Ed. by Rev. Principal [J. M.] Hodgson. [Lib. of the Soul.] 8vo. EDIN., [1907].

—— *See* Clarkson (G. E.); Hoyles (J.)

Lawler (John) Book auctions in England in the seventeenth century (1676-1700). With a chronological list of the book auctions of the period. 8vo. LOND., 1906.

Lawrence (David) *See* Smith (A. A.) and Lawrence (D.)

Lawrence (David Herbert) *See* Magnus (M.); Murry (J. M.)

Layamon. *See* Suppt. Early Eng. Text. Soc., O.S., 277.

Lazerowitz (Morris) *ed. See* Ambrose (A.) and Lazerowitz (M.) *ed.*

Lea (Frank A.) The life of John Middleton Murry. 8vo. LOND., 1959.

Leach (A. F.) *See* Tate (W. E.)

Leaders of Religion. *See* Suppt.

Leake (Richard) *See* Wilson (E. M.)

Leary (William) Lincolnshire Methodist Chapels now closed. Vol. 1. 4to. *Duplicated.* LINCOLN, 1970. [Pamph.]

Leary (William) *and others.* 200 years of Methodism in Messingham. 8vo. MESSINGHAM, 1971. [Pamph.]

Leaver (R. A.) A short history of St. Mary's Chapel, Castle Street, Reading, publ. during the 175th year. 8vo. [READING,] 1973. [Pamph.]

Le Brun (Jacques) Les oeuvres spirituelles de Pierre Jurieu. 8vo. STRASBOURG, 1975. [Pamph.]

Leckie (J. H.) Fergus Ferguson, D.D.: his theology and heresy trial: a chapter in Scottish church history. 8vo. EDIN., 1923.

Lecler (Joseph) *See* Dumeige (G.) *ed.*

Leclerq (Henri) *See* Suppt. Jahrbuch für Antike u. Christentum. Erg. Bd. 5.

Lee (A. E.) *ed.* A history and record of the activities of the United Methodist Church, Derby Road, Lenton, Nottingham, 1851-1931. 8vo. [NOTTINGHAM, 1931.] [Pamph.]

[**Lee** (Ben)] A history of Cheadle Hulme and its Methodism, 1787-1968. obl. 8vo. CHEADLE HULME, 1967. [Pamph.]

Lee (Ernest George) Christianity and sex morality. [Religion: its Modern Needs and Problems, 17.] 8vo. LOND., 1933.

Lee (George) *ed. See* Bridge (A.) and Lee (G.) *ed.*

Lee (George Mervyn) Had Apollonius of Tyana read St. Mark? 8vo. [OSLO,] 1973. [Pamph.]

Lee (*Sir* Henry) *See* Chambers (*Sir* E. K.)

Lee (Joan D.) *comp. See* Liturgies. *Latin Rite.* [Hours.]

Lee (Roy Stuart) Principles of pastoral counselling. [Lib. of Pastoral Care.] 8vo. LOND., 1968.

Leeds City Museums. The bicentenary of the discovery of oxygen by Joseph Priestley. 8vo. [LEEDS, 1974.] [Pamph.]

Leenhardt (Franz-J.) *See* Bible. N.T. Commentaries. Commentaire du N.T.

Leeson (Spencer) Christian education reviewed. 8vo. LOND., 1957.

Leeuwen (A. T. van) Critique of heaven and earth. [Gifford Lects., 1970 and 1972.] 2 vols. 8vo. LOND., 1972-74.
   1. Critique of heaven. 1972.
   2. Critique of earth. 1974.

Leeuwenberg (Huib) *ed. See* Buijtenen (M. P. van) *and others, ed.*

Leeves (Bridget) Kidlington: the story of a growing church. 8vo. [KIDLINGTON, 1978.] [Pamph.]

Lefebvre (Charles) *See* Dumeige (G.) *ed.*

Lefèvre d'Étaples (Jacques) *See* Bedouelle (G.)

Leff (Gordon) William of Ockham: the metamorphosis of scholastic discourse. 8vo. MANCHESTER, 1975.

Lehmann (Henning J.) Per piscatores: studies in the Armenian version of a collection of homilies by Eusebius of Emesa and Severian of Gabala. fol. AARHUS, 1975.

Lehrer (Adrienne) and **Lehrer** (Keith) *ed.* Theory of meaning. [Central Issues in Philos. Ser.] 8vo. ENGLEWOOD CLIFFS (N.J.), 1970.

Lehrer (Keith) *ed. See* Lehrer (A.) and Lehrer (K.) *ed.*

Leibholz (G.) *See* Bonhoeffer (D.)

Leibnitz (Gottfried Wilhelm) Fragmente zur Logik. Ausgewählt, übersetzt und erläutert von Franz Schmidt. [Philosophische Studientexte.] 8vo. BERLIN, 1960.

—— *See* Broad (C. D.); Collins (A.); Hostler (J.); Robinet (A.); Suppt. Mitteilungen der Gottfried-Wilhelm-Leibniz-Gesellschaft.

Leicester. *Clarendon Park Baptist Church.* The Clarendon Baptist, souvenir number, Oct. 1936: to mark the opening of the re-constructed church and school buildings. 8vo. LEICESTER, 1936. [Pamph.]

Leigh (R. A.) Rousseau and the problem of tolerance in the eighteenth century. A lecture delivered in the Taylor Institution, Oxford, 26 Oct. 1978. 8vo. OXF., 1979. [Pamph.]

Leloir (Louis) *See* Suppt. Corpus Script. Christ. Orient., Subsid., 42-43, 47, 51.

Lemerle (Paul) Le premier humanisme byzantin: notes et remarques sur enseignement et culture à Byzance des origines au Xe siècle. [Bibliothèque Byzantine, Études, 6.] 4to. PARIS, 1971.

—— Le monde de Byzance: histoire et institutions. [Variorum Reprs.] 8vo. LOND., 1978.

—— Essais sur le monde byzantin. [Variorum Reprs.] 8vo. LOND., 1980.

Lemos (Ramon M.) Rousseau's political philosophy: an exposition and interpretation. 8vo. ATHENS (Ga.), 1977.

Le Moyne (Jean) Les Sadducéens. [Études Bibliques.] 8vo. PARIS, 1972.

Le Neve (John) Fasti Ecclesiae Anglicanae. (1716.) [Rev. and expanded ed.] 1066-1300. 8vo. LOND., 1968-
    2. Monastic cathedrals (Northern and Southern Provinces): Diana E. Greenway. 1971.
    3. Lincoln: Diana E. Greenway. 1977.
No more yet published, 1980.

—— —— 1541-1857. 8vo. LOND., 1969-
    2. Chichester Diocese: Joyce M. Horn. 1971.
    3. Canterbury, Rochester and Winchester Dioceses: Joyce M. Horn. 1974.
    4. York Diocese: Joyce M. Horn and David M. Smith. 1975.
    5. Bath and Wells Diocese: Joyce M. Horn and Derrick Sherwin Bailey. 1979.
No more yet published, 1980.

Lenwood (Frank) *See* Papers for War Time, 17, 28.

Leo III, *Emperor of the East, 'the Isaurian'. See* Suppt. Corpus Script. Christ. Orient., Subsid., 41.

Leonard (George Hare) *See* Papers for War Time, 11.

Leontius, *priest, of Constantinople. See* Aubineau (M.) *ed.*

Lessenich (R. P.) Elements of pulpit oratory in eighteenth-century England (1660-1800). 8vo. KÖLN & WEIN, 1972.

Lester (D. N. R.) The history of Batley Grammar School, 1612-1962. 8vo. BATLEY, [1962].

Levin (David) Cotton Mather: the young life of the Lord's Remembrancer, 1663-1703. 8vo. CAMB. (Mass.) & LOND., 1979.

Levin (Salmond S.) *ed.* A century of Anglo-Jewish life (1870-1970). Lectures to commemorate the centenary of the United Synagogue. 8vo. LOND., [1973].

Levine (David) *See* Wrightson (K.) and Levine (D.)

Levine (Joseph M.) Dr. Woodward's shield: history, science, and satire in Augustan England. 8vo. BERKELEY (Calif.), *etc.,* 1977.

Levitt (Ruth) George Eliot: the Jewish connection. Foreword by Abba Eban. 8vo. JERUSALEM, 1975.

Levy (Babette May) Early Puritanism in the southern and island colonies. 8vo. WORCESTER (Mass.), 1960. [Pamph.]

Levy (Matthias) *See* Roth (C.)

Levy (Samuel) *ed. See* Suppt. Jewish Annual.

Lewalski (Barbara K.) and **Sabol** (Andrew J.) *ed.* Major poets of the earlier seventeenth century: Donne, Herbert, Vaughan, Crashaw, Johnson, Herrick, Marvell. 8vo. NEW YORK, 1973.

Lewes. *Westgate Chapel.* A brief history of Westgate Chapel, High Street, Lewes, Sussex. 8vo. [LEWES,] n.d. [Pamph.]

Lewes (George Henry) *See* Catalogues. *Dr. Williams's Lib.*

Lewis (Arnold H.) The friendly church. [Religion: its Modern Needs and Problems, 6.] 8vo. LOND., 1932.

Lewis (Clarence Irving) *See* Suppt. Library of Living Philosophers, 13.

Lewis (Clive Staples) Letters to Malcolm, chiefly on prayer. 8vo. LOND., 1964.

Lewis (Howell Elvet) The life of E. Herber Evans, D.D., frcm his letters, journals, etc. 8vo. LOND., 1900.

—— *See* Parry (E. W.)

Lewis (Hywel David) Morals and the new theology. 8vo. LOND., 1947.

—— The self and immortality. [Philos. of Relig. Ser.] 8vo. LOND., 1973.

—— *ed.* Contemporary British philosophy: personal statements. Fourth ser. [Muirhead Lib. of Philos.] 8vo. LOND., 1976.

—— *ed. See* Suppt. Library of Philosophy.

Lewis (Hywel David) *and others.* Persons and life after death. Essays by Hywel D. Lewis and some of his critics. [Lib. of Philos. and Relig.] 8vo. LOND., 1978.

Lewis (Vivian) "Come with us and we will surely do you good": the story of the Loughton Union Church, 1813-1973. 8vo. LEAMINGTON SPA [printed], [1974]. [Pamph.]

Lexington Theological Quarterly. *See* Suppt.

Leytonstone. *Congregational Church.* Manual for 1927, containing reports and subscriptions for 1926. 8vo. [LEYTONSTONE, 1927.] [Pamph.]

Libellus. Libellus de diversis ordinibus et professionis qui sunt in aecclesia. Ed. and trans. G. Constable and B. Smith. [Oxford Medieval Texts.] 8vo. OXF., 1972.

Library. *See* Suppt.

Library of . . . *See* Suppt.

Lidbetter (Hubert) Quaker meeting houses, 1670-1850. fol. [CHEAM, 1946.] [Pamph.]

Lidgett (J. Scott) Apostolic ministry. Sermons and addresses. 8vo. LOND., [1910].

—— God, Christ and the Church. 8vo. LOND., 1927.

—— My guided life. 8vo. LOND., 1936.

—— God and man. 8vo. LOND., 1944.

—— Salvation as proclaimed by prophets, apostles, and by our Lord Jesus Christ. 8vo. LOND., 1952.

Liebeschuetz (J. H. W. G.) Antioch: city and imperial administration in the later Roman Empire. 8vo. OXF., 1972.

—— Continuity and change in Roman religion. 8vo. OXF., 1979.

Lietzmann (Hans) Mass and Lord's Supper: a study in the history of the liturgy. Trans. with appendices by Dorothea H. G. Reeve. With introd. and further inquiry by Robert Douglas Richardson. 8vo. Publ. in 11 fascicles. LEIDEN, 1953-79.

Lilburne (John) Come out of her my people: or an answer to the questions of a gentlewoman (a professour in the antichristian Church of England) about hearing the public ministers. (1639.) facsim. repr. 8vo. EXETER, 1971. [Pamph.]

Lilla (S. R. C.) Clement of Alexandria: a study in Christian Platonism and Gnosticism. [Oxford Theological Monographs.] 8vo. OXF., 1971.

Lincoln Record Society. *See* Suppt.

Lindars (Barnabas) *See* Bible. Commentaries. New Century Bible.

Lindars (Barnabas) and **Smalley** (S. S.) *ed. See* Moule (C. F. D.) [Misc.]

Lindberg (Conrad) The manuscripts and versions of the Wycliffite Bible: a preliminary survey. 8vo. UPPSALA, 1971. [Pamph.]

Lindley (Jeanne) Seeking and finding: the life of Emile Cammaerts. 8vo. LOND., 1962.

Lindon (J. M. A.) La 'Practica col Rev. Signor Shepherd" e la ripresa dei rapporti fra Ugo Foscolo e Francis Jeffrey nel 1827. 8vo. [TORINO, 1975.] [Pamph.]

—— A 'warmhearted, highminded' friend of Ugo Foscolo and an unnoticed obituary of the poet. 8vo. [CAMB., 1975.] [Pamph.]

Lindsay (A. D.) Karl Marx's "Capital": an introductory essay. (1925.) repr. 8vo. LOND., 1931.
—— *See* Scott (D.)
Lings (Martin) A Moslem saint of the twentieth century: Shaikh Ahmad al- 'Alawi: his spiritual heritage and legacy. [Ethical and Religious Classics of East and West.] 8vo. LOND., 1961.
Linnell (C. L. S.) Norfolk church dedications. [St. Anthony's Hall Publs., 21.] 8vo. LOND., 1962. [Pamph.]
Linscott (R. E.) *ed.* Totteridge Road Baptist Church, Enfield, 1868-1968. obl. 8vo. [ENFIELD, 1968.] [Pamph.]
Lips (Hermann von) *See* Suppt. Forschungen zur Religion u. Lit., 122.
Littell (F. H.) The Anabaptist concept of the Church. 8vo. SCOTTDALE (Pa.), [1957.] [Pamph.]
—— Landgraf Philipp und die Toleranz: ein christlicher Fürst, der Linke Flügel der Reformation und der christliche Primitivismus. Vorlesung. 8vo. BAD NAUHEIM, 1957.
— *ed.* *See* Dictionaries. Christianity.
Little (B. D. G.) Catholic churches since 1623: a study of Roman Catholic churches in England and Wales from penal times to the present decade. 8vo. LOND., 1966.
Little (F. G.) and **Walker** (E. T. F.) The story of the Northern Baptists. 8vo. NEWCASTLE-UPON-TYNE, 1945. [Pamph.]
Little (G. A.) Brendan the Navigator: an interpretation. 8vo. DUBLIN, 1945.
Littleboy (Anna L.) A history of Jordans. (1909.) 10th rev. ed. (1949.) repr. 8vo. LOND., 1967. [Pamph.]
LITURGIES: CHRISTIAN.
Eastern Rites. *Greek Rite.* [Misc.] *See* Wagner (G.)
—— **Lesser Eastern Rites.** *Malabar Rite.* [Misc.] *See* Howard (G. B.)
—— —— *Maronite Rite.* [Misc.] *See* Spinks (B. D.)
Western Rites. *Latin Rite.* [Benedictionals. Local.] *Freising. See* Suppt. Henry Bradshaw Soc., 88.
—— —— [Customaries.] *Benedictine. See* Suppt. Henry Bradshaw Soc., 99.
—— —— [Graduals. Local.] *Sarum.* Graduale Sarisburiense: a reprod. in facsim. of a MS. of the 13th cent., with a dissertation and hist. index illustrating its development from the Gregorian Antiphonale Missarum. By Walter Howard Frere. (1894.) facsim. repr. 4to. FARNBOROUGH, 1966.
—— —— [Hours. Local.] *England.* Horae beatae Mariae Virginis, or Sarum and York primers, with kindred books and primers of the reformed Roman Use. Introd. by Edgar Hoskins. (1901.) facsim. repr. 8vo. FARNBOROUGH, 1969.
—— —— —— —— A miniature book of hours. [An abridgement of the Sarum Use, with other devotions, compiled by Joan D. Lee for the Henry VI Society.] 8vo. LOND., 1978.
—— —— [Missals. Local.] *Sarum.* Missale ad usum insignis et praeclarae ecclesiae Sarum. Labore ac studio Francisci Henrici Dickinson. (1861-63.) facsim. repr. 8vo. FARNBOROUGH, 1969.
—— —— —— *York.* The lay folk's mass book of the 14th century. Ed. by the Duke of Argyll. 16mo. LOND., 1916.
—— —— [Pontificals.] *See* Suppt. Henry Bradshaw Soc., 97.
—— —— [Pontificals. Local.] *Cracow. See* Suppt. Henry Bradshaw Soc., 100.
—— —— [Processionals. Local.] *Sarum.* Processionale ad usum insignis ac praeclarae ecclesiae Sarum. [Ed. W. G. Henderson.] (1882.) facsim. repr. 8vo. FARNBOROUGH, 1969.
—— **Lesser Western Rites.** *Gallican Rite.* [Misc.] *See* Suppt. Henry Bradshaw Soc., 98.
Anglican Rite. [General Collections.] *See* Buchanan (C. O.) *ed.*
—— *Church of England.* [Common Prayer. Misc.] *See* Suppt. Alcuin Club Collections, 53, 54, 55.
—— —— [Common Prayer. *French.* Misc.] *See* Griffiths (D. N.)
—— —— [Common Prayer. *Welsh.* Misc.] *See* Griffiths (D. N.)
—— —— [Common Prayer. Revision.] Fragmentary illustrations of the history of the Book of Common Prayer from MS. sources (Bishop Sanderson and Bishop Wren). Ed. William Jacobson. (1874.) facsim. repr. 8vo. FARNBOROUGH, 1969.
—— —— —— *See* Cope (G. F.) *and others.*

Liturgies Christian—*continued*
Reformed Churches, etc. *Methodist* [Misc.] *See* Suppt. Methodist Sacramental Fellowship, M.S.F. Booklets, N.S., 2.
—— *Pentecostal.* A manual for ministers. By J. T. Bradley. [Assemblies of God and Elim Pentecostal Church.] 8vo. NOTTINGHAM & CHELTENHAM, [1975].
—— *Unitarian.* Every nation kneeling, and other services of prayer and praise. Compiled by Will Hayes for use in the Church of the Great Companions. 8vo. MEOPHAM GREEN (Kent), 1954.
—— —— [Local.] *Halifax: Northgate End Chapel.* Service and chant book. 8vo. HALIFAX, 1913.
—— —— *Sheffield: Upper Chapel.* Services for divine worship. (1906.) 2nd ed. 8vo. SHEFFIELD, 1950.
—— *Universalist.* Prayers of the larger faith. [Compiled by William Arthur Peacock for the Universalist Church, London.] 8vo. UCKFIELD, [194-].
Miscellaneous. *See* Brown (Leslie W.)
LITURGIES: JEWISH. Gate of repentance: services for the High Holydays. [Union of Liberal and Progressive Synagogues.] 4to. LOND., 1973.
—— [Hagadah. *Hebrew and English.*] The Passover Haggadah. With English trans. [by Jacob Sloan], introd. and commentary, based on the commentaries of E. D. Goldschmidt. Ed. Nahum N. Glatzer. 8vo. NEW YORK, 1953.
Liu (Tai) Discord in Zion: the Puritan divines and the Puritan Revolution, 1640-1660. [Internat. Archives of the Hist. of Ideas, 61.] 8vo. THE HAGUE, 1973.
—— The founding of the London Provincial Assembly, 1645-47. 8vo. [LOND.,] 1978. [Pamph.]
Liverpool. *Allerton Presbyterian Church.* The first twenty-five years, 1932-1957: Allerton Presbyterian Church, Mather Avenue, Liverpool 18, in which is incorporated the congregation of Mount Pleasant Church. 8vo. LIVERPOOL, [1957]. [Pamph.]
Liverpool. *Fairfield Presbyterian Church.* A brief history issued on the occasion of the congregational jubilee, 1864-1914. 8vo. [LIVERPOOL, 1914.] [Pamph.]
Liverpool. *Richmond Baptist Church.* Suffer little children to come unto me: Richmond Baptist Sunday School anniversary, 1865-1965. 8vo. [LIVERPOOL, 1965.] [Pamph.]
Liverpool. *Union Presbyterian Church.* Union Presbyterian Church of England, Fountains Road, Kirkdale, Liverpool, 1875-1902. 8vo. [LIVERPOOL, 1902.] [Pamph.]
Livingstone (Elizabeth A.) *ed. See* Dictionaries. Christianity; Suppt. Texte u. Untersuchungen, 5te. Reihe, 112, 115-117.
Llywelyn-Williams (Alun) R. T. Jenkins. [Writers of Wales.] 8vo. [CARDIFF,] 1977.
Lloyd, *family of. See* Lloyd (H.)
Lloyd (Humphrey) The Quaker Lloyds in the industrial revolution. 8vo. LOND., 1975.
Lloyd (L. J.) The library of Exeter Cathedral. With a description of the archives by Audrey M. Erskine. 8vo. EXETER, [1967]. [Pamph.]
Lloyd (Morgan) 1619-59, *Welsh mystic.* [Works.] Gweithiau Morgan Llwyd o Wynedd. 2 vols. 8vo. BANGOR & LOND., 1899-1908.
    1. Danolygiaeth Thomas E. Ellis. 1899.
    2. Danolygiaeth John H. Davies. 1908.
—— *See* Bevan (H.)
Lloyd (R. Glynne) John Owen, Commonwealth Puritan. 8vo. PONTYPRIDD & LIVERPOOL, 1972.
Lloyd (Roger B.) The borderland: an exploration of theology in English literature. 8vo. LOND., 1960.
Lluyd (Edward) *See* Roberts (B. F.)
Loader (J. A.) *See* Suppt. Zeitschr. für A. T. Wiss. Beihefte, 152.
Lock (John) and **Dixon** (W. T.) A man of sorrow: the life, letters and times of the Rev. Patrick Brontë, 1777-1861. (1965.) 2nd ed. 8vo. LOND. & WESTPORT (Conn.), 1979.
Locke (Don) A fantasy of reason: the life and thought of William Godwin. 8vo. LOND., *etc.*, 1980.
Locke (John) Correspondence. Ed. E. S. de Beer. 8vo. OXF., 1976-
    1. Introd. Letters nos. 1-461. 1976.

Locke (John) Correspondence—*continued*
  2. Letters nos. 462-848. 1976.
  3. Letters nos. 849-1241. 1978.
  4. Letters nos. 1242-1701. 1979.
  5. Letters nos. 1702-2198. 1979.
  No more yet published, 1980.
—— *See* Collins (A.); Franklin (J. H.); Gough (J. W.); Woolhouse (R. S.); Suppt. Locke Newsletter.
Locke Newsletter. *See* Suppt.
Lockett (W. E. A.) *ed.* The modern architectural setting of the liturgy. Papers read at a conference held at Liverpool, Sep. 1962. 8vo. LOND., 1964.
Lodge (*Sir* Oliver) *See* Love and death.
Loeb Classical Library. *See* Suppt.
Loen (A. E.) Secularization: science without God? [Trans. Margaret Kohl.] 8vo. LOND., 1967.
Lohse (Bernhard) *ed. See* Kretschmar (G.) and Lohse (B.) *ed.*
Lohse (Eduard) *ed. See* Dead Sea Scrolls.
Lok (Henry) *See* Lupton (L. F.)
London. *Bevis Marks Synagogue. See* Suppt. Jewish Hist. Soc. Publs., 1973.
London. *Bunhill Fields.* [Short guide.] 8vo. LOND., 1974. [Pamph.]
London. *City Temple.* Retrospect and prospect, 1916-17. Report of the Church Committee, presented at the Annual Meeting, Mar. 9th, 1918. 8vo. LOND., [1918]. [Pamph.]
London. *Crown Court Church.* [Historical brochure.] (1951.) rev. ed. 8vo. EDIN. [printed], 1971. [Pamph.]
London, *Diocese of,* and **Southwark,** *Diocese of.* Syllabus of church teaching and prayer book instruction. 8vo. LOND., 1944. [Pamph.]
London. *Guildhall Library. See* Catalogues.
London. *King's College. See* Hearnshaw (F. J. C.); Huelin (G.)
London. *King's Weigh House Church. See* Suppt. King's Weigh House Monthly.
London. *New College. See* Catalogues; Nuttall (G. F.)
London. *St. Paul's Presbyterian Church, Westbourne Terrace.* Jubilee, May 9th, 1911. 8vo. [LOND., 1911.] [Pamph.]
London. *University. Institute of Historical Research.* Bulletin. *See* Suppt.
London. *University College. See* Catalogues; Harte (N. B.) and North (J. A.)
London. *University Library. See* Catalogues.
London Bible College. *See* Suppt. Vox Evangelica.
London Congregational Union. *See* Taylor (J. H.)
London County Council. *See* Suppt. Greater London Council.
London Head Teachers' Association. The London Head Teachers' Association, 1888-1938. 8vo. LOND., 1938.
London Missionary Society. *See* Harris (J. C.)
London Quarterly and Holborn Review. *See* Suppt. Church Quarterly.
London (H. S.) *See* Suppt. Harleian Soc. Publs., 111-112.
London's liberties; or a learned argument of law & reason, upon . . . December 14. 1650 . . . at Guild Hall, London, between Mr. Maynard, Mr. Hales & Mr. Wilde . . . and Major John Wildman and Mr. John Price. (1651.) facsim. repr. 8vo. EXETER, 1972. [Pamph.]
Long (A. J.) Fifty years of theology, 1928-1978: the vindication of liberalism. [Essex Hall Lect., 1978.] 8vo. LOND., 1978. [Pamph.]
Longe (F. D.) Lowestoft in olden times. (1898.) 2nd ed. 8vo. LOWESTOFT, 1905.
Longford (Elizabeth Pakenham, *Countess of*) Piety in Queen Victoria's reign. [Friends of Dr. Williams's Lib. Lect., 27.] 8vo. LOND., 1973. [Pamph.]
Longstaff (T. R. W.) *ed. See* Orchard (J. B.) and Longstaff (T. R. W.) *ed.*
Longuet-Higgins (H. C.) *See* Kenny (A. J. P.) *and others.*
Lonsdale (John) 1737-1807,*Vicar of Darfield. See* Suppt. Surtees Soc., 188.
Loomie (A. J.) *See* Suppt. London University. Inst. of Hist. Research. Bulletin. Special Suppts., 9.
Loos (Milan) Dualist heresy in the Middle Ages. [Trans. Iris Lewitová.] 8vo. PRAGUE & THE HAGUE, 1974.
Lord (F. Townley) Christ in the modern scene. 8vo. LOND., 1936.
—— Conquest of death: a Christian interpretation of immortality. 8vo. LOND., 1940.

Lorimer (D. A.) The role of anti-slavery sentiment in English reactions to the American Civil War. 8vo. [CAMB.,] 1976. [Pamph.]

Lossky (Vladimir) In the image and likeness of God. Introd. by A. M. Allchin. [Ed. John H. Erickson and Thomas E. Bird.] 8vo. LOND., 1975.

Lott (Eric J.) Vedantic approaches to God. Foreword by John Hick. [Lib. of Philos. and Relig.] 8vo. LOND. & BASINGSTOKE, 1980.

Loukaris (Kyrillos) *Patriarch of Alexandria and Constantinople.* Sermons, 1598-1602. Ed. Keetje Rozemond. [Byzantina Neerlandica, 4.] 8vo. LEIDEN, 1974.

Love and death. A narrative of fact. Foreword by Sir Oliver Lodge. 8vo. LOND., [1926].

Loveridge (S. M.) and **Whiting** (Arthur) New Baptist Church, Devizes, 1852-1952: an historical account. 8vo. [DEVIZES, 1952.] [Pamph.]

Lowe (Norman) *See* Suppt. Chetham Soc., 3rd Ser., 20.

Lowe (Walter Bezant) The heart of Northern Wales, at is was and as it is. 2 vols. 8vo. LLANFAIRFECHAN, 1912-27.

—— Llansannan: its history and associations. 8vo. LLANFAIRFECHAN, 1915.

Lowell, *family of, of New England. See* Greenslet (F.)

Lowndes (G. A. N.) The silent social revolution: an account of public education in England and Wales, 1895-1935. 8vo. LOND., 1937.

Lowrie (D. A.) Rebellious prophet: a life of Nicolai Berdyaev. 8vo. LOND., 1960.

Lowrie (Walter) A short life of Kierkegaard. (1942.) 2nd ed. 8vo. PRINCETON, 1965.

Lowther, *family of. See* Suppt. Surtees Soc., 191.

Lowther (*Sir* Christopher) *See* Suppt. Surtees Soc., 189.

Lubbock (*Lady* Sybil Marjorie) The child in the crystal. 8vo. LOND., 1939.

Lucas (J. R.) The freedom of the will. 8vo. OXF., 1970.

—— A treatise on time and space. 8vo. LOND., 1973.

—— *See* Kenny (A. J. P.) *and others.*

Lucian, *of Samosata.* [Works. *Greek.*] Luciani opera. Recognovit brevique adnotatione critica instruxit M. D. Macleod. [Oxford Classical Texts.] 8vo. OXF. 1. Libelli 1-25. 1972.

—— *See* More (*Sir* T.)

Ludendorff (Mathilde) The triumph of the Immortal-Will. Trans. Alice Brechta. 8vo. TUTZING, n.d.

Ludlow (Edmund) 1617?-1692. *See* Suppt. Royal Hist. Soc. Camden 4th Ser., 21.

Lüdemann (Gerd) *See* Suppt. Forschungen zur Religion u. Lit., 123.

Lüling (Günter) Der christliche Kult an der vorislamischen Kaaba als Problem der Islamwissenschaft und christlichen Theologie. 8vo. ERLANGEN, 1977. [Pamph.]

Luffield Priory. Charters. Pt. 2. Ed. with an introd. by G. R. Elvey. [Northants. Record Soc. Publs., 21, 1973.] 8vo. [NORTHAMPTON,] 1975. [*Pt. 1 not in Library.*]

Lukacs (John) Historical consciousness, or the remembered past. 8vo. NEW YORK, *etc.*, 1968.

Lull (Ramon) *See* Hillgarth (J. N.)

Lunn (Stead) History of the Meltham Baptist Church, 1813-1913. 8vo. MELTHAM, 1913.

Lupton (L. F.) A history of the Geneva Bible. 13 vols. 8vo. LOND., 1966-81.
1. The quarrel. 1966.
2. Reform. 1969.
3. Truth. 1971.
4. Travail. 1972.
5. Vision of God. 1973.
6. Hope's anchor. 1974.
7. Welcome joy. 1975.
8. Faith: Henry Lok. 1976.
9. Love: Katherine Willoughby de Eresby, Duchess of Suffolk. 1977.
10. Courage: Peregrine Bertie. 1978.
11. Endurance: Miles Coverdale. 1979.
12. Heaven: Miles Coverdale [contd.]. 1980.
13. Index. 1981.

—— Calvin, the Geneva Bible and eschatology. 8vo. [LOND., 1969.] [Pamph.]

—— Conrad Badius. 8vo. [EXETER, 1969.] [Pamph.]

Luscombe (D. E.) *See* Suppt. Historical Assn. Gen. Ser., 95.

Lusty (F. C.) Walgrave Baptist Church, 1700-1950: a brief record of two-hundred-and-fifty years' witness and service. 8vo. NORTHAMPTON, 1950.

Luther (Martin) *See* Agate (L. D.); Bainton (R. H.); Borth (W.); Köstlin (J.); Moore (W. G.); Oberman (H. A.) *ed.;* Rublack (H.-C.); Suppan (K.); Thomas (J. H.); Wernle (P.)

Lutheran Council of Great Britain. [Anniversary, 1948-73.] 8vo. LOND., [1975].

Luton. *Ebenezer Strict Baptist Chapel.* Centenary services, Nov. 18th, 1953, Ebenezer Strict Baptist Chapel, Hastings Street, Luton, Beds. 8vo. [LUTON, 1953.] [Pamph.]

Luton. *Park Street Baptist Church.* 299th church anniversary: souvenir brochure. 8vo. [LUTON, 1974.] [Pamph.]

Luton. *Ramridge Baptist Church.* A pioneer venture: the story of a missionary work and the growth of a church in a new housing-estate at Ramridge, Luton, Beds. 8vo. [LUTON,] 1958. [Pamph.]

Lyall (Edna) *pseud. See* Payne (G. A.)

Lyles (A. M.) Methodism mocked: the satiric reaction to Methodism in the eighteenth century. 8vo. LOND., 1960.

Lyndwood (William) Provinciale, (seu Constitutiones Angliae,) continens constitutiones provinciales quatuordecim Archiepiscorum Cantuariensium. (1679.) facsim. repr. fol. FARNBOROUGH, 1968.

Lyne (J. L.) *See* Calder-Marshall (A.)

Lyte (Henry Francis) *See* Skinner (B. G.)

Lyttelton (Edith S.) The faculty of communion. 8vo. LOND., 1925.

Lyttelton (Edward) The mind and character of Henry Scott Holland. 8vo. LOND., 1926.

Mabillon (Jean) and **Ruinart** (Thierri) Ouvrages posthumes de D. Jean Mabillon et de D. Thierri Ruinart, Bénédictins de la Congrégation de Saint Maur. Par D. Vincent Thuillier. (1724.) facsim. repr. 3 vols. 8vo. FARNBOROUGH, 1967.

MacAlpine (Neil) *See* Dictionaries. Languages. *Gaelic.*

Macarius, *Saint, of Corinth. See* Philokalia.

Macaulay (T. B., *1st Baron*) *See* Knowles (D.)

MacBeath (John) Fillebrook's fifty years: the jubilee story, 1878-1928. 8vo. LOND., [1928]. [Pamph.]

McBee (Silas) An eirenic itinerary: impressions of our tour. With addresses and papers on the unity of Christian churches. 8vo. LOND., 1911.

McCafferty (W. H.) Belfast Domestic Mission, 1853-1953: a century of social service. 8vo. [BELFAST, 1953.] [Pamph.]

McClelland (W. G.) And a new earth: making tomorrow's society better than today's. [Swarthmore Lect., 1976.] 8vo. LOND., 1976.

McClure (Kevin Paul) and **McClure** (Susan) Stars, and rumours of stars: reports of the paranormal in the Welsh religious revival, 1904-5. 8vo. [MARKET HARBOROUGH, 1980.] [Pamph.]

McCormack (James) and **Condon** (Kevin) Monsieur Vincent: an account of Vincent de Paul and his place in the world of today. 8vo. DUBLIN, 1970. [Pamph.]

McCutchan (Helen C.) *See* Suppt. Hymn Soc. of America. Papers, 28.

McCutchan (R. G.) *See* Suppt. Hymn Soc. of America. Papers, 28.

Macdonald (Allan J. M.) Episcopi vagantes in church history. 8vo. LOND., 1945. [Pamph.]

McDonald (Frances M. S.) Monument to faith: a history of the United Reformed Church, Aston Tirrold, Oxfordshire. 8vo. ASTON TIRROLD, 1978. [Pamph.]

MacDonald (George) *See* Johnson (J.)

McDonald (J. I. H.) Kerygma and didache: the articulation and structure of the earliest Christian message. [Soc. for N.T. Studies, Monograph Ser., 37.] 8vo. CAMB., 1980.

McDougall (Eleanor) *See* Papers for War Time, 16.

McEwen (Gilbert D.) The oracle of the coffee house: John Dunton's Athenian Mercury. 8vo. SAN MARINO (Calif.), 1972.

Macfarlane (Alan) The family life of Ralph Josselin, a seventeenth-century clergyman: an essay in historical anthropology. 8vo. CAMB., 1970.

Macfayden (Dugald) *ed.* Constructive Congregational ideals: a series of addresses. 8vo. LOND., 1902.

McGee (James Sears) The godly man in Stuart England: Anglicans, Puritans, and the Two Tables, 1620-1670. [Yale Historical Publs., Miscellany, 110.] 8vo. NEW HAVEN & LOND., 1976.

McGehee (C. W.) Answers in the wind. [Meditations.] 8vo. BOSTON (Mass.), 1969. [Pamph.]

McGiffert (Arthur Cushman) Pilot of a liberal faith: Samuel Atkins Eliot, 1862-1950. 8vo. [BOSTON (Mass.),]1976.

Macgregor (George H. C.) The relevance of the impossible: a reply to Reinhold Niebuhr. 8vo. LOND., 1941.

Machin (G. I. T.) Politics and the churches in Great Britain, 1832 to 1868. 8vo. OXF., 1977.

Machray (W. F.) The first Bishop of Liverpool: biographical sketch of the Rt. Rev. John Charles Ryle. 8vo. LOND., 1900. [Pamph.]

McInnes (Angus) *See* Suppt. Historical Assn. Appreciations in Hist., 7.

Macintyre (R. G.) The other side of death: a study in Christian eschatology. 8vo. LOND., 1920.

McKay (J. W.) *See* Suppt. Studies in Bibl. Theol., 2nd Ser., 26.

McKenna (J. H.) *See* Suppt. Alcuin Club. Collections, 57.

MacKenzie (John) *See* Dictionaries. Languages. *Gaelic.*

McKenzie (John Grant) Nervous disorders and religion: a study of souls in the making. [Tate Lects., Manchester Coll., Oxford, 1947.] 8vo. LOND., 1951.

McKenzie (John Lawrence) The world of the Judges. 8vo. LOND., 1967.

Mackenzie (K. D.) *ed.* Union of Christendom. 8vo. LOND. & NEW YORK, 1938.

Mackie (John Duncan) Presbyterianism and nationality. [Presbyterian Hist. Soc. of England Annual Lect., 5, 1927.] 8vo. LOND., 1927. [Pamph.]

MacKinnon (D. M.) The problem of metaphysics. [Gifford Lects., 1965-66.] 8vo. LOND., 1974.

[**McKinnon** (I. A.)] United Reformed Church, Long Eaton: the first hundred years, 1876-1976. 4to. [LONG EATON, 1977.] [Pamph.]

MacKinnon (John G.) The MacKinnon years. [Poems and summarised sermons.] 8vo. INDIANAPOLIS, 1968.

Mackintosh (H. R.) Some aspects of Christian belief. 8vo. LOND., [1923].

Mackintosh (Robert) 1858-1933. *See* Sell (A. P. F.)

Mackintosh (W. H.) Disestablishment and liberation: the movement for the separation of the Anglican Church from state control. 8vo. LOND., 1972.

McLachlan (Herbert) 1876-1958. Cross Street Chapel in the life of Manchester. 8vo. MANCHESTER, 1941. [Pamph.]

—— The Ancient Chapel of Toxteth. An address at the 334th anniversary, 30th Nov. 1952. 8vo. LOUGHBOROUGH [printed], [1952]. [Pamph.]

McLachlan (Herbert John) *b.* 1908. The Old Nonconformity in Fulwood. 8vo. SHEFFIELD, 1940. [Pamph.]

MacLachlan (Lewis) C.P.F.L.U.: a short history of the Christian Pacifist Forestry and Land Units, 1940-1946. With a memoir to Henry Carter, by E. C. Urwin. 8vo. LOND., 1952.

MacLennan (Kenneth) *See* Papers for War Time, 23.

McLoughlin (William G.) New England Dissent, 1630-1833: the Baptists and the separation of church and state. 2 vols. 8vo. CAMB. (Mass.), 1971.

Macmurray (John) A challenge to the churches: religion and democracy. [The Democratic Order, 9.] 8vo. LOND., 1941.

—— Constructive democracy. Two lectures delivered at University Coll., London, Dec. 1942. (1943.) repr. 8vo. LOND., 1943.

McMillan (William) A profile in courage: Henry Montgomery, 1788-1865. 8vo. NEWRY, 1966. [Pamph.]

McNabb (Vincent) *See* Siderman (E. A.)

MacNeice (F. J.) Reunion: the open door. A call from Ireland. 8vo. BELFAST, 1929. [Pamph.]

McNeill (John) *See* Gammie (A.)

Macquarrie (John) Three issues in ethics. 8vo. LOND., 1970.

—— Existentialism. [Theological Resources.] 8vo. LOND., 1972.

—— Paths in spirituality. 8vo. NEW YORK, *etc.*, 1972.

Macrae (Florence A.) The history of the Old Meeting House, Ditchling. (1950.) With additions and emendations. 8vo. *Duplicated.* n.p., [1974]. [Pamph.]

McTaggart (J. McT. E.) *See* Geach (P. T.)

Madan (Falconer) *See* Catalogues. *Bodleian Lib.*

[Magnus (Maurice)] Memoirs of the Foreign Legion. By M. M. Introd. by D. H. Lawrence. 8vo. LOND., 1924.

Magraw (Charles) The problem of human immortality. 8vo. LOND., [1923].

Maguire (L. J.) *See* Ditchling. *Old Meeting House.*

Mahoney (A. G.) The origins of the Society of Saint Vincent de Paul and its establishment in England and Wales. 4to. LOND., [1967.] [Pamph.]

Maidenhall. *Stoke Green Baptist Church.* A guide to 200 years of witness, 1757 to 1957. 8vo. *Duplicated.* [MAIDENHALL, 1957.] [Pamph.]

Maier (Anneliese) Studien zur Naturphilosophie der Spätsscholastik. (1949-58.) [Storia e Letteratura Raccolta di Studi e Testi, 22, 37, 41, 52, 69.] 5 vols. in 3. 8vo. ROMA 1952-68.

Maier (Franz Georg) *ed.* Byzanz. [Fischer Weltgeschichte, 13.] 8vo. FRANKFURT AM M., 1973.

Maier (Gerhard) Mensch und freier Wille nach den jüdischen Religionspartien zwischen Ben Sira und Paulus. [Wissenschaftl. Untersuch. zum N.T., 12.] 8vo. TÜBINGEN, 1971.

Maimonides (Moses) *See* Suppt. Yale Judaica Ser.

Maitland (F. W.) *See* Fifoot (C. H. S.)

Major (H. D. A.) and **Wigley** (Thomas) The Christian church, yesterday and tomorrow. [Modernist Pamphs. on Relig., Life and Thought, 1.] 8vo. LOND., [1943]. [Pamph.]

Makarios. *See* Macarius.

Makemie (Francis) Life and writings. Ed. with an introd. by Boyd S. Schlenther. [Presbyterian Historical Soc. Publs., 11.] 8vo. PHILADELPHIA, 1971.

Malcolm (C. W.) Twelve hours in the day: the life and work of Rev. Lionel B. Fletcher, D. D. 8vo. LOND., 1956.

Maltby (Thomas R.) [Selections.] T.R.M.: a memorial. [Comp. Arnold Longman.] 8vo. FROME, [c. 1943]. [Pamph.]

Maltby (W. R.) *See* Papers for War Time, 6.

Malthus (T. R.) *See* James (P.)

Manchester. *Brookfield Church.* Brookfield Church Sunday School, Hyde Road, Gorton Manchester: jubilee (1900-1950) and 29th rose fete and crowning of the queen, July 1st and 2nd, 1950. 8vo. LEVENSHULME [printed] [1950]. [Pamph.]

Manchester. *John Rylands Library.* *See* John Rylands Library, *Manchester.*

Mandeville (*Sir* John) *See* Suppt. Early Eng. Text Soc., O.S., 269.

Mango (Cyril A.) Byzantine literature as a distorting mirror. Inaugural lect., Univ. of Oxford, 21 May 1974. 8vo. OXF., 1975. [Pamph.]

—— Byzantium: the empire of New Rome. [Hist. of Civilisation.] 8vo. LOND., 1980.

Mani. *See* Suppt. Corpus Script. Christ. Orient., Subsid., 55.

Mann (C. S.) *See* Bible. Commentaries. Anchor Bible, 26.

Mannering (Enid P.) The story of St. Martin's United Reformed Church, Saltdean. 8vo. *Duplicated.* n.p., 1979. [Pamph.]

Manning (Bernard Lord) This latter house: the life of Emmanuel Congregational Church, Cambridge, from 1874 to 1924. 8vo. CAMB., 1924.

—— The making of modern English religion: an historical impression of certain religious forces in modern English history. 8vo. LOND., 1929.

Manor Park, *E. Ham. Rehoboth.* 1830-1930: a brief record of the history of the church worshipping at Rehoboth, High Street North, Manor Park. Centenary services, Nov. 12, 1930. 8vo. LOND., [1930]. [Pamph.]

Mantle (J. Gregory) Hugh Price Hughes. [New Century Leaders Ser.] 8vo. LOND., 1901.

Manton (Jo) Mary Carpenter and the children of the streets. 8vo. LOND., 1976.

Manuel (F. E.) The religion of Isaac Newton. [Fremantle Lects. 1973.] 8vo. OXF. 1974.

Marcel (Gabriel) *See* Widmer (C.)

Marc' Hadour (G. P.) The Bible in the works of Thomas More. 5 vols. in 2. 8vo. NIEUWKOOP, 1969-72.

Marchant (James) J. B. Paton, educational and social pioneer. 8vo. LOND., 1909.
Marchant (*Sir* James) *ed.* Survival. 8vo. LOND., 1924
—— Life after death according to Christianity and spiritualism. 8vo. LOND., 1925.
Margate. *Cecil Square Baptist Church.* 1762-1962: a bicentenary souvenir and short history. 8vo. [MARGATE, 1962.] [Pamph.]
Margery (Ralph) *See* King (D. W.)
Margolis (Joseph) Psychotherapy and morality: a study of two concepts. 8vo. NEW YORK, 1966.
Marha Krestos, *Abbot of Dabra Libanos. See* Suppt. Corpus Script. Christ. Orient., Aethiop., 62-63.
Mark (Thiselton) Human nature and human survival. An essay. 8vo. LOND., [1929].
Markert (Ludwig) *See* Suppt. Zeitschr. für A. T. Wiss. Beihefte, 140.
Markus (R. A.) Christianity in the Roman world. [Currents in the Hist. of Culture and Ideas.] 8vo. LOND., 1974.
Marsden (G. M.) Perry Miller's rehabilitation of the Puritans: a critique. 8vo. [CHICAGO, 1970.] [Pamph.] [Photocopy.]
Marsh (Colin) Why this church? A history of Counterslip Baptist Church, Bristol. 8vo. [BRISTOL,] 1979. [Pamph.]
Marshall (I. Howard) Luke: historian and theologian. 8vo. EXETER, 1970.
—— The Gospel of Luke: a commentary on the Greek text. [New Internat. Greek Test. Comm.] 8vo. EXETER, 1978.
—— *ed.* New Testament interpretation. Essays on principles and methods. 8vo. EXETER, 1977.
Marshall (Mary Paley, *Mrs. Alfred*) What I remember. Introd. by G. M. Trevelyan. 8vo. CAMB., 1947.
Martin (Alfred von) *ed. See* Arseniev (N.) and Martin (A. von) *ed.*
Martin (Arthur D.) Foreshewings of Christ: Old Testament studies in the preparation for the Advent. 8vo. LOND., 1930.
—— Doctor Vanderkemp. 8vo. [LOND., 1931.]
Martin (Aubrey J.) Hanes Llwynrhydowen. 8vo. LLANDYSUL, 1977.
Martin (David Alfred) The dilemmas of contemporary religion. 8vo. OXF., 1978.
—— *ed. See* Suppt. Sociological Yearbook of Religion in Britain.
Martin (G. T.) *See* Suppt. Egypt Exploration Soc. Arch. Survey, 35.
Martin (Hugh) Benjamin Keach (1640-1704): pioneer of congregational hymn singing. [Heritage Biographies.] 8vo. LOND., 1961. [Pamph.]
[**Martin** (R. S.)] "One Church": the story of Wembley Park United Reformed Church Golden jubilee, 1930-1980. 4to. *Duplicated.* n.p., 1980. [Pamph.]
Martin (Ralph P.) Colossians: the Church's Lord and the Christian's liberty: an expository commentary with a present-day application. 8vo. EXETER, 1972.
—— Mark: evangelist and theologian. 8vo. EXETER, 1972.
—— *See* Bible. Commentaries. New Century Bible.
—— *ed. See* Bruce (F. F.) [Misc.]
Martin (Raymond G.) John Robinson (1575-1625). [Heritage Biographies.] 8vo. LOND., 1961. [Pamph.]
Martius (Galeottus) *See* Briggs (E. R.)
Martival (Roger) *Bp. of Salisbury. See* Suppt. Canterbury and York Soc., 58, 68.
Marvell (Andrew) The rehearsal transpros'd (1672) and The rehearsal transpros'd, the second part (1673). Ed. D. I. B. Smith. 8vo. OXF., 1971.
—— *See* Bagguley (W. H.) *ed.*; Lewalski (B. K.) and Sabol (A. J.) *ed.*
Marx (Karl) *See* Lindsay (A. D.)
Mary, *the Blessed Virgin. See* Goodall (J. A.); Orchard (W. E.); Suppt. Corpus Script. Christ. Orient., Aethiop., 66-69.
Mary Magdalene. *See* Suppt. Analecta Bollandiana. Subsid. Hagiog., 57.
Mary, *Queen of Scots. See* Paul (J. E.); Vessey (D. W. T.)
Mascall (E. L.) Theology and images. [Contemp. Studies in Theol., 7.] 8vo. LOND., 1963. [Pamph.]
—— The openness of being: natural theology today. [Gifford Lects., 1970-71.] 8vo. LOND., 1971.
—— Theology and the Gospel of Christ. 8vo. LOND., 1977.
Mason (Leonard) Bold antiphony: meditations in contrasting moods. obl. 8vo. LOND., 1967. [Pamph.]
—— Hinge of the year: Christmas crosstalk. obl. 8vo. LOND., 1967. [Pamph.]

Massie (John)   An Established Church "conveyance." Memorandum on the New England Company, prepared at the request of the Protestant Dissenting Deputies. 8vo.   LOND., [1913].   [Pamph.]

Mather, *family of.   See* Middlekauff (R.)

Mather (Cotton)   *See* Levin (D.)

Matheson (Peter)   Cardinal Contarini at Regensburg.   8vo.   OXF., 1972.

Mathew (David)   *R.C. Abp. of Apamea.*   Sir Tobie Mathew.   8vo.   LOND., 1950.

Mathew (David) *and others.*   Richard Challoner, 1691-1781, the greatest of the Vicars-Apostolic: his life, times, works, influence, &c.   4to.   LOND., 1946.   [Pamph.]

Mathew (*Sir* Toby)   *See* Mathew (D.)

Mathews (H. F.)   Methodism and the education of the people, 1791-1851.   8vo. LOND., 1949.

Mathews (T. F.)   The early churches of Constantinople: architecture and liturgy. 8vo.   UNIVERSITY PARK (Pa.) & LOND., 1971.

Mathilda, *of Magdeburg.   See* Deutsche Mystiker, 2.

Matson (William Tidd)   *See* Playdon (M. C.)

Matthaei (Louise E.)   *See* Papers for War Time, 34.

Matthai (John)   *See* Papers for War Time, 30.

Matthew, *Metropolitan of Ephesus.*   [Epistles. *Greek and German.*] Die Briefe des Matthaios von Ephesos im Codex Vindobonensis Theol. Gr. 174.   Hrsg. Diether Reinsch.   8vo.   BERLIN, 1974.

Matthews (Timothy R.)   *See* Varley (J.)

Matthews (Walter R.) *Dean of St. Paul's.*   Some modern problems of faith.   8vo. LOND., 1928.

—— Seven words.   8vo.   LOND., 1933.

—— Our faith in God.   [Diocesan Ser., 1.]   8vo.   LOND., 1936.

—— Memories and meanings.   8vo.   LOND., 1969.

—— *See* Owen (H. P.)

Maty (Matthieu)   *See* Janssens (U.)

Mauchline (John)   *See* Bible. Commentaries. New Century Bible.

Maurer (Wilhelm)   Melanchthon-Studien.   [Schriften des Vereins für Reformationsgesch., 181, Jg. 70.]   8vo.   GÜTERSLOH, 1964.

—— Der junge Melanchthon: zwischen Humanismus und Reformation.   2 vols. 8vo.   GÖTTINGEN, 1967-69.

   1.   Der Humanist.   1967.

   2.   Der Theologe.   1969.

Maurice (F. D.)   *See* Brose (O. J.); Christensen (T.); Flesseman-Van Leer (E.)

Mauser (U. W.)   Gottesbild und Menschwerdung: eine Untersuchung zur Einheit des Alten und Neuen Testaments.   [Beiträge zur Hist. Theol., 43.]   8vo.   TÜBINGEN, 1971.

Maximus, *Saint, Abbot and Confessor.   See* Riou (A.)

Mayes (A. D. H.)   *See* Bible. Commentaries. New Century Bible; Suppt. Studies in Bibl. Theol., 2nd Ser., 29.

[**Mayhew** (W. H.)]   1859-1959: a history of Edmonton Baptist Church, the Broadway, N.9.   8vo.   [LOND., 1959.]   [Pamph.]

Mayor (S. H.)   The Lord's Supper in early English Dissent.   8vo.   LOND., 1972.

Mays (James Luther)   Micah: a commentary.   [Old Test. Lib.]   8vo.   LOND., 1976.

Mays (John Barron)   Urban problems and moral issues.   [Essex Hall Lect., 1975.] 8vo.   LOND., 1975.   [Pamph.]

[**Mead** (Marjory)]   God building: the story of one hundred years.   Flinders Street Baptist Church, Adelaide.   8vo.   [ADELAIDE, 1961.]   [Pamph.]

Medd (P. G.)   *See* Bright (W.)

Medieval Classics   [*also* Medieval Texts].   *See* Suppt. Oxford Medieval Texts.

Medina (*Sir* Solomon de)   *See* Suppt. Jewish Hist. Soc. Publs., 1974.

Medley (Samuel) 1738-99, *Baptist minister.   See* Ramsbottom (B. A.)

Megaw (A. H. S.)   *See* Suppt. Dumbarton Oaks Studies, 14.

Meiser (Hans)   *See* Heiwik (H.)

Melanchthon (Philip)   *See* Maurer (W.)

Melchizedek, *King of Salem.   See* Horton (F. L.)

Melito, *Bp. of Sardis.*   Sur la Pâque, et fragments. Introd., texte critique, trad. et notes par Othmar Perler.   [Sources Chrétiennes, 123.]   8vo.   PARIS, 1966.

Méliusz (Peter)   *See* Bucsay (M.) *and others.*

Mellanby (Kenneth) The threat of world pollution. [Essex Hall Lect., 1971.] 8vo. LOND., 1971. [Pamph.]

Mellink (A. F.) *ed. See* Kossman (E. H.) and Mellink (A. F.) *ed.*

Mellor (S. A.) Stanley Alfred Mellor. [His last written message, with addresses by L.P. Jacks and Arthur Fitch.] 8vo. [LIVERPOOL, 1926.] [Pamph.]

Melon (Jean-François) Opere. II. Scritti editi. A cura di Onofrio Nicastro e Severina Perona. [Studi sull' illuminismo, 7.] 8vo. *Photo. repr.* SIENA, 1977.

Melton (William) *Abp. of York. See* Suppt. Canterbury and York Soc., 70, 71.

Melugin (R. F.) *See* Suppt. Zeitschr. für A. T. Wiss. Beihefte, 141.

Mendelssohn (Moses) *See* Altmann (A.)

Mendenhall (G. H.) The tenth generation: the origins of the biblical tradition. 8vo. BALTIMORE & LOND., 1973.

Mendl (Wolf) Prophets and reconcilers: reflections on the Quaker Peace Testimony. [Swarthmore Lect., 1974.] 8vo. LOND., 1974.

Mennonite Quarterly Review. *See* Suppt.

Merrick (M. M.) James Duckett: a study of his life and times. 8vo. LOND., 1947.

Merry (D. H.) *See* Suppt. Oxford Hist. Soc., N.S., 25.

Methodist Church. *Local Preachers Department.* Report, 1957-58. 8vo. LOND., [1958]. [Pamph.]

—— *South India Provincial Synod. See* Proposed scheme of union.

Methodist Conferences. The official directory of the Conference, Nottingham, 1945. 8vo. [NOTTINGHAM, 1945.] [Pamph.]

—— The handbook to the Methodist Conference, 1970, in the Whitworth Hall, Univ. of Manchester. 8vo. [MANCHESTER, 1970.]

Methodist Sacramental Fellowship. *See* Suppt.

Methodius, *Saint, Bp. of Olympus and Patara. See* Dvornik (F.)

Metzger (B. M.) A textual commentary on the Greek New Testament. A companion volume to the United Bible Societies' Greek New Testament (3rd ed.). 8vo. LOND. & NEW YORK, 1971.

—— The early versions of the New Testament: their origin, transmission, and limitations. 8vo. OXF., 1977.

Metzger (Martin) Die Paradieseserzählung: die Geschichte ihrer Auslegung von J. Clericus bis W. M. L. de Wette. [Abhandlungen zur Philos., Psychol. u. Pädagogik, 16.] 8vo. BONN, 1959.

Meyendorff (John) Byzantine hesychasm: historical, theological and social problems. Collected studies. [Variorum Reprs.] 8vo. LOND., 1974.

—— Byzantine theology: historical trends and doctrinal themes. 8vo. NEW YORK, 1974.

Meyer (C. S.) *ed. See* Suppt. Sixteenth Century Essays and Studies.

Meyer (F. B.) Abraham: or, the obedience of faith. (1888.) 12th imp. 8vo. LOND., 1911.

—— John the Baptist. (1900.) [Another ed.] 8vo. LOND., 1922.

—— Peter: fisherman, disciple, apostle. 8vo. LOND., [1919].

Meyer (Louis) *ed. See* Fundamentals.

Mezezers (Valdis) The Herrnhuterian Pietism in the Baltic and its outreach into America and elsewhere in the world. 8vo. NORTH QUINCY (Mass.), 1975.

Michaelson (Sidney) *ed. See* Bible. N.T. Misc. John, Epistles of.

Michel, *Dan, See* Suppt. Early Eng. Text Soc., O.S., 278.

Micklem (Nathaniel) The creed of a Christian, being monologues upon great themes of the Christian faith. 8vo. LOND., 1940.

[——] No more apologies, and other B[ritish] W[eekly] papers. By Ilico. 8vo. LOND., 1941.

—— Congregationalism and episcopacy. 8vo. LOND., [1950]. [Pamph.]

—— The box and the puppets (1888-1953). 8vo. LOND., 1957.

—— Faith and reason. 8vo. LOND., 1963.

—— *See* Thomas (H. A.)

Middlekauff (Robert) The Mathers: three generations of Puritan intellectuals. 1596-1728. 8vo. NEW YORK, 1971.

Middleton (Thomas) *See* Heinemann (M.)

Midland Christian Union. The Midland Christian Union of Presbyterian, Unitarian, and other non-subscribing churches: historical summary (1806-1925). 8vo. WALSALL [printed], 1925. [Pamph.]

Midland Union of Unitarian and Free Christian Churches. Commemorating the "Great Ejection", 1662-1962. [Ed. Charles Simpson.] 8vo. WEST BROMWICH [printed], [1962]. [Pamph.]

Miege (Guy) Nouvelle méthode pour apprendre l'Anglois. (1685.) facsim. repr. [English Linguistics, 1500-1800, 216.] 8vo. MENSTON, 1970.

Miles (Michael) *See* Suppt. Christian Brethren Research Fellowship, Occ. Papers, 7.

Milik (J. T.) *See* Discoveries in the Judaean Desert.

Mill (John Stuart) Later letters, 1849-1873. Ed. Francis E. Mineka and Dwight N. Lindley. [Collected works, 14-17.] 4 vols. 8vo. TORONTO, 1972.

—— *See* Garforth (F. W.); Halliday (R. J.)

Miller (J. H. D.) From the other side: talks of a dead son with his father. 8vo. LOND., 1925.

Miller (J. Maxwell) *ed. See* Hayes (J. H.) and Miller (J. M.) *ed.*

Miller (John) Popery and politics in England, 1660-1668. 8vo. CAMB., 1973.

Miller (Perry) *See* Marsden (G. M.)

Miller (Samuel J. T.) and **Spielman** (J. P.) Cristobal Rojas y Spinola: cameralist and irenicist, 1626-1695. [Trans. of the Amer. Philos. Soc., N.S., 52, 5.] fol. PHILADELPHIA, 1962.

Miller (Spencer) and **Fletcher** (J. F.) The Church and industry. 8vo. NEW YORK, 1930.

Miller (W. D.) *See* Smith (J. S.)

Mills (Thomas) 1623-1703. *See* Packard (J.) and Packard (F.) *ed.*

Millson (F. E.) The story of the life of the Rev. Oliver Heywood: a service of song. 8vo. HALIFAX, 1902. [Pamph.]

Milne (A. T.) A history of Broadwindsor, Dorset. 8vo. DORCHESTER, [1935]. [Pamph.]

Milne (J. G.) The early history of Corpus Christi College, Oxford. 8vo. OXF., 1946.

Milton (John) Complete prose works. [General editor: Don M. Wolfe.] 8vo. NEW HAVEN & LOND., 1953-
   5.i. 1648?-1671. Ed. French Fogle. 1971.
   5.ii. 1649-1659. Ed. J. Max Patrick. 1971.
   6.   ca.1658 – ca.1660. Ed. Maurice Kelley. 1973.
   7.   1659-1660. Ed. Robert W. Ayers. 1974.

—— *See* Bickley (H.); Eliot (T. S.); Fogle (F. R.) and Trevor-Roper (H. R.); Gardner (H. L.); Hill (C.); Hunter (W. B.) *and others;* Hutchinson (F. E.); Steadman (J. M.); Williamson (G.)

Milward (R. J.) History of Wimbledon. Pt. 3. Wimbledon in the time of the Civil War. 8vo. [LOND.,] 1976.

Mind. *See* Suppt.

Mind Association. *See* Suppt. Aristotelian Society. Suppt. vols.

Minear (P. S.) Commands of Christ. 8vo. EDIN., [1973].

—— *See* Suppt. Studies in Bibl. Theol., 2nd Ser., 18.

Minn (H. R.) The thorn that remained: materials for the study of St. Paul's thorn in the flesh, 2 Cor. 12: 1-10. 8vo. AUCKLAND, 1972.

Mishnah. Die Mischna. Text, Übersetzung und ausführliche Erklärung. . .begrundet von G. Beer und O. Holtzmann. 8vo. BERLIN, *etc.*, 1912-
   III. Naschim. 4. Näzir (Nasiräer). Von Maas Boertien. 1971.
   V. Kodaschim. 5. 'Arakin (Schätzungen). Von Michael Krupp. 1971.
   VI. Toharot. 1. Kelim (Gefässe). Von Wolfgang Bunte. 1972.
      —— 7. Nidda (Unreinheit der Frau). Von Benyamin Z. Barslai. 1980.

[**Missen** (F. G.) and **Blyth** (K.) *ed.*] Achievement: the story of the rebuilding of Teddington Baptist Church, 1956. 8vo. [TEDDINGTON, 1956.] [Pamph.]

Mitchell (Basil) The justification of religious belief. [Philos. of Relig. Ser.] 8vo. LOND., 1973.

Mitchell (Fred) *See* Thompson (P.)

Mitchell (L. G.) Charles James Fox and the disintegration of the Whig party, 1782-1794. [Oxford Historical Monographs.] 8vo. LOND., 1971.

Mitchell (Marjory G.) History of the British League of Unitarian and Other Liberal Christian Women. 8vo. LOND., [1949]. [Pamph.]

Mitteilungen der Gottfried-Wilhelm-Leibniz-Gesellschaft. *See* Suppt.

Mitteilungen und Neuerwerbungen. *See* Suppt.
Mittmann (Siegfried) *See* Suppt. Zeitschr. für A. T. Wiss. Beihefte, 139.
Mitton (C. Leslie) *See* Bible. Commentaries. New Century Bible.
Moberly (W. H.) *See* Papers for War Time, 8.
Modbury. *Baptist Church.* [Brief history.] 8vo. *Duplicated.* n.p., [*c.*1970]. [s.sh.fold.]
Modern Churchman. *See* Suppt.
Modern Free Churchman. *See* Suppt.
[**Módis** (László)] A debreceni református kollégium és nagytemplom. 8vo. BUDA-PEST, 1966. [Pamph.]
Møller (Jens Glebe) Doctrina secundum pietatem: Holger Rosenkrantz den Laerdes teologi. 4to. KØBENHAVN, 1966.
Mohammed. *See* Stubbs (H.)
Mohrmann (Christine) Études sur le latin des chrétiens. [Storia e Letteratura Raccolta di Studi e Testi, 65, 87, 103.] 3 vols. in 2. 8vo. ROMA, 1961-65.
Mol. (Hans) *ed.* Western religion: a country by country sociological inquiry. Ed. Hans Mol in collab. with Margaret Hetherton and Margaret Henty. [Religion and Reason, 2.] 8vo. THE HAGUE & PARIS, 1972.
Molitor (Joseph) *See* Suppt. Corpus Script. Christ. Orient., Subsid., 49.
Molland (Einar) Reformasjonens fedre eller "Lysestaken": et tema i protestantismens ikonografi og dets forekomst i Norge. 8vo. ARENDAL, 1974. [Pamph.]
Moltmann (Jürgen) Perspektiven der Theologie. Gesammelte Aufsätze. 8vo. MÜNCHEN & MAINZ, 1968,
—— —— Hope and planning. [Trans. Margaret Clarkson.] 8vo. NEW YORK, *etc.*, 1971.
—— Theology of play. Trans. Reinhard Ulrich. 8vo. NEW YORK, *etc.*, 1972.
—— The crucified God: the cross of Christ as the foundation and criticism of Christian theology. [Trans. R. A. Wilson and J. S. Bowden.] 8vo. LOND., 1974.
—— Man: Christian anthropology in the conflicts of the present. Trans. John Sturdy. 8vo. LOND., 1974.
—— The Church in the power of the Spirit: a contribution to Messianic ecclesiology. [Trans. Margaret Kohl.] 8vo. LOND., 1977.
Money (Agnes L.) *comp.* History of the Girls' Friendly Society. rev. ed. 8vo. LOND., 1905.
[**Monkcom** (Donald)] Winchmore Hill Baptist Church magazine, Apr. 1957. Jubilee issue, containing the story of the church: "Glasshouse Yard", 1670-1905; Winchmore Hill, 1907- . 8vo. LOND., 1957. [Pamph.]
Monmouthshire Baptist Association. *See* Roberts (W.)
Montefiore (Claude J. G.) *See* Bentwich (N.); Montefiore (H. W.)
Montefiore (H. W.) Sir Moses Montefiore and his great nephew: a study in contrasts. [Montefiore Memorial Lect., 11, 1979.] 8vo. SOUTHAMPTON, 1979. [Pamph.]
Montefiore (Moses) *See* Montefiore (H. W.)
Montgomery (Henry) *See* McMillan (W.)
Month. *See* Suppt.
[**Moody** (A. W.) *comp.*] Horfield Baptist Church, Bristol: diamond jubilee celebrations, June 8th and 11th, 1952. 4to. [BRISTOL, 1952.] [Pamph.]
Moody (Michael E.) *ed.* *See* Carlson (L. H.) [Misc.]
Moon (N. S.) Caleb Evans, founder of the Bristol Education Society. 8vo. LOND., 1971. [Pamph.]
—— Education for ministry: Bristol Baptist College, 1679-1979. Foreword by David S. Russell. 8vo. BRISTOL, 1979.
[**Moon** (N. S.) *and others.*] The Bristol Education Society, 1770-1970. 8vo. BRISTOL, [1970?]. [Pamph.]
Moore (Clifford Herschel) Pagan ideas of immortality during the early Roman Empire. [Ingersoll Lect., 1918.] 8vo. CAMB. (Mass.), 1918.
Moore (Giles) 1617-79. Journal. Ed. Ruth Bird. 8vo. LEWES, 1971.
Moore (W. G.) La réforme allemande et la littérature française: recherches sur la notoriété de Luther en France. [Publs. de la Faculté des Lettres de l'Univ. de Strasbourg, 52.] 8vo. STRASBOURG, 1930.
Morales (José L.) El cántico espiritual de San Juan de la Cruz: su relación con el Cantar de los cantares y otras fuentes escriturísticas y literarias. Tesis. 8vo. MADRID, 1971.

Morard (Françoise-E.) Monachos, moine: histoire du terme grec jusqu'au 4 siècle: influences bibliques et gnostiques. Thèse. 8vo. FRIBOURG (Suisse), [1974].

Moravcsik (Gyula) Byzantium and the Magyars. [Trans. Mihály Szegedy-Maszák, rev. Miklós Szenczi and Zsigmond Ritoók.] 8vo. AMSTERDAM [& BUDAPEST], 1970.

Moravian Almanack. *See* Suppt.

More (Henry) 1614-87. *See* Hoyles (J.)

More (*Sir* Thomas) *Saint.* Complete works. 8vo. NEW HAVEN & LOND., 1963-
3.i. Translations of Lucian. Ed. Craig R. Thompson. 1974.
    8. The confutation of Tyndale's answer. Ed. Louis A. Schuster, *etc.* 3 vols. 1973.
—— The last letters of Blessed Thomas More. Introd. by Cardinal Gasquet and ed. with connecting narrative by W. E. Campbell. [Catholic Lib., 18.] 8vo. LOND., 1924.
—— *See* Marc'Hadour (G. P.); O'Sullivan (R.) *and others.*

Morey (Adrian) The Catholic subjects of Elizabeth I. 8vo. LOND., 1978.
—— David Knowles: a memoir. 8vo. LOND., 1979.

Morgan (George Campbell) The Gospel according to Luke. 8vo. NEW YORK, *etc.*, 1931.
—— The triumphs of faith. 8vo. LOND., [1944].
—— *See* Harries (J.); Murray (H.).

Morgan (George Ernest) Mighty days of revival: R. C. Morgan, his life and times. Introd. by Lord Kinnaird. 8vo. LOND., [1909].

Morgan (Irvonwy) Puritan spirituality. Illustrated from the life and times of the Rev. John Preston. 8vo. LOND., 1973.
—— A rent for love, and other poems. 8vo. LOND., 1973.

Morgan (Paul) *comp.* Oxford libraries outside the Bodleian: a guide. (1972). repr. 8vo. OXF., 1974.

Morgan (Richard Cope) *See* Morgan (G. E.)

Morgan (Robert Chowen) *See* Suppt. Studies in Bibl. Theol., 2nd Ser., 25.

Morgan-Wynne (J. E.) History of Botley Baptist Church, 1892-1963. 8vo. [BOTLEY, 1963.] [Pamph.]

Morison (James) *See* Smeaton (O.)

Morison (Stanley) Some fruits of theosophy: the origins and purpose of the so-called Old Catholic Church. Preface by Herbert Thurston, S. J. 8vo. LOND., 1919.

Morley. *Baptist Church.* Diamond jubilee, 1932. 8vo. MORLEY, [1932]. [Pamph.]

[**Morley** (E. K.) *ed.*] Camberley Congregational Church: jubilee souvenir outlook, Oct. 1969. 8vo. [FLEET, printed, 1969.] [Pamph.]

Morrill (J. S.) Cheshire, 1630-1660: county government and society during the English Revolution. [Oxford Historical Monographs.] 8vo. OXF., 1974.
—— The revolt of the provinces: conservatives and radicals in the English Civil War, 1630-1650. [Historical Problems: Studies and Documents, 26.] 8vo. LOND., 1976.

Morris (Caleb) *See* Evans (D. T.)

Morris (Irene) Three hundred years of Baptist life in Coventry (the story of Queen's Road Church). 8vo. LOND., [1925].

Morris (John) *c.* 1580-1658. *See* Birrell (T. A.)

Morris (Leon) The apostolic preaching of the Cross. (1955.) 2nd ed. 8vo. LOND., 1960.
—— Studies in the Fourth Gospel. 8vo. EXETER 1969.

Morrison (Christine Marie) Morrison of Wellington. 8vo. LOND., [1930].

Morrison (George Herbert) *See* Gammie (A.); Morrison (C. M.)

Mortier (Jeanne) and **Aboux** (M.-L.) *ed. See* Teilhard de Chardin (P.) [Misc.]

Mortimer (R. C.) *Bp. of Exeter. See* Skinner (B. G.)

Morton (Andrew Q.) *ed. See* Bible. N.T. Misc. John, Epistles of.

Morton (Arthur L.) The world of the Ranters: religious radicalism in the English revolution. 8vo. LOND., 1970.

Moses. *See* Suppt. Corpus Script. Christ. Orient., Aethiop., 73-74.

Moss (C. B.) *See* Barnard (L. W.)

Mott (J. R.) The present-day summons to the world mission of Christianity. 8vo. LOND., 1932.

Mott (J. R.)—*continued*
—— Five decades and a forward view. [Sprunt Lects., 1939.] (1939.) 2nd ed. 8vo. NEW YORK & LOND., 1939.
Mottram (R. H.) The window seat, or life observed. 8vo. LOND., 1954.
Mottram (William) *ed. See* Hughes (F. C.) and Mottram (W.) *ed.*
Moulam (G. E.) and **Freeman** (P.) The Melton Mowbray Congregational Church, 1821-1971. 8vo. [MELTON MOWBRAY, 1971.] [Pamph.]
Mould (Daphne D. C. P.) The monasteries of Ireland: an introduction. 8vo. LOND., 1976.
Moule (C. F. D.) The meaning of hope: a biblical exposition with concordance. 8vo. LOND., 1953.
—— The origin of Christology. 8vo. CAMB., 1977.
—— The Holy Spirit. [Mowbrays Lib. of Theol.] 8vo. LOND. & OXF., 1978.
—— [Misc.] Christ and Spirit in the New Testament. Ed. Barnabas Lindars and Stephen S. Smalley, in honour of Charles Francis Digby Moule. 8vo. CAMB., 1973.
Moule (H. C. G.) *Bp. of Durham.* The school of suffering: a brief memorial of Mary E. E. Moule. By her father. (1905.) 5th imp. 8vo. LOND., 1906.
Moule (Mary E. E.) *See* Moule (H. C. G.)
Moulton (J. H.) A grammar of New Testament Greek. 4 vols. 8vo. EDIN., 1906-76.
   4. Style. By Nigel Turner. 1976.
—— *See* Moulton (W. F.); Papers for War Time, 31.
[**Moulton** (William Fiddian) *the younger.*] James Hope Moulton. By his brother. Foreword by Bishop [H. E.] Ryle. 8vo. LOND., 1919.
Moxey (E. W.) The Independent Chapel in Liscard: foundation and early years. fol. *Duplicated.* WALLASEY, 1976. [Pamph.]
Mueller (D. L.) An introduction to the theology of Albrecht Ritschl. 8vo. PHILA-DELPHIA, 1969.
Müller (Friedrich Max) *See* Chaudhuri (N. C.)
Müller (George) *See* Bergin (G. F.) *comp.*
Müller (Richard) Adventisten—Sabbat—Reformaticn: geht das Ruhetagsverständnis der Adventisten bis zur Zeit der Reformation zurück? Eine theologiegeschichtliche Untersuchung. [Studia Theologica Lundensia, 38.] 8vo. LUND, 1979.
Müller-Schwefe (Hans-Rudolf) *ed.* Was ist Wahrheit? Ringvorlesung der Evangelisch-Theologischen Fakultät der Universität Hamburg. 8vo. GÖTTINGEN, 1965.
Müntzer (Thomas) *c.* 1489-1525. *See* Rupp (E. G.)
Muggleton (Lodowick) *See* Reay (B. G.)
Muirhead's Library of Philosophy. *See* Suppt. Library of Philosophy.
Mullett (Michael) *ed.* Early Lancaster Friends. [Univ. of Lancaster Centre for N.W. Regional Studies, Occ. Paper, 5.] 4to. LANCASTER, 1978. [Pamph.]
Mummery (J. S.) *See* Carpenter (W. H.) *ed.*
Mundle (C. W. K.) A critique of linguistic philosophy. 8vo. OXF., 1970.
Murdoch (Iris) The sovereignty of good. [Studies in Ethics and the Philos. of Relig.] 8vo. LOND., 1970.
Mure (G. R. C.) Idealist epilogue. 8vo. OXF., 1978.
Murphy (Francis-Xavier) *See* Dumeige (G.) *ed.*
Murphy (James) Church, state and schools in Britain, 1800-1970. [Students Lib. of Education.] 8vo. LOND., 1971.
Murphy (M. J.) Cambridge newspapers and opinion, 1780-1930. 8vo. CAMB., 1977.
Murray (Albert Victor) The school and the church: the theory and practice of Christian education under the Butler Act. 8vo. LOND., 1944.
Murray (Alexander) Reason and society in the Middle Ages. 8vo. OXF., 1978.
Murray (D. B.) The first hundred years: the Baptist Union of Scotland. 8vo. [GLASGOW, 1969.]
Murray (Harold) Sixty years an evangelist: an intimate study of Gipsy Smith. 8vo. LOND., [1937].
—— Campbell Morgan, Bible teacher: a sketch of the great expositor and evangelist. 8vo. LOND., [1938].
—— Dinsdale Young, the preacher: an intimate sketch (1938.) 2nd imp. 8vo. LOND., 1938.

Murray (I. H.) The Puritan hope: a study in revival and the interpretation of prophecy. 8vo. LOND., 1971.

Murray (John) The Epistle to the Romans: the English text [Amer. R.V. (1901)] with introd., exposition and notes. [New Internat. Comm. on the N.T.] (1960-65.) 2 vols. in 1. 8vo. LOND. & EDIN., 1967.

Murray (Robert H.) The hereafter and the undying hope. 8vo. CAMB., 1926.

Murray (Robert P. R.) Symbols of church and kingdom: a study in early Syriac tradition. 8vo. CAMB., 1975.

Murry (John Middleton) Still life. [A novel.] 8vo. LOND., 1916.
—— Poems: 1916-20. 8vo. LOND., 1921.
—— Countries of the mind. (1922.) [Collins' Kings' Way Classics, 27.] 8vo. LOND., etc., [1927].
—— Pencillings: little essays on literature. (1923.) [Collins' Kings' Way Classics, 34.] 8vo. LOND., etc., [1928].
—— The life of Jesus. (1926.) [Life and Letters Ser., 58.] 8vo. LOND. & TORONTO, 1934.
—— Things to come: essays. 8vo. LOND., 1928.
—— God: being an introduction to the science of metabiology. 8vo. LOND., 1929.
—— Studies in Keats new and old. (1930.) 2nd ed. 8vo. LOND., etc., 1939.
—— Son of woman: the story of D. H. Lawrence. 8vo. LOND. & TORONTO, 1931.
—— The necessity of Communism. 8vo. LOND. & TORONTO, 1932.
—— William Blake. 8vo. LOND., 1933.
—— Shakespeare. 8vo. LOND. 1936.
—— The necessity of pacifism. 8vo. LOND., 1937.
—— Heaven—and earth. 8vo. LOND., 1938.
—— The price of leadership. 8vo. LOND., 1939.
—— Europe in travail. [Christian News-letter Books, 2.] 8vo. LOND. & NEW YORK, 1940.
—— Christocracy. (1942.) repr. 8vo. LOND., 1943.
—— Adam and Eve: an essay towards a new and better society. 8vo. LOND., 1944.
—— Community farm. 8vo. LOND. & NEW YORK, 1952.
—— See Lea (F. A.)

Murry (Mary Middleton) To keep faith. 8vo. LOND., 1959.

Mussies (G.) See Suppt. Novum Testamentum. Suppts., 27.

Mutimer (G.) and **Goddard (H. E.)** Rendham Congregational Church: a brief history. fol. Duplicated. n.p., n.d. [s.sh.]

Myers (Jacob M.) See Bible. Commentaries. Anchor Bible, 12-14.

Myers (Sydney) R. W. Dale (1829-1895). [Heritage Biographies.] 8vo. LOND., 1961. [Pamph.]

Myles (John) See Edmunds (E.)

Nabyud. Abbot of Dabra Sihat. See Suppt. Corpus Script. Christ. Orient., Aethiop., 70-71.

Nagel (L. C.) Prince Rupert's Bluecoats: the story of a Civil War regiment. 8vo. LOND., 1973. [Pamph.]

Nag Hammadi Papyri. See Pistis Sophia.

Nagle (A. F.) The Hampshire Congregational Union: a review. 8vo. FAREHAM [printed], [1972]. [Pamph.]

Nairne (Alexander) Immortality: the Christian view. A lecture to churchmen at Norwich, 11 Feb. 1931. 8vo. CAMB., 1931. [Pamph.]

Napper (Charles) The art of political deception. 8vo. LOND., 1972.

Narsai. See Suppt. Patrologia Orientalis, XL.1.

Nash (G. B.) Quakers and politics: Pennsylvania, 1681-1726. 8vo. PRINCETON, 1968.

National Portrait Gallery. The portraits of members of the Kit Cat Club painted during the years 1700-1720 by Sir Godfrey Kneller for Jacob Tonson. [Introd. and 42 brief biographies by Mary Ransome.] 8vo. LOND., [c.1946]. [Pamph.]

Nauman (St. Elmo) See Dictionaries. Religion.

Nauta (D.) De Nederlandsche Gereformeerden en het Independentisme in de zeventiende eeuw. 8vo. AMSTERDAM, 1936.
—— [Misc.] Opstellen aangeboden aan Prof. Dr. D. Nauta bij zijn afscheid als hoogleraar aan de Vrije Universiteit te Amsterdam op 7 juni 1968. 8vo. LEIDEN, 1968.

Neale (*Sir* John Ernest) The Elizabethan age. [Creighton Lect. in Hist., 1950.] 8vo. LOND., 1951. [Pamph.]

Neame (Alan) The Holy Maid of Kent: the life of Elizabeth Barton, 1506-1534. 8vo. LOND., 1971.

Needham (G. R.) The FOY [Fellowship of Youth] Society: 50 years. fol. LOND., [1974]. [Pamph.]

Needham (*Sir* Joseph) Science and civilisation in China. With the research assistance of Wang Ling. 8vo. CAMB., 1954-
    4. Physics and physical technology.
      iii. Civil engineering and nautics. 1971.
    5. Chemistry and chemical technology.
      i. *Not yet published*, 1980.
      ii. Spagyrical discovery and invention: magisteries of gold and immortality. 1974.
      iii. —— historical survey, from cinnabar elixirs to synthetic insulin. 1967.

Neil (William) *See* Bible. Commentaries. New Century Bible.

Neill (Stephen C.) Towards church union, 1937-1952: a survey of approaches to closer union among the churches. [Faith and Order Commission Papers, 11.] 8vo. LOND., 1952. [Pamph.]

—— *ed.* The ministry of the church: a review by various authors of a book [ed. K. E. Kirk] entitled "The apostolic ministry". 8vo. LOND., 1947.

Nelson's Medieval Classics [*also* Texts]. *See* Suppt. Oxford Medieval Texts.

Neri (Philip) *Saint. See* Trevor (M.)

Nestle (Wilhelm) Griechische Weltanschauung in ihrer Bedeutung für die Gegenwart. Vorträge und Abhandlungen. 8vo. STUTTGART, 1946.

Neusner (Jacob) The idea of purity in ancient Judaism. [Haskell Lects., 1972-73.] With a critique and commentary by Mary Douglas. [Studies in Judaism in Late Antiquity, 1.] 8vo. LEIDEN, 1973.

Neville (Sylas) Diary, 1767-88. Ed. Basil Cozens-Hardy. 8vo. LOND., 1950.

New-Church Magazine. *See* Suppt.

New Haw. *Heathervale Road Baptist Church.* A brief account of the Heathervale Road Baptist Church, New Haw, Surrey, 1938-1957. 8vo. [NEW HAW, 1957]. [Pamph.]

New Studies in the Philosophy of Religion. *See* Suppt.

New Testament Abstracts. *See* Suppt.

New Testament Library. *See* Suppt.

New Testament Studies. *See* Suppt.

Newcastle-upon-Tyne. *Heaton United Reformed Church.* A history of the Heaton Presbyterian Congregation from 1877 to 1977, now part of the United Reformed Church. 4to. *Duplicated.* [NEWCASTLE-UPON-TYNE, 1977.] [Pamph.]

Newey (Vincent) *ed.* The Pilgrim's Progress: critical and historical views. [Liverpool English Texts and Studies.] 8vo. LIVERPOOL, 1980.

Newman (Aubrey) The United Synagogue, 1870-1970. 8vo. LOND., 1977.

—— *See* Suppt. Jewish Hist. Soc. Publs., 1971.

Newland (F. W.) Newland of Claremont and Canning Town. 8vo. LOND., 1932.

Newman (J. H.) *Cardinal.* [Selections.] A Newman synthesis. Arranged by Erich Przywara. 8vo. LOND., 1930.

—— Letters and diaries. Ed. at the Birmingham Oratory with notes and an introd. by Ian Ker and Thomas Gornall. Vols. 1-10. 8vo. OXF., 1978-
    1. Ealing, Trinity, Oriel, Feb. 1801 to Dec. 1826. 1978.
    2. Tutor of Oriel, Jan. 1827 to Dec. 1831. 1979.
    3. New bearings, Jan. 1832 to Jun. 1833. 1979.
    4. The Oxford Movement, Jul. 1833 to Dec. 1834. 1980.
    5-10. *Not yet published*, 1980.

—— —— Ed...Charles Stephen Dessain (and [23+] Thomas Gornall). Vols. 11-31. 8vo. LOND. & OXF., 1961-77.
    21. The Apologia, Jan. 1864 to Jun. 1865. 1971.
    22. Between Pusey and the extremists, Jul. 1865 to Dec. 1866. 1972.
    23. Defeat at Oxford, defence at Rome, Jan. to Dec. 1867. 1973.
    24. A grammar of assent, Jan. 1868 to Dec. 1869. 1973.
    25. The Vatican Council, Jan. 1870 to Dec. 1871. 1973.
    26. Aftermaths, Jan. 1872 to Dec. 1873. 1974.

Newman (J. H.) *Cardinal—continued*
    27. The controversy with Gladstone, Jan. 1874 to Dec. 1875. 1975.
    28. Fellow of Trinity, Jan. 1876 to Dec. 1878. 1975.
    29. The cardinalate, Jan. 1879 to Sep. 1881. 1976.
    30. A cardinal's apostolate, Oct. 1881 to Dec. 1884. 1976.
    31. The last years, Jan. 1885 to Aug. 1890. With a suppt. of addenda to vols. 11-30. 1977.
—— Theological papers on faith and certainty. Partly prepared for publ. by Hugo M. de Achaval. Selected and ed. by J. Derek Holmes, with introd. by C. S. Dessain. 8vo. OXF., 1976.
—— Theological papers on biblical inspiration and on infallibility. Selected, ed. and introd. by J. Derek Holmes. 8vo. OXF., 1979.
—— *See* Barry (W. F.); Coulson (J.) and Allchin (A. M.) *ed.*; Parkinson (H. J.) *ed.*
Newman (M. L.) The people of the covenant: a study of Israel from Moses to the monarchy. (1962.) Brit. ed. 8vo. LOND., 1965.
Newman (R. M.) A history of Shortwood Baptist Church, 1715-1965. 4to. LOND. & STROUD [printed], [1965]. [Pamph.]
Newsome (David) Two classes of men: Platonism and English Romantic thought. [Birkbeck Lects., 1972.] 8vo. LOND., 1974.
Newton (*Sir* Isaac) Correspondence. Ed. H. W. Turnbull [1-3]; J. F. Scott [4]; A. Rupert Hall and Laura Tilling [5-]. 4to. CAMB.: for the Royal Society, 1959-
    5. 1709-1713. 1975.
    6. 1713-1718. 1976.
    7. 1718-1727. 1977.
—— Opticks, or a treatise of the reflections, refractions, inflections and colours of light. (1704.) Based on the 4th ed., Lond., 1730. Foreword by Albert Einstein; introd. by Sir Edmund Whittaker. (1931.) [Repr. with] preface by I. Bernard Cohen and an analytical table of contents by Duane H. D. Roller. [Dover Ed.] 8vo. NEW YORK, 1952.
—— *See* Ault (D. D.); Hurlbutt (R. H.); Manuel (F. E.)
Newton (John A.) Search for a saint: Edward King. 8vo. LOND., 1977.
Newton (K. J.) *See* Suppt. Christian Brethren Research Fellowship, Occ. Papers, 6.
Nicastro (Onofrio) Lettere di Henry Stubbe a Thomas Hobbes (8 luglio 1656-6 maggio 1657). 8vo. *Duplicated.* SIENA, 1973.
—— Note sul Behemoth di Thomas Hobbes. fol. PISA, 1977. [Pamph.]
Nicephorus, *Patriarch of Constantinople. See* O'Connell (P.)
Nicetas, *Choniates. See* Dieten (J. L. van)
Nicetas, *of Paphlagonia. See* Suppt. Analecta Bollandiana. Subsid. Hagiog., 58.
Nichol (J. T.) Pentecostalism. (1966.) rev. ed. 8vo. PLAINFIELD (N.J.), 1971.
Nicholas, *of Cusa, Cardinal.* Opera omnia, iussu et auctoritate Academiae Litteratum Heidelbergensis ad codicum fidem edita. 4to. LEIPZIG, *etc.*, 1932-
    3. De coniecturis. Ed. Iosephus Koch et Carolus Bormann, Iohanne Gerhardo Senger comite. 1972.
Nicholas (Islwyn ap) Heretics at large: the story of a Unitarian Chapel [in Aberystwyth]. 8vo. LLANDYSUL, 1977. [Pamph.]
Nicholls (D. G.) Church and state in Britain since 1820. [Readings in Politics and Society.] 8vo. LOND., 1967.
Nicholson (E. W.) Preaching to the exiles: a study of the prose tradition in the Book of Jeremiah. 8vo. OXF., 1970.
Nicholson (H. M.) A history of the Baptist Church now meeting in George Street Chapel, Plymouth, from 1620. (1870.) Rev. ed., with an introd. by Samuel Vincent. 8vo. LOND. & PLYMOUTH, 1904.
Nicholson (J. F. V.) Vavasor Powell (1617-1670). [Heritage Biographies.] 8vo. LOND., 1961. [Pamph.]
Nickelsburg (G. W. E.) Resurrection, immortality, and eternal life in intertestamental Judaism. [Harvard Theological Studies, 36.] 8vo. CAMB. (Mass.) & LOND., 1972.
Nicodemus, *Saint, of the Holy Mountain. See* Philokalia; Scupoli (L.)
Nicol (D. M.) Byzantium and Greece. Inaugural lect. in the Koraës Chair of Modern Greek and Byzantine Hist., Lang. and Lit. at Univ. of London King's Coll., Oct. 26th 1971. 8vo. [LOND., 1971.] [Pamph.]
—— Byzantium: its ecclesiastical history and relations with the western world. Collected studies. [Variorum Reprs.] 8vo. LOND., 1972.

Nicol (D. M.)—*continued*
——— The last centuries of Byzantium, 1261-1453. 8vo. LOND., 1972.
——— Church and society in the last centuries of Byzantium. [Birkbeck Lect., 1977.]
8vo. CAMB., 1979.
——— The end of the Byzantine Empire. [Foundations of Medieval Hist.] 8vo.
LOND., 1979.
Nicol (W.)   *See* Suppt. Novum Testamentum. Suppts., 32.
Niebuhr (Reinhold)   *See* Macgregor (G. H. C.)
Niederwimmer (Kurt)   *See* Suppt. Forschungen zur Religion u. Lit., 113.
Nielsen (Kai)   Contemporary critiques of religion.   [Philos. of Relig. Scr.] 8vo.
LOND., 1971.
——— Scepticism.   [New Studies in the Philos. of Relig.] 8vo. LOND., *etc.*, 1973.
Nieto (J. C.)   Juan de Valdés and the origins of the Spanish and Italian Reformation.
[Travaux d'Humanisme et Renaissance, 108.]   4to. GENÈVE, 1970.
Nietzsche (Friedrich)   [Works. *German.*] [*Odd vols. of various editions.*]
Nietzsches Werke. Kleinoktavausgabe. Erste Abtheilung. 8vo. LEIPZIG.
   2-3.   Menschliches, Allzummenschliches: ein Buch für freie Geister. 2 vols. 1903.
   5.   Die fröhliche Wissenschaft ("la gaya scienza"). 1905.
——— ——— Nietzsches Werke. Taschen-Ausgabe. 8vo. LEIPZIG & STUTTGART.
   2.   Unzeitgemässe Betrachtungen.—Aus dem Nachlass 1873-75. (1906.) repr.
     1921.
   8.   Jenseits von Gut und Böse.—Zur Genealogie der Moral.—Aus dem Nachlass
     1885-86. 1906.
——— ——— Nietzsches Werke. Klassiker-Ausgabe. 8vo. STUTTGART.
   5.   Die fröhliche Wissenschaft ("la gaya scienza").—Dichtungen. 1921.
——— ——— Nietzsches Werke. Kröners Taschenausgabe. Mit Nachwörter von Alfred
Baeumler. 8vo. STUTTGART & LEIPZIG.
   70.   Die Geburt der Tragödie.—Der greichische Staat. [And other works.] (1930.)
     repr. 1945.
   71.   Unzeitgemässe Betrachtungen. [And other works.] (1930.) repr. 1938.
   72.   Menschliches, Allzumenschliches: ein Buch für freie Geister. 2 vols. in 1.
     1930.
   75.   Also sprach Zarathustra: ein Buch für Alle und Keinen. (1930.) repr. 1941.
   76.   Jenseits von Gut und Böse.—Zur Genealogie der Moral. (193-.) repr. 1959.
   77.   Götzendämmerung.—Der Antichrist.—Ecce homo.—Gedichte. [And other
     works.] (193-.) repr. 1964.
   78.   Der wille zur Macht: Versuch einer Umwertung aller Werte. 1930.
  170.   Nietzsche-Register: alphabetisch-systematische Ubericht über Friedrich
     Nietzsches Gedankenwelt. Von Richard Oehler. 1943.
Nigg (Walter)   Grosse Heilige. (1946.) 6te. Aufl. 8vo. ZÜRICH & STUTTGART, 1958.
Nightingale (Benjamin)   Providence Particular Baptist Chapel, Freetown, Bury:
souvenir of the centenary of the opening of the chapel in 1836, and the jubilee of the
opening of the new Sunday School in 1886. 8vo. LOND. [printed], 1936. [Pamph.]
Nijenhuis (W.)   Ecclesia Reformata: studies on the Reformation.   [Kerkhistorische
Bijdragen, 3.] 8vo. LEIDEN, 1972.
Nikodimos.   *See* Nicodemus.
Nilus, *Saint and ascetic.*   *See* Cameron (A. D. E.)
Nineham (D. E.)   New Testament interpretation in an historical age.   [Ethel M.
Wood Lect., 1975.] 8vo. LOND., 1976. [Pamph.]
Noon (F. E.) and **Valentine** (Peter)   Kingsthorpe Baptist Church, Northampton, ter
jubillee [*sic*], 1823-1973: a brief history.   8vo. [NORTHAMPTON, 1973.] [Pamph.]
Norden (Eduard)   Die antike Kunstprosa, vom 6. Jahrhundert v. Chr. bis in die Zeit
der Renaissance. (1898.) 5te. Aufl. 2 vols. 8vo. DARMSTADT, 1958.
——— Agnostos theos. Untersuchungen zur Formengeschichte: religiöse Rede. (1913.)
4te. Aufl. 8vo. DARMSTADT, 1956.
Norena (Carlos G.)   Juan Luis Vives.   [Internat. Archives of the Hist. of Ideas, 34.]
8vo. THE HAGUE, 1970.
Norman (E. R.)   Church and society in England, 1770-1970: a historical study.   8vo.
OXF., 1976.
——— Christianity and world order.   [B.B.C. Reith Lects., 1978.] 8vo. OXF., 1979.
Norman (Richard)   Reasons for actions: a critique of Utilitarian rationality.   [Lib. of
Philos. and Logic.] 8vo. OXF., 1971.

Norris (John)   *See* Hoyles (J.)

North (Frank Mason)   *See* Suppt. Hymn Soc. of America. Misc. Publs., 1970.

North (John A.)   *See* Harte (N. B.) and North (J. A.)

Northamptonshire Association of Congregational Ministers and Churches.
Report, 1922.   8vo.   NORTHAMPTON, 1923.   [Pamph.]

Northamptonshire Past and Present.   *See* Suppt.

Northcott (R. J.)   Dick Sheppard and St. Martin's. Introd. by Pat McCormick.
(1937.)   2nd imp.   8vo.   LOND., 1937.

Norton (John) 1606-63.   The answer to the whole set of questions of the celebrated Mr.
William Apollonius, Pastor of the Church of Middelberg. (1648.) Trans. from the
Latin by Douglas Horton.   8vo.   CAMB. (Mass.), 1958.

Norton (Thomas)   *See* Suppt. Early Eng. Text Soc., O.S., 272.

Norwich. *Octagon Chapel.* [Brief history.] (1930.) [rev. ed.] 8vo. [NORWICH,
1956.]   [Pamph.]

—— *St. Mary's Baptist Church.*   Opening of new church building and celebration of
the 283rd anniversary of the church.   8vo.   [NORWICH, 1952.]   [Pamph.]

Notestein (Wallace)   The Scot in history: a study of the interplay of character and
history. (1946.) repr.   8vo.   LOND., 1947.

—— Four worthies: John Chamberlain, Anne Clifford, John Taylor, Oliver Heywood.
8vo.   LOND., 1956.

Noth (Martin)   Gesammelte Studien zum Alten Testament. II. Mit einem Nachruf
von Rudolf Smend und der von Hermann Schult zusammengestellen Bibliographie.
Hrsg. Hans Walter Wolff. [Theologische Bucherei, 39.] 8vo. MÜNCHEN, 1969.

—— A history of Pentateuchal traditions. Trans. with an introd. by Bernhard W.
Anderson.   8vo.   ENGLEWOOD CLIFFS (N.J.), 1972.

Nott (L. P.)   Gideon, 1810 to 1910: the vicissitudes of a city chapel. (Being the centenary
history of Gideon Congregational Church, Bristol.)   8vo.   BRISTOL, 1909.

Nottingham. *High Pavement Chapel.*   Some notes on the memorials and other objects
of interest and beauty in the High Pavement Chapel, Nottingham.   8vo.   [NOTTING-
HAM, 1936?]

Nouro (Abrohom)   My tour in the parishes of the Syrian Church in Syria and Lebanon.
[In English, Syriac and Arabic.] fol.   BEIRUT, 1967.

Novak (Michael)   The experience of nothingness. [Bross Lects., 1969.] 8vo.
NEW YORK, *etc.*, 1970.

Novatian.   Opera, quae supersunt, nunc primum in unum collecta ad fidem codicum.
Ed. G. F. Diercks. [Corpus Christianorum, Ser. Latina, 4.] 8vo. TURNHOUT, 1972.

Novum Testamentum.   *See* Suppt.

Noxon (James)   Hume's philosophical development: a study of his methods.   8vo.
OXF., 1973.

Numen.   *See* Suppt.

Nurmi (M. K.)   William Blake. [Hutchinson Univ. Lib.]   8vo.   LOND., 1975.

Nuttall (G. F.)   Christian prayer: the theological background.   8vo.   [WALTON-ON-
THAMES, 1938.]   [Pamph.]

—— Early Quaker letters from the Swarthmore MSS. to 1660, calendared, indexed and
annotated. fol.   *Duplicated.*   LOND., 1952.

—— Better than life: the lovingkindness of God.   8vo.   LOND., 1962.

—— Assembly and Association in Dissent, 1689-1831.   8vo.   CAMB., 1971.   [Pamph.]

—— Puritans and Nonconformists round Puttenham and Wanborough, 1640-90.
4to. n.p., [1971].   [Pamph.]

—— Christianity and violence. [Frederick Denison Maurice Lect., 1970.] 8vo.
[ARRINGTON,] 1972.   [Pamph.]

—— Overcoming the world: the early Quaker programme.   8vo.   OXF., 1973.
[Pamph.]

—— John Horne of Lynn.   8vo.   [LOND., 1975.]   [Pamph.]

—— A Puritan prayer-journal [of Samuel Birch], 1651-1663.   8vo.   BIELFELD, 1975.
[Pamph.]

—— George Whitefield's 'curate' [Thomas Cole]: Gloucestershire Dissent and the
Revival.   8vo.   CAMB., 1976.   [Pamph.]

—— New College, London, and its library. Two lectures delivered on 19 May 1977 at
Dr. Williams's Library on the occasion of the transfer of the books, and on 16 June
1977 at St. Andrew's Church, Frognal, at the closure of the College. 8vo. [LOND.,]
1977.   [Pamph.]

Nuttall (G. F.)—*continued*
—— Continental Pietism and the Evangelical movement in Britain. 8vo. [LEIDEN, 1978.] [Pamph.]
—— Dr. Philip James and his family: Joshua Thomas at work. 8vo. [LLANDEILO, 1978.] [Pamph.]
—— The genius of R. T. Jenkins. [R. T. Jenkins Memorial Lect., 1976.] 8vo. DENBIGH, 1978. [Pamph.]
—— The moment of recognition: Luke as story-teller. [Erhel M. Wood Lect., 1978.] 8vo. LOND., 1978. [Pamph.]
—— Welsh students at Bristol Baptist College, 1720-1797. 8vo. DENBIGH, 1978. [Pamph.]
——English Dissenters in the Netherlands, 1640-1689. 8vo. ['S GRAVENHAGE, 1979.] [Pamph.]
—— [Misc.] Reformation, conformity, and Dissent. Essays in honour of Geoffrey Nuttall. Ed. R. Buick Knox. 8vo. LOND., 1977.
—— *See* Suppt. Historical MSS. Comm. Joint Publs., 26.

Obelkevich (James) Religion and rural society: South Lindsey, 1825-1875. 8vo. OXF., 1976.
Oberman (H. A.) *ed.* Luther: sol, ratio, erudio, Aristoteles. Probeartikel zum Sachregister der Weimarer Lutherausgabe. 8vo. BONN, 1971.
Obolensky (Dimitri) The Byzantine commonwealth: Eastern Europe, 500-1453. [Hist. of Civilization.] 8vo. LOND., 1971.
—— Byzantium and the Slavs. Collected studies. Preface by Ivan Dujčev. [Variorum Reprs.] 8vo. LOND., 1971.
O'Brien (P. T.) *See* Suppt. Novum Testamentum. Suppts., 49.
Ockham (William) *See* Leff (G.); Weinberg (J. R.)
O'Connell (Patrick) The ecclesiology of St. Nicephorus I (758-828), Patriarch of Constantinople: pentarchy and primacy. [Orientalia Christiana Analecta, 194.] 8vo. ROMA, 1972.
O'Connell (Robert J.) Art and the Christian intelligence in St. Augustine. 8vo. OXF., 1978.
O'Day (Rosemary) The English clergy: the emergence and consolidation of a profession, 1558-1642. 8vo. LEICESTER, 1979.
—— *ed.* *See* Heal (F.) and O'Day (R.) *ed.*
O'Day (Rosemary) and **Heal** (Felicity) *ed.* Continuity and change: personnel and administration in the Church in England, 1500-1642. 8vo. LEICESTER, 1976.
O'Donnell (J. J.) Cassiodorus. 8vo. BERKELEY (Calif.), *etc.*, 1979.
Oeconomos (Lysimaque) La vie religieuse dans l'empire byzantin au temps des Comnènes et des Anges. (1918.) repr. [Burt Franklin Research and Source Works, Byzantine Ser., 35.] 8vo. NEW YORK, 1972.
Oehl (Wilhelm) *ed.* *See* Deutsche Mystiker.
Oehler (Richard) Nietzsche-Register. *See* Nietzsche (F.)
Oetinger (Friedrich Christoph) 1702-82. Weinsberger Evangelienpredigten. (1758-61). [Neu hrsg. auf der Grundlage der Ausgabe von E. Ehmann (1856-58).] 8vo. METZINGEN, 1972.
Ogilvie (J. N.) The Presbyterian churches of Christendom. (1896.) new ed. 8vo. LOND. & EDIN., 1925.
Ogilvie (R. M.) The library of Lactantius. 8vo. OXF., 1978.
Oglethorpe (W. J.) Shrewsbury Street Methodist Church and School, Glossop: the story of one hundred years, 1856-1956. 8vo. GLOSSOP, [1955]. [Pamph.]
O'Higgins (James) Anthony Collins: the man and his works. [Internat. Archives of the Hist. of Ideas, 35.] 8vo. THE HAGUE, 1970.
—— *See* Collins (A.)
Oikonomidès (Nicolas) Documents et études sur les institutions de Byzance (VIIe-XVe s.). [Variorum Reprs.] 8vo. LOND., 1976.
Old Testament Library. *See* Suppt.
Oldenburg (Henry) Correspondence. Ed. and trans. A. Rupert Hall and Marie Boas Hall. 8vo. MADISON (Wis.), *etc.*, 1965-
    7. 1670-1671. 1970.
    8. 1671-1672. 1971.
    9. 1672-1673. 1973.

Oldenburg (Henry)—*continued*
  10. Jun. 1673-Apr. 1674. 1975.
  11. May 1674-Sep. 1675. 1977.
Oldham (J. H.) Florence Allshorn and the story of St. Julian's. 8vo. LOND., 1951.
—— *See* Papers for War Time, 5, 36.
Oliver (Robert W.) *See* Chambers (R. F.)
Olivi (Petrus Joannis) *c.* 1248-98. *See* Burr (D.)
Olney Hymns. *See* Suppt. Hymn Soc. of America. Papers, 20.
Olsen (V. N.) The New Testament logia on divorce: a study of their interpretation from Erasmus to Milton. [Beiträge zur Gesch. der Bibl. Exegese, 10.] 8vo. TÜBINGEN, 1971.
—— John Foxe and the Elizabethan church. 8vo. BERKELEY (Calif.), *etc.*, 1973.
Olson (Alison G.) and **Brown** (R. M.) *ed.* Anglo-American political relations, 1675-1775. 8vo. NEW BRUNSWICK (N.J.), 1970.
Oman (John Wood) A dialogue with God, and other sermons and addresses. 8vo. LOND., [1950.]
Oort (Elizabeth) *and others, ed.* Feestbundel, uitgegeven ter gelegenheid van het 75-jarig bestaan van het kerkhistorisch gezelschap S.S.S. Redactie: E. Oort, H. Beck, H. Wevers. 8vo. n.p., [1977].
Oppenheimer (Laetitia H.) Incarnation and immanence. [Lib. of Practical Theol.] 8vo. LOND., 1973.
Orange (A. Derek) Joseph Priestley: an illustrated life, 1733-1804. [Lifelines, 31.] 8vo. AYLESBURY, 1974. [Pamph.]
Orchard (J. B.) and **Longstaff** (T. R. W.) *ed.* J. J. Griesbach: synoptic and text-critical studies, 1776-1976. [Soc. for N.T. Studies, Monograph Ser., 34.] 8vo. CAMB., 1978.
Orchard (W. E.) Problems and perplexities. 8vo. LOND., 1912.
—— Advent sermons: discourses on the first and second coming of Christ. 8vo. LOND., 1914.
—— The Christian International. [King's Weigh House Pulpit, 1.] 8vo. [LOND.,] 1918. [Pamph.]
—— Six sermons. 16mo. LOND., [c. 1918].
—— The Church founded on the Apostles St. Peter and St. Paul. [King's Weigh House Pulpit, 11.] 8vo. [LOND.,] 1919. [Pamph.]
—— The Church. [Free Catholic Tracts, 1.] 8vo. BIRMINGHAM, 1920. [Pamph.]
—— The safest mind cure, and other sermons. 8vo. LOND., 1920.
—— Six sermons. 8vo. LOND., [c. 1920].
—— The finality of Christ, and other sermons. 8vo. LOND., 1921.
—— Foundations of faith. 4 vols. 8vo. NEW YORK & LOND., 1924-26.
  1. Theological. 1924
  2. Christological. 1926.
  3. Ecclesiological. 1926.
  4. *Not in Library.*
—— The Charter of Congregational Catholicism: a defence of our position. A sermon. 8vo. [LOND., 1931.] [Pamph.]
—— The way of simplicity: a guide for the perplexed. 8vo. LOND., 1934.
—— The cult of Our Lady: a defence, an explanation, and an appeal. 8vo. LOND., 1937.
—— *See* Papers for War Time, 10.
Ordericus Vitalis. [Historia Ecclesiastica *Latin and English.*] Ecclesiastical history. Ed. and trans. with introd. and notes by Marjorie Chibnall. [Oxford Medieval Texts.] 6 vols. 8vo. OXF., 1969-80.
  1. General introd. Books I and II. Index. 1980.
  3. Books V and VI. 1972.
  4. Books VII and VIII. 1973.
  5. Books IX and X. 1975.
  6. Books XI, XII and XIII. 1978.
Origen. [Commentaries. John. *Greek and French.*] Commentaire sur saint Jean. Texte grec, avant-propos, trad. et notes par Cécile Blanc. [Sources Chrétiennes.] 8vo. PARIS, 1966-
  1. Livres I-IV. 1966.
  2. Livres VI et X. 1970.
  3. Livre XIII. 1975.

Origen—*continued*
—— [Commentaries. Matthew. *Greek and French.*] Commentaire sur l'évangile selon Matthieu. Introd., [texte,] trad. et notes par Robert Girod. [Sources Chrétiennes.] 8vo. PARIS, 1970-
  1. Livres X et XI. 1970.
—— [Contra Celsum. *Greek and French.*] Contre Celse. Introd., texte critique, trad. et notes par Marcell Borret. [Sources Chrétiennes.] 8vo. PARIS, 1967-
  3. Livres V et VI. 1969.
—— [Dialogue with Heraclides. *Greek and French.*] Entretien avec Héraclide. Introd., texte, trad. et notes de Jean Scherer. [Sources Chrétiennes, 67.] 8vo. PARIS, 1960.
—— [Homilies. Joshua. *Latin and French.*] Homélies sur Josué. Texte latin, introd., trad. et notes de Annie Jaubert. [Sources Chrétiennes, 71.] 8vo. PARIS, 1960.
—— [Homilies. Song of Songs. *Latin and French.*] Homélies sur le Cantique des Cantiques. Introd., [texte,] trad. et notes de Dom Olivier Rousseau. [Sources Chrétiennes, 37.] (1954.) 2e éd. 8vo. PARIS, 1966.
—— [Philocalia. *Greek and French.*] Philocalie 21-27: sur le libre arbitre. Introd., texte, trad. et notes par Eric Junod. [Sources Chrétiennes, 226.] 8vo. PARIS, 1976.
Osborn (A. R.) Schleiermacher and religious education. 8vo. LOND., 1924.
Osborn (John) 1743-1814. *See* Gilles (A.)
Osborn (R. R.) Forbid them not: the importance and the history of general baptism. 8vo. LOND., 1972.
Osborne (S. C.) The Hinckley Baptist Church: the first two hundred years. 8vo. HINCKLEY, [1966].
Osten-Sacken (Peter von der) *See* Suppt. Forschungen zur Religion u. Lit., 112.
Ostrogorsky (George) Zur byzantinischen Geschichte: ausgewählte kleine Schriften. 8vo. DARMSTADT, 1973.
[O'Sullivan (Richard) *and others.*] Under God and the law. Papers read to the Thomas More Society of London. 2nd Ser. 8vo. OXF., 1949.
Otto (Rudolf) Das Heilige: über das Irrationale in der Idee des Göttlichen und sein Verhältnis zum Rationalen. (1917.) 26. bis 28. Aufl. 8vo. MÜNCHEN, 1947.
—— Das Gefühl des Uberweltlichen (sensus numinis). [5th and 6th ed. of Aufästze das Numinose betreffend (1923), Teil I.] 8vo. MÜNCHEN, 1932.
—— [Misc.] Rudolf Otto: zum Gedachtnis. Trauerfeier für den am 6. Marz 1937 heimgegangenen. . .und Gedächtnisrede an seinem Sarg gehalten von Heinrich Frick am 10. Marz 1937. 8vo. LEIPZIG, 1937. [Pamph.]
Outka (Gene) Agape: an ethical analysis. [Yale Publs. in Religion, 17.] 8vo. NEW HAVEN & LOND., 1972.
Owen (Dorothy M.) Church and society in medieval Lincolnshire. [Hist. of Lincs., ed. Joan Thirsk, vol. 5.] 8vo. LINCOLN, 1971.
Owen (Frank) Tempestuous journey: Lloyd George, his life and times. 8vo. LOND., 1954.
Owen (H. Gareth) The liberty of the Minories: a study in Elizabethan religious radicalism. 8vo. LOND., 1965. [Pamph.]
Owen (H. P.) Concepts of deity. [Philos. of Relig. Ser.] 8vo. LOND., 1971.
—— A principle of Christian doctrine. Inaugural lect. in the Chair of Christian Doctrine, Univ. of London King's Coll., Oct. 14th 1971. 8vo. [LOND., 1971.] [Pamph.]
—— W. R. Matthews: philosopher and theologian. 8vo. LOND., 1976.
Owen (*Sir* John) 1600-66, *Royalist major-general. See* Tucker (N.)
Owen (John) 1616-83, *Puritan divine.* Correspondence. With an account of his life and work. Ed. Peter Toon. Foreword by Geoffrey F. Nuttall. 8vo. CAMB. & LOND., 1970.
—— Oxford orations. Ed. Peter Toon. Trans. supervised by John Glucker. 8vo. LINKINHORNE (Cornw.), 1971.
—— The true nature of a Gospel Church and its government. (1689.) Abridged and ed. by John Huxtable. 8vo. LOND., 1947.
—— *See* Barraclough (P.); Lloyd (R. G.); Toon (P.)
Owen (W. T.) Wales and the Congregational Fund Board: 'a beauty-spot of ecclesiastical history'. 8vo. DENBIGH [printed], [1978]. [Pamph.]
Owens (Ben G.) *See* John (J. M.) *ed.*

Oxbury (H. F.) From St. Paul's to Unthank Road: being a history of the Baptist Church formed at St. Paul's, Norwich, in 1788, removed to St. Clement's in 1814, and since 1875 meeting at Unthank Road. 8vo. [NORWICH,] 1925. [Pamph.]

Oxenham (Erica) "J.O." [A biography of John Oxenham, *i.e.* William Arthur Dunkerley.] 8vo. LOND., 1924.

Oxenham (John) *pseud. See* Oxenham (E.)

Oxford. *John Bunyan Baptist Church, Cowley.* On sure foundations: the story of John Bunyan Baptist Church, Cowley, founded Apr. 1939. 8vo. [OXF., 1964.] [Pamph.]

Oxford. *New Road Baptist Church.* 300th anniversary, 1653-1953: tercentenary booklet and souvenir of celebrations, Oct. 1953. 8vo. [OXF., 1953.] [Pamph.]

Oxford. *Woodstock Road Baptist Church.* Jubilee, 1898-1948, 8vo. [LOND., 1948.] [Pamph.]

Oxford dictionary of quotations. *See* Dictionaries. Quotations.

Oxford dictionary of saints. *See* Dictionaries. Biography.

Oxford English dictionary. *See* Dictionaries. Languages. *English.*

Oxford Group. The Oxford Group and its work of moral re-armament. [Foreword by Sir Lynden Macassey.] 8vo. LOND., 1954.

Oxford Historical Monographs. *See* Suppt.

Oxford Historical Society. *See* Suppt.

Oxford Latin dictionary. *See* Dictionaries. Languages. *Latin.*

Oxford Medieval Texts. *See* Suppt.

Oxford Theological Monographs. *See* Suppt.

Oxfordshire Record Society. *See* Suppt.

[**Oxley** (J. E.)] Palmers Green Baptist Church: golden jubilee anniversary, 1905-1955. 8vo. [LOND., 1955] [Pamph.]

Ozment (S. E.) Mysticism and Dissent: religious ideology and social protest in the sixteenth century. 8vo. NEW HAVEN & LOND., 1973.

Pace (Richard) *See* Wegg (J.)

Pachter (H. M.) Paracelsus: magic into science. [Life of Science Lib.] 8vo. NEW YORK, 1951.

Packard (Faith) Henry Sampson, 1629-1700: Nonconformist minister and physician. 8vo. IPSWICH, 1977. [Pamph.]

Packard (John) and **Packard** (Faith) Thomas Mills: Suffolk Baptist and benefactor. 8vo. IPSWICH, [1980.] [Pamph.]

Packer (J. I.) The Evangelical Anglican identity problem: an analysis. [Latimer Studies, 1.] 8vo. OXF., 1978. [Pamph.]

—— *ed.* All in each place: towards reunion in England. Ten Anglican essays with some Free Church comments. 8vo. APPLEFORD, 1965.

Page (G. E.) Some Baptist churches in the Bedford area. 8vo. LOND., 1953. [Pamph.]

Paget (Elma Katie) Henry Luke Paget: portrait and frame. 8vo. LOND., *etc.*, 1939.

—— *See* Papers for War Time, 3.

Paget (Henry Luke) *See* Paget (E. K.)

Pakenham (Elizabeth) *Countess of Longford. See* Longford (Elizabeth Pakenham, *Countess of*)

Pakington, *family of. See* Pakington (H. A.) and Pakington (R. H. R.)

Pakington (Humphrey A.) *5th Baron Hampton* and **Pakington** (Richard H. R.) *6th Baron Hampton.* The Pakingtons of Westwood. fol. [UPTON-ON-SEVERN,] 1975.

Palaeologus (Jacobus) *of Khios.* Catechesis Christiana dierum duodecim. Primum edidit Ružen Dostálová. [Instytut Filozofii i Socjologii Polskiej Akademii Nauk, Biblioteka Pisarzy Reformacyjnych, 8.] 8vo. WARSAW, 1971.

Palamas (Gregory) *Saint., Abp. of Thessalonica. See* Papademetriou (G. C.)

Palestine Exploration Quarterly. *See* Suppt.

Palfrey (H. E.) Foleys of Stourbridge. 8vo. WORCESTER, 1945. [Pamph.]

Pálfy (Miklós) *ed. See* Pap (L.) and Pálfy (M.) *ed.*

Palladius, *Bp. of Helenopolis. See* Suppt. Corpus Script. Christ. Orient., Syri, 169-170, 173-174.

Palliser (D. M.) The Reformation in York, 1534-1553. [Borthwick Papers, 40.] 8vo. YORK, 1971. [Pamph.]

Palmer (Edwin James) *Bp. of Bombay.* South India: the meaning of the scheme. 8vo. WINCHESTER, 1944. [Pamph.]

Palmer (Helen M.) *ed. See* Dictionaries. Biography.
Palmer (Humphrey) Analogy: a study of qualification and argument in theology. [New Studies in the Philos. of Relig.] 8vo. LOND., 1973.
[**Palmer** (P. R.)] Silver jubilee, 1935-1960: Holland-on-Sea Baptist Church. 8vo. [HOLLAND-ON-SEA, 1960.] [Pamph.]
Palmer (W. M.) *See* Catalogues. *Bodleian Lib.*
Panagopoulos (Johannes) *ed. See* Suppt. Novum Testamentum. Suppts., 45.
Pancaro (Severino) *See* Suppt. Novum Testamentum. Suppts., 42.
Pannenberg (Wolfhart) Was ist der Mensch? Die Anthropologie der Gegenwart im Lichte der Theologie. (1962.) 2te. Aufl. 8vo. GÖTTINGEN, 1964.
Pantzer (Katharine F.) *See* Suppt. Bibliographical Soc. Publs., 1973-75.
[**Pap** (László) and **Pálfy** (Miklós) *ed.*] Hungarian Protestantism: its past and present. fol. BUDAPEST, 1956. [Pamph.]
Papademetriou (George C.) Introduction to Saint Gregory Palamas. 8vo. NEW YORK, 1973.
Papadopoulos-Kerameus (A. I.) *ed.* Varia Graeca sacra. Sbornik greceskich neizdannych bogoslovskich tekstov IV-XV vekov. (1909.) Editionem phototypicam praefatione instruxit Jürgen Dummer. [Subsidia Byzantina, 6.] 8vo. LEIPZIG, 1975.
Papers for War Time. [Ed. William Temple.] 8vo. LOND., 1914-15. [36 pamphs. bound in 1 vol.]
  1. Christianity and war: William Temple.
  2. Are we worth fighting for? Richard Roberts.
  3. The woman's part: Elma K. Paget.
  4. Brothers all: the war and the race question: Edwyn Bevan.
  5. The decisive hour: is it lost? J. H. Oldham.
  6. Active service: the share of the combatant: W. R. Maltby.
  7. The war spirit in our national life: A. Herbert Gray.
  8. Christian conduct in war time: W. H. Moberly.
  9. The witness of the Church in the present crisis: X.
  10. The real war: W. E. Orchard.
  11. Love came down at Christmas: George Hare Leonard.
  12. An answer to Bernhardi: D. S. Cairns.
  13. Patriotism: Percy Dearmer.
  14. Spending in war time: E. J. Urwick.
  15. Christianity and force: A. G. Hogg.
  16. Germany and Germans: Eleanor McDougall.
  17. Pharisaism and war: Frank Lenwood.
  18. The cure for war: A Clutton-Brock.
  19. Our need of a Catholic Church: William Temple.
  20. War, this war, and the Sermon on the Mount: B. H. Streeter.
  21. The removing of mountains. By the author of 'Pro Christo et Ecclesia' [*i.e.* Lily Dougall].
  22. International control: W. G. S. Adams.
  23. The price of blood: Kenneth MacLennan.
  24. Biology and war: J. Arthur Thomson.
  25. The visions of youth: [E. S. Talbot].
  26. Bernhardism in England: A Clutton-Brock.
  27. The only alternative to war: A. Herbert Gray.
  28. Chariots of fire: Frank Lenwood.
  29. The ethics of international trade: Henri Lambert.
  30. India and the war: John Matthai.
  31. British and German scholarship: James Hope Moulton.
  32. Are we to punish Germany, if we can? A. Clutton-Brock.
  33. Peace with empire: the problem: Edwyn Bevan.
  34. The reasonable direction of force: a plea for investigation before war: Louise E. Matthaei.
  35. What is at stake in the war: R. W. Seton-Watson.
  36. The Church the hope of the future: J. H. Oldham.
Paracelsus (Philip Aurel Theophrastus) Sozialethische und sozialpolitische Schriften. Aus dem theologisch-religionsphilosophischen Werk ausgewählt, eingeleitet und mit erklärenden Anmerkungen. Hrsg. Kurt Goldammer. [Civitas Gentium: Schriften

Paracelsus (Philip Aurel Theophrastus)—*continued*
zur Soziol. u. Kulturphilos.] 8vo. TÜBINGEN, 1952.
—— *See* Pachter (H. M.)
Pare (P. N.) and **Harris** (D. B.) Eric Milner-White, 1884-1963: a memoir. Epilogue
by the Archbishop of Canterbury [A. M. Ramsey]. 8vo. LOND., 1965.
Pareus (David) *See* Brinkmann (G.)
[**Parker** (Carol)] It started in a garage: Trinity Baptist Church Sunday School,
Gloucester, 1928-1978. 8vo. [GLOUCESTER, 1978.] [Pamph.]
Parker (Joseph) *See* Bywater (M.); Dawson (A.)
Parker (Theodore) *See* Cloyd (R.)
Parker (Thomas H. L.) Portrait of Calvin. 8vo. LOND., 1954.
—— Calvin's New Testament commentaries. 8vo. LOND., 1971.
—— John Calvin: a biography. 8vo. LOND., 1975.
Parker-Rhodes (Damaris) Truth: a path and not a possession: a Quaker woman's
journey. [Swarthmore Lect., 1977.] 8vo. LOND., 1977.
[**Parkhurst** (K. W.)] Souvenir of the centenary of Camden Road Baptist Church,
1854-1954. 8vo. [LOND., 1954.] [Pamph.]
Parkinson (H. J.) *ed.* Centenary addresses on Newman's Idea of a university, to the
Newman Association's London Circle and the Union of Catholic Students in 1952.
8vo. LOND., 1953.
Parmiter (Geoffrey de C.) *See* Suppt. London University. Inst. of Hist. Research.
Bulletin. Special Suppts., 11.
Parrinder (Geoffrey) Religion in Africa. 8vo. HARMONDSWORTH, 1969.
—— Mysticism in the world's religions. 8vo. LOND., 1976.
Parry, *family of.* *See* Horton-Smith (L. G. H.)
Parry (Emyr Wyn) Howell Elfed Lewis. 8vo. LOND., 1958.
Parry (L. L.) *See* Brown (Cecil L.) and Parry (L. L.)
Parry (Thomas) Hanes llenyddiaeth Gymraeg hyd 1900. (1945.) 3rd ed. (1953.)
repr. 8vo. CAERDYDD, 1964.
—— John Morris-Jones, 1864-1929. [In Welsh and English.] 8vo. CARDIFF, 1958.
Parsons (K. A. C.) *ed.* St. Andrew's Street Baptist Church, Cambridge: three
historical lectures [by G. F. Nuttall, B. R. White, G. W. Byrt] given on the occasion
of the 250th anniv., Apr. 1971. 8vo. CAMB., 1971. [Pamph.]
Partee (Charles) Calvin and classical philosophy. [Studies in the Hist. of Christian
Thought, 14.] 8vo. LEIDEN, 1977.
Partridge (E. H.) Freedom in education: the function of the public boarding school.
8vo. LOND., 1943.
Passmore (J. A.) The perfectibility of man. 8vo. LOND., 1970.
Patlagean (Evelyne) Pauvreté économique et pauvreté sociale à Byzance, 4e-7e
siècles. [Civilisations et Sociétés, 48.] 8vo. PARIS & LA HAYE, 1977.
Paton (John Brown) *See* Marchant (J.)
Patrick (John Max) and **Roper** (Alan) The editor as critic and the critic as editor.
Introd. by Murray Kreiger. [Clark Lib. Seminar Papers.] 8vo. LOS ANGELES,
1973. [Pamph.]
Patrides (C. A.) *See* Hunter (W. B.) *and others.*
Patrologia Orientalis. *See* Suppt.
Patton (J. G.) A country Independent chapel (Swanland, E. Yorks., Congregational
Church). 8vo. LOND., 1943.
Patton (K. L.) Songs of simple thanksgiving. The Unitarian Universalist Association
meditation manual for 1978. 8vo. BOSTON (Mass.), 1977. [Pamph.]
Pauck (Wilhelm) and **Pauck** (Marion) Paul Tillich: his life and thought. 8vo.
LOND., 1977-
    1. Life. 1977.
    2. *Not yet published*, 1980.
Paul, *Saint and Apostle.* *See* Bornkamm (G.); Glover (T. R.); Goppelt (L.); Hanson
(A. T.); Howard (G.); Hunt (E. W.); Käsemann (E.); Rengstorf (K. H.) *ed.;* Sanders
(E. P.); Schütz (J. H.); Stendahl (K.); Stewart (J. S.); Wiles (G. P.); Ziesler (J. A.);
Suppt. Forschungen zur Religion u. Lit., 103, 123; Novum Testamentum. Suppts.,
26, 35, 40, 49.
Paul (J. E.) Mary, Queen of Scots: the last days. [Royal Stuart Papers, 1.] 8vo.
ILFORD, [1972]. [Pamph.]

Paul (Leslie A.) Alternatives to Christian belief: a critical survey of the contemporary search for meaning. (1967.) repr. 8vo. LOND., 1970.
Paul (R. S.) Oliver Cromwell (1599-1658). [Heritage Biographies.] 8vo. LOND., 1961. [Pamph.]
—— The accidence and essence of Puritan piety. 8vo. AUSTIN (Tex.), 1978. [Pamph.]
—— See Goodwin (T.) *and others*
Paul (S. F.) Memorial of John Hervey Gosden, comprising a selection of his letters and sermons, together with some account of his life and labours. 8vo. BEXHILL, 1965.
—— Further history of the Gospel Standard Baptists. 6 vols. 8vo. [BRIGHTON, etc.,] 1951-69.
　　6. Some Wiltshire and other western churches. 1969.
Paulsen (Friedrich) Geschichte des gelehrten Unterrichts, auf den deutschen Schulen und Universitäten vom Ausgang des Mittelalters bis zur Gegenwart. Mit besonderer Rücksicht auf den klassischen Unterricht. (1885.) 3te. Aufl., hrsg. Rudolf Lehmann. Erster Bd. 8vo. LEIPZIG, 1919. [Photocopy in 3 vols.]
Paulson (Ronald) See Carlson (L. H.) and Paulson (R.)
Pauly (August Friedrich von) See Dictionaries. Classical.
Payne (E. A.) The Church awakes: the story of the modern missionary movement. 8vo. LOND., 1942.
—— The Association at the 141st milestone. Presidential address to the Oxfordshire and East Gloucestershire Baptist Association, May 19th 1943. 8vo. [OXF.,] 1943. [Pamph.]
—— South-East from Serampore: more chapters in the story of the Baptist Missionary Society. 8vo. LOND., 1945.
—— The growth of the world Church: the story of the modern missionary movement. 8vo. LOND., 1955.
—— Thirty years of the British Council of Churches, 1942-1972. 8vo. LOND., [1972]. [Pamph.]
—— The City Temple and the Free Churches: retrospect and prospect. Centenary lecture, City Temple, 19th June 1974. 8vo. [LOND., 1974.] [Pamph.]
　　Out of great tribulation: Baptists in the U.S.S.R. 8vo. LOND., [1974]. [Pamph.]
[——] A 20th century minister: John Oliver Barrett (1901-78). 8vo. ONGAR [printed], [1979]. [Pamph.]
—— A venerable Dissenting institution: Dr. Williams's Library, 1729-1979. [Friends of Dr. Williams's Lib. Lect., 33.] 8vo. LOND., 1979. [Pamph.]
Payne (George Andrew) Mrs. Gaskell and Knutsford. 8vo. MANCHESTER & LOND., [1900].
—— "Edna Lyall": an appreciation. 8vo. MANCHESTER, [1903].
Payne (James) "Ebenezer" past and present: an historical sketch of the Baptist Church at "Ebenezer", Richmond Street, Brighton, from its commencement to the opening of the new chapel, 1824-1962. 8vo. *Duplicated.* n.p., [1964]. [Pamph.]
Payne (John Orlebar) Old English Catholic missions. (1889.) facsim. repr. 8vo. FARNBOROUGH, 1970.
—— *ed.* Records of the English Catholics of 1715, compiled wholly from original documents. (1889.) facsim. repr. 8vo. FARNBOROUGH, 1970.
—— *ed. See* Estcourt (E. E.) and Payne (J. O.) *ed.*
Payne (William L.) Defoe in the pamphlets. 8vo. [IOWA CITY,] 1973. [Pamph.]
Peacocke (A. R.) Science and the Christian experiment. 8vo. OXF., 1971.
—— Creation and the world of science. [Bampton Lects., 1978.] 8vo. OXF., 1979.
Peake (A. S.) *See* Peake (L. S.); Wilkinson (J. T.)
Peake (Lesile S.) Arthur Samuel Peake: a memoir. 8vo. LOND., 1930.
Pearce (G. J. M.) Charles Haddon Spurgeon (1834-1892). [Heritage Biographies.] 8vo. LOND., 1961. [Pamph.]
Pearce-Higgins (J. D.) and **Whitby** (G. S.) *ed.* Life, death, and psychical research: studies on behalf of the Churches' Fellowship for Psychical and Spiritual Studies. 8vo. LOND., 1973.
Pearson (A. F. S.) Der älteste englische Presbyterianismus. 8vo. EDIN., 1912.
Pearson (Samuel C.) The Campbell Institute: herald of the transformation of an American religious tradition. 8vo. ST. LOUIS (Mo.), 1978. [Pamph.]

Pearson (W. W.) Shantiniketan: the Bolpur School of Rabindranath Tagore. 8vo. LOND., 1917.

Peart (R. C.) *comp.* Ebenezer Baptist Church, Scarborough: bicentenary, 1771 to 1971. 8vo. SCARBOROUGH, [1971]. [Pamph.]

Peart-Binns (J. S.) Blunt. [Life of A. W. F. Blunt, Bishop of Bradford.] 8vo. QUEENSBURY (Yorks.), [1969].

Peel (Albert) Robert Crowley: Puritan, printer, poet. [Presbyterian Hist. Soc. of England Lect. 14, 1937.] 8vo. MANCHESTER, [1937]. [Pamph.]

—— A brief history of English Congregationalism. (1931.) repr. 8vo. LOND., 1945. [Pamph.]

Peel (Albert) and **Horton** (Douglas) International Congregationalism. 8vo. LOND., 1949.

Peers (E. Allison) Saint Teresa, foundress. [Publs. of the Institute of Hispanic Studies, Lects. and Addresses, 5.] 4to. LIVERPOOL, 1946. [Pamph.]

Pellow (J. D. C.) *See* Suppt. Methodist Sacramental Fellowship. M.S.F. Booklets. N.S., 4.

Pelzer (Auguste) *See* Dictionaries. Abbreviations.

Penelhum (Terence) Problems of religious knowledge. [Philos. of Relig. Ser.] 8vo. LOND., 1971.

Penn (Gulielma, *Mrs. William*) *See* Hodgkin (L. V.)

Penn (William) *See* Comfort (W. W.); Endy (M. B.)

Pennington (Donald H.) and **Thomas** (K.) *ed. See* Hill (C.) [Misc.]

Penry (John) 1559-93. Three treatises concerning Wales. Introd. by David Williams. 8vo. CARDIFF, 1960.

—— *See* Williams (S.)

Pentecostal. *See* Suppt.

Pepys (Samuel) Diary. A new and complete transcription, ed. Robert Latham and William Matthews. 8vo. LOND., 1970-
    4. 1663. 1971.
    5. 1664. 1971.
    6. 1665. 1972.
    7. 1666. 1972.
    8. 1667. 1974.
    9. 1668-69. 1976.

Percival (Janet) *See* Catalogues. *London. University Coll.*

Percy (Thomas) *Bp. of Dromore. See* Gaussen (A. C. C.)

Perham (Michael) *See* Suppt. Alcuin Club. Manuals, 1.

Perkins (Ephraim Henry) A brief account of the Congregational Church, Milborne Port, Somerset. 8vo. n.p. [priv. printed], 1907.

Perkins (Ernest Benson) So appointed: an autobiography. Foreword by Harold Roberts. 8vo. LOND., 1964.

Perkins (William) 1558-1602. Works. Introd. and ed. by Ian Breward. [Courtenay Lib. of Reformation Classics, 3.] 8vo. APPLEFORD, 1970.

Perman (David) Change and the churches: an anatomy of religion in Britain. 8vo LOND., 1977.

Perrin (J. M.) and **Thibon** (Gustave) Simone Weil as we knew her. [Trans. Emma Craufurd.] 8vo. LOND., 1953.

Perrin (Norman) Jesus and the language of the kingdom: symbol and metaphor in New Testament interpretation. [New Test. Lib.] 8vo. LOND., 1976.

—— The resurrection narratives: a new approach. 8vo. LOND., 1977.

Perrot (John) *See* Suppt. Friends' Hist. Soc. Journal Suppt., 33.

Perry (B. E.) *See* Babrius and Phaedrus.

Perry (Herbert E.) A century of liberal religion and philanthropy in Manchester, being a history of the Manchester Domestic Mission Society, 1833-1933. 8vo. MANCHESTER, 1933. [Pamph.]

Pert (K. G.) and **Cotgrove** (Barbara) Reflections on an old meeting house: an appreciation of the achievement of the Ipswich Dissenters of 1699. 4to. IPSWICH, 1976. [Pamph.]

Peskett (Hugh) Guide to the parish and non-parochial registers of Devon and Cornwall, 1538-1837. [Devon and Cornwall Record Soc., Extra Ser., 2.] 8vo. TORQUAY [printed], 1979.

Peter, *of Abano,* 1250-1317, *astrologer and physician. See* Agrippa (H. C.)

Peterborough. *Oundle Road Baptist Church.* Centenary, 1958. 8vo. [PETER-
BOROUGH, 1958.] [Pamph.]
Peterken (H. T.) *ed.* The Eastbourne Baptist: monthly magazine of the Victoria
Drive Baptist Church, Eastbourne. Aug. 1961. [With hist. notes on the church.]
4to. EASTBOURNE, 1961. [Pamph.]
Peterkiewicz (Jerzy) The third Adam. [Jan Maria Michal Kowalski.] 8vo.
LOND., 1975.
Peters (R. S.) Reason, morality and religion. [Swarthmore Lect., 1972.] 8vo.
LOND., 1972.
—— *ed.* John Dewey reconsidered. [Internat. Lib. of the Philos. of Education.]
8vo. LOND., 1977.
—— *ed. See* Suppt. Royal Inst. of Philos. Lects., 8.
Pétrement (Simone) Simone Weil: a life. Trans. from the French by Raymond
Rosenthal. 8vo. LOND., 1977.
Pettman (Kathleen) and **Kingsford** (H. E.) Sutton Baptist Church, 1869-1969.
8vo. [SUTTON, 1969.] [Pamph.]
Petty (C. P.) A history of Trinity Church (Huntingdon) in the nineteenth century.
4to. [HUNTINGDON, 195-.] [Pamph.]
Phaedrus. *See* Babrius and Phaedrus.
Pheasant (J. L. N.) Death; its cause and its conquest: a suggestion. A paper read
before the Caistor Rural Deanery Clerical Society, Mar. 7th, 1922. 8vo. OXF.,
1923. [Pamph.]
Phelan (Margaret H.) The story of New Meeting House, home of Richard Baxter's
pulpit and of his spirit. 8vo. KIDDERMINSTER, [1974]. [Pamph.]
Philip, *Landgraf of Hesse. See* Littell (F. H.); Varrentrapp (C.)
Phillimore (W. P. W.) and **Ruston-Harrison** (C. W.) *ed.* Cumberland parish
registers. Marriages. Vol. 2. 8vo. LOND., 1912. [*No more in Library.*]
Phillips (C. S.) Canterbury Cathedral in the Middle Ages. 8vo. LOND., 1949.
[Pamph.]
Phillips (D. Z.) Death and immortality. [New Studies in the Philos. of Relig.]
8vo. LOND., 1970.
Phillips (F. B.) Is war Christian? 8vo. LOND., 1936.
Phillips (George) 1593-1644. *See* Foote (H. W.)
Phillips (J. B.) *See* Bible. N.T. *English.*
Phillips (P. T.) *ed.* The view from the pulpit: Victorian ministers and society. 8vo.
TORONTO, 1978.
Philo, *of Alexandria. See* Sandmel (S.); Schwarz (W.)
Philokalia. The complete text compiled by St. Nikodimos of the Holy Mountain
and St. Makarios of Corinth. Trans. from the Greek and ed. by G. E. H. Palmer,
Philip Sherrard, Kallistos Ware, *etc.* 8vo. LOND. & BOSTON, 1979-
1. 1979.
No more yet published, 1980.
Philosophical Books. *See* Suppt.
Philosophical Quarterly. *See* Suppt.
Philosophy. *See* Suppt.
Philosophy of Religion. *See* Suppt.
Philoxenus, *Bp. of Hierapolis (Mabug). See* Chesnut (R. C.); Suppt. Corpus Script.
Christ. Orient., Syri, 165-166, 171-172; Patrologia Orientalis, XXXVIII.3,
XXXIX.4.
Philpot (J. C.) *See* Howard (K. W. H.) *comp.*
Photius, *Patriarch of Constantinople. See* Dvornik (F.); Hergenröther (J. A. G.) *ed.*
Picciotto (James) Sketches of Anglo-Jewish history. (1875.) Rev. and ed. with a
prologue, notes, and an epilogue, by Israel Finestein. 8vo. LOND., 1956.
Pickard (Irene) Memories of J. Rendel Harris. 8vo. [SELLY OAK, 1979.]
Piercy (Josephine K.) Studies in literary types in seventeenth-century America
(1607-1710). [Yale Studies in English, 91.] (1939.) 2nd ed. (1969.) repr. 8vo.
[HAMDEN (Conn.),] 1969.
Pierhal (Jean) Albert Schweitzer: the life of a great man. (1956.) 3rd imp. 8vo.
LOND., 1960.
Pietzner (Carlo) *comp. See* Allen (P. M.) and Pietzner (C.) *comp.*
Piggott (W. Charter) The Christ imperative: studies in the commands of Jesus.
8vo. LOND., 1912.

Piggott (W. Charter)—*continued*
—— The imperishable word. 8vo. LOND., 1912.
—— [Misc.] William Charter Piggott, 1872-1943. [Memorial volume.] 8vo. LOND., 1944.
Pineau (J.-B.) Érasme: sa pensée religieuse. 8vo. PARIS, 1924.
Piper (John) 'Love your enemies': Jesus' love command in the Synoptic Gospels and in the early Christian paraenesis: a history of the tradition and interpretation of its uses. [Soc. for N.T. Studies, Monograph Ser., 38.] 8vo. CAMB., 1979.
Pirot (Louis) *See* Dictionaries. Biblical.
Pistis Sophia. [*Coptic and English.*] Text ed. Carl Schmidt. Trans. and notes by Violet MacDermot. Volume ed. R. McL. Wilson. [Nag Hammadi Studies, 9.] [Coptic Gnostic Lib.] 8vo. LEIDEN, 1978.
Pittenger (W. Norman) The Christian Church as social process. 8vo. LOND., 1971.
Plan of church union in North India and Pakistan. Prepared by the Negotiating Committee representative of the Church of India, Burma and Ceylon, churches associated with the Baptist Missionary Society, the Methodist Church, and the United Church of Northern India. 8vo. MADRAS, 1951. [Pamph.]
Plantin (Christopher) *See* Gulik (E. van) and Vervliet (H. D. L.)
Plantinga (Alvin) God and other minds: a study of the rational justification of belief in God. [Contemp. Philos.] (1967.) 3rd imp. 8vo. ITHACA (N.Y.) & LOND., 1972.
—— The nature of necessity. [Clarendon Lib. of Logic and Philos.] 8vo. OXF., 1974.
—— God, freedom and evil. [Essays in Philos.] 8vo. LOND., 1975.
—— *ed.* The ontological argument from St. Anselm to contemporary philosophers. Introd. by Richard Taylor. (1965.) repr. 8vo. LOND. & MELBOURNE, 1968.
Plath (Uwe) Calvin and Basel in den Jahren 1552-1556. [Basler Beiträge zur Geschichtswiss., 133.] 8vo. BASEL & STUTTGART, 1974.
—— Der Streit um C. S. Curiones "De amplitudine beati regni Dei" im Jahre 1554 in Basel. 8vo. FIRENZE & CHICAGO, 1974. [Pamph.]
—— Sebastiani Castellionis annotationes ad Johannis Calvini Institutiones Christianae religionis anno 1533 excusas. 8vo. GENÈVE, 1975. [Pamph.]
—— Zur Entstehungsgeschichte des Wortes "Calvinist". 8vo. [GÜTERSLOH,] 1975. [Pamph.]
Plato. *See* Allen (R. E.); Field (G. C.); Guthrie (W. K. C.); Jaspers (K.)
Platt (Frederic) Two tracts for the times. I. Evangelical and sacramental: a plea for synthesis. II. The evangel and 'the breaking of bread': an apostolic synthesis. 8vo. LOND., 1944. [Pamph.]
[Playdon (M. C.)] Providence Chapel, Swanwick Lane [Fareham], 1803-1974. 8vo. *Duplicated.* n.p., 1974. [Pamph.]
—— "This sweet singer of songs for the sanctuary": William Tidd Matson, 1833-1899. 4to. *Duplicated.* n.p., 1974. [Pamph.]
Plöger (Otto) *See* Bible. O.T. Commentaries. Handbuch zum A.T. I, 18.
[Plowman (Max)] A subaltern on the Somme in 1916. By Mark VII [Max Plowman]. 8vo. LOND. & TORONTO, 1927.
—— The faith called pacifism. 8vo. LOND., 1936.
—— Bridge into the future: letters of Max Plowman. Ed. D.L.P. [Dorothy Lloyd Plowman]. 8vo. LOND., 1944.
Plowright (B. C.) Rebel religion: Christ, community and church. Introd. by John MacMurray. 8vo. LOND., 1936.
Plumb (J. H.) and **Dearing** (V. A.) Some aspects of eighteenth-century England. Introd. by Maximillian E. Novak. [Clark Lib. Seminar Papers.] 8vo. LOS ANGELES, 1971. [Pamph.]
Plutarch. *See* Schwarz (W.)
Pohlmann (K. F.) *See* Suppt. Forschungen zur Religion u. Lit., 104, 118.
Pole (Reginald) *Cardinal.* *See* Fenlon (D.); Gasquet (F. A.); Haile (M.)
Polin (Raymond) La politique de la solitude: essai sur la Philosophie politique de Jean-Jacques Rousseau. [Philosophie Politique.] 8vo. PARIS, 1971.
Pollard (Alfred W.) [Misc.] A select bibliography of the writings of Alfred W. Pollard. [With a short autobiography, completed and with a preface by Henry Thomas.] 8vo. OXF., 1938.
—— *See* Suppt. Bibliographical Soc. Publs., 1973-75.

Pollins (H.) *See* Brennan (T.) *and others.*
Pollock (*Sir* Frederick) *See* Fifoot (C. H. S.)
Poole (Joshua) The English Parnassus. (1657.) facsim. repr. [English Linguistics, 1500-1800, 359.] 8vo. MENSTON, 1972.
—— Practical rhetoric. (1663.) facsim. repr. [English Linguistics, 1500-1800, 341.] 8vo. MENSTON, 1972.
Pope (Marvin H.) *See* Bible. Commentaries. Anchor Bible, 15.
Popham (James Kidwell) [Misc.] A brief biography [by S.L.H.], and addresses delivered in connection with the Sovereign Grace Union, together with a foreword by J. H. Gosden. 8vo. LOND., 1938.
Popper (Karl) *See* Suppt. Library of Living Philosophers, 14.
Porritt (Arthur) More and more of memories. 8vo. LOND., 1947.
Porter (C. E.) Congregational memoirs. [Old Presbyterian Congregation of Larne and Kilwaughter.] 8vo. [LARNE, 1929.]
Porter (Ellen Jane) *See* Suppt. Hymn Soc. of America. Papers, 30.
Porter (Harry Boone) *See* Suppt. Alcuin Club. Collections, 61.
Porter (Harry Culverwell) *ed.* Puritanism in Tudor England. [History in Depth.] 8vo. LOND., 1970.
Porter (J. R.) The non-juring bishops. [Royal Stuart Papers, 4.] 8vo. ILFORD, 1973. [Pamph.]
—— *ed.* *See* Davies (Gwynne H.) [Misc.]
Porter (Mary) *and others.* Mary Sumner: her life and work. I. Memoir of Mrs. Sumner. By Mary Porter. II. A short history of the Mothers' Union. By Mary Woodward, compiled from the MS. hist. of the Society by Lady Horatia Erskine. 8vo. WINCHESTER, 1921.
Porteus (C. A.) *See* Taylor (J.) and Porteus (C. A.)
Portsmouth. *John Pounds Memorial Church.* An introduction. 8vo. [PORTSMOUTH, 195-.] [Pamph.]
Poskitt (F. R.) *See* Brown (W. E.)
Posthumus Meyjes (G. H. M.) Richard Jean De Nerée en zijn 'Inventaire General' (1610). 8vo. [NIEUWKOOP, 1975.] [Pamph.]
—— Quasi stellae fulgebunt: plaats en functie van de theologische doctor in de middeleeuwse maatschappij en kerk. Rede, 8 Feb. 1979. 8vo. LEIDEN, 1979. [Pamph.]
Potter (G. R.) Zwingli. 8vo. CAMB., 1976.
—— *See* Suppt. Historical Assn. Gen. Ser., 89.
Potters Bar. *Baptist Church.* Do you know? [Brief history of the church.] 12mo. [LOND.,] n.d. [Pamph.]
Potz (Richard) Patriarch und Synode in Konstantinopel: das Verfassungsrecht des ökumenischen Patriarchates. [Kirche u. Recht, 10.] 8vo. WIEN, 1971.
Pounds (John) *See* Portsmouth. *John Pounds Memorial Church.*
Powell (J. R.) The navy in the English Civil War. Introd. by C. V. Wedgwood. 8vo. HAMDEN (Conn.) & LOND., 1962.
[Powell (M. W.) *and others.*] Desborough Baptist Church: a brief history, 1848 to 1948 8vo. [NORTHAMPTON, 1948.] [Pamph.]
Powell (Vavasor) *See* Nicholson (J. F. V.)
Powley (P. J.) *comp.* Wycombe Marsh Union Baptist Church, 1857-1957. 8vo. *Duplicated.* [WYCOMBE MARSH, 1957.] [Pamph.]
Prabhavananda, *Swami.* *See* Johnson (C.) *ed.*
[Pratt (Josiah) 1768-1844.] [Eclectic notes.] The thought of the Evangelical leaders: notes of the discussions of the Eclectic Society, London, during the years 1798-1814. Ed. John H. Pratt. (1856.) repr. 8vo. EDIN., 1978.
Praxis. *See* Suppt.
Presbyterian Church in Ireland. *See* Suppt.
Presbyterian Church of England. Index to the Proceedings of the General Assembly, 1921-1972. Comp. J. M. Ross. 4to. *Duplicated.* LOND., 1973.
—— *See* Suppt.
Presbyterian Historical Society of England. *See* Suppt.
Preston (John) *See* Morgan (I.)
Preus (J. S.) From shadow to promise: Old Testament interpretation from Augustine to the young Luther. 8vo. CAMB. (Mass.), 1969.

Price (H. H.)   Essays in the philosophy of religion. Based on the Sarum Lects., 1971. 8vo. OXF., 1972.
Price (Milburn) *ed.*   *See* Reynolds (W. J.)
Price (Richard) *See* Laboucheix (H.); Thomas (D. O.); Suppt. Price-Priestley News-Letter.
Price (S. J.)   Bloomsbury. [Bloomsbury Central Baptist Church centenary celebrations, Apr. 1948.] 8vo. LOND., [1948]. [Pamph.]
Prickett (Stephen)   Romanticism and religion: the tradition of Coleridge and Wordsworth in the Victorian church. 8vo. CAMB., 1976.
Prideaux (John) *Bp. of Worcester*.   *See* Prideaux (S. P. T.)
Prideaux (Sherburne P. T.)   John Prideaux: in piam memoriam. 8vo. SALISBURY, 1938. [Pamph.]
Priestley, *family of*.   *See* Catalogues. *Dickinson Coll.*
Priestley (Joseph)   A course of lectures on the theory of language and universal grammar. (1762.) facsim. repr. 8vo. FARNBOROUGH, 1971.
—— *See* Garrett (C.); Leeds City Museums; Orange (A. D.); Priestley Centenary Fund; Smith (W. D. A.); Suppt. Price-Priestley Newsletter.
Priestley Centenary Fund.   An illustrated handbook of the Presbyterian, Unitarian, and other liberal Christian churches in the Midlands. With a short life of Dr. Priestley. obl. 8vo. BIRMINGHAM, 1904. [Pamph.]
Pringle (Arthur) *ed.*   The war and our faith. Papers by Congregationalists. 8 pamphs. in 1 vol. 8vo. LOND., [1916].
  1.   Providence and the world: W. B. Selbie.
  2.   Providence and the individual: E. Griffith-Jones.
  3.   The Cross and the war: R. S. Franks.
  4.   The peace-maker and the pacifist: J. M. Gibbon.
  5.   The war and humanity: R. F. Horton.
  6.   Immortality: R. W. Thompson.
  7.   The church after the war: D. L. Ritchie.
  8.   The unity of humanity: G. E. Darlaston.
Prior (A. N.)   Objects of thought. Ed. P. T. Geach and A. J. P. Kenny. 8vo. OXF., 1971.
Priscillian.   *See* Chadwick (H.)
Pritchard (Arnold)   Catholic loyalism in Elizabethan England. 8vo. LOND., 1979.
Pritchard (J. B.) *ed.*   The ancient Near East: supplementary texts and pictures relating to the Old Testament. 4to. PRINCETON, 1969.
Pritchard (R. A.)   Thomas Charles, 1755-1814. 8vo. CARDIFF, 1955.
Proceedings of . . .   *See* Suppt.
Proctor (David)   *See* Scott (D. V.)
Probert (J. C. C.)   Fore Street Methodist Church, Redruth, 1865-1965: a social history. 8vo. [REDRUTH, 1965.] [Pamph.]
Proposed scheme of union.   Prepared by the Joint Committee of the Church of India, Burma and Ceylon, the South India United Church, and the South India Provincial Synod of the Methodist Church. (1929.) 7th ed. 8vo. MADRAS, 1943. [Pamph.]
—— [Misc.] The scheme of church union in South India: a statement submitted to the archbishops and bishops of the Anglican Communion. 8vo. LOND., n.d. [Pamph.]
Prowting (D. C.)   From the beginning: the story of High Cross Congregational Church, Tottenham, publ. on the occasion of the centenary. 8vo. LOND., 1966. [Pamph.]
Pruett (J. H.)   The parish clergy under the later Stuarts: the Leicestershire experience. 8vo. URBANA (Ill.), *etc.*, 1978.
Pryke (E. J.)   Redactional style in the Marcan Gospel: a study of syntax and vocabulary as guides to redaction in Mark. [Soc. for N.T. Studies, Monograph Ser., 33.] 8vo. CAMB., 1978.
Pryke (W. W.)   Barnham Chapel, Suffolk. 8vo. LAVENHAM, 1970. [Pamph.]
Puddicombe (*Mrs.* Anne Adaliza)   *See* Raine (Allen) *pseud.*
Pugh (Robert) 1610-79, *R.C.*   Blacklo's cabal. (1680.) facsim. repr. Introd. by T. A. Birrell. 8vo. FARNBOROUGH, 1970.
[Puleston (Winnie)]   The United Reformed Church, Alkrington: jubilee, 1926-1976. 8vo. *Duplicated.* [ALKRINGTON, 1976.] [Pamph.]

Pullen (G. F.) *ed.* *See Catalogues. St. Mary's Seminary, Oscott.*
Purey-Cust (A. P.) *comp.* Edward Vesey Bligh: a memoir. 8vo. LEEDS, 1908.
Pye (Jonathan H.) A bibliography of the published works of Ian Thomas Ramsey. 8vo. *Duplicated.* DURHAM, 1979. [Pamph.]

Quervain (Alfred de) Humanismus und evangelische Theologie. [Mainzer Universitäts-Reden, 10.] 8vo. MAINZ, 1947. [Pamph.]
Quiller-Couch (*Sir* Arthur) *See* Brittain (F.)
Quin (W. F.) Brentwood Congregational Church: a brief history, 1672-1972. fol. *Duplicated.* [BRENTWOOD, 1972.]
Quine (W. V. O.) Methods of logic. (1952.) 2nd ed. 8vo. LOND., 1962.
—— From a logical point of view: 9 logico-philosophical essays. (1953.) 2nd ed. (1961.) repr. 8vo. NEW YORK & EVANSTON, 1963.
—— Selected logic papers. 8vo. NEW YORK, 1966.
—— The ways of paradox, and other essays. (1966.) rev. and enl. ed. 8vo. CAMB. (Mass.) & LOND., 1976.
—— Word and object. (1960.) repr. 8vo. CAMB. (Mass.), 1976.
Quinn (P. L.) Divine commands and moral requirements. [Clarendon Lib. of Logic and Philos.] 8vo. OXF., 1978.
Quinton. *Carters Lane Baptist Church.* 150 years (1811-1961): anniversary. 4to. [QUINTON, 1961.] [Pamph.]
Quispel (Gilles) The secret book of Revelation: the last book of the Bible. 4to. LOND., 1979.

Raban (Edward) *d.* 1658. [Misc.] Record of the celebration of the tercentenary of the introduction of the art of printing into Aberdeen by Edward Raban in the year 1622. 16th and 17th June 1922. 8vo. ABERDEEN, 1922.
Rabb (Theodore K.) *See* Suppt. Jewish Hist. Soc. Publs., 1974.
Rabinowicz (Oskar K.) *See* Suppt. Jewish Hist. Soc. Publs., 1974.
Rad (Gerhard von) Weisheit in Israel. 8vo. NEUKIRCHEN-VLUYN, 1970.
—— —— Wisdom in Israel. [Trans. James D. Martin.] 8vo. LOND., 1972.
—— *See* Bible. O.T. Commentaries. Das A. T. Deutsch; Suppt. Studies in Bibl. Theol., 2nd Ser., 30.
Rae (T. H. H.) John Dury, reformer of education. [Schriften des Instituts für wiss. Irenik der J. W. Goethe Univ., Frankfurt am M., 8.] 8vo. MARBURG, 1970.
Rahner (Karl) Free speech in the Church. [Trans. G. R. Lamb.] 8vo. LOND. & NEW YORK, 1959.
—— Theological investigations. 8vo. LOND., *etc.*, 1961-
    7-8. Further theology of the spiritual life. Trans. David Bourke. 2 vols. 1971.
    9-10. Writings of 1965-67. 1. Trans. Graham Harrison. 2. Trans. David Bourke. 2 vols. 1972-73.
    11-12. Confrontations. Trans. David Bourke. 2 vols. 1974.
    13. Theology, anthropology, Christology. Trans. David Bourke. 1975.
    14. Ecclesiology, questions in the Church, the Church in the world. Trans. David Bourke. 1976.
    15. *Not yet published,* 1980.
    16. Experience of the Spirit: source of theology. Trans. David Morland. 1979.
—— The Trinity. Trans. Joseph Donceel. 8vo. LOND., 1970.
—— Christian at the crossroads. [Trans. V. Green.] 8vo. LOND., 1975.
Raible (Christopher) and **Darling** (Edward) *ed.* 73 voices, personal, wistful, hopeful: an anthology of aspirations, meditations, prayers. 8vo. BOSTON (Mass.), 1971. [Pamph.]
Raine (Allen) *pseud.* *See* Jones (S. R.)
Raine (Kathleen) Blake and the new age. 8vo. LOND., 1979.
Rainy (Robert) *See* Simpson (P. C.)
Ramsbottom (B. A.) Samuel Medley: preacher, pastor, poet. 8vo. [BEDFORD,] 1978. [Pamph.]
[Ramsden (G. M.)] A record of the Kay family of Bury, Lancashire, in the 17th and 18th centuries, with notes on the families of Gaskell, Mangnall, Darbishire. fol. *Duplicated.* n.p., 1979.

Ramsey (Arthur Michael) *Abp. of Canterbury.* Jesus Christ in faith and history. Inaugural lect., Univ. of Durham, Oct. 25 1940. [Theology Occ. Papers, N.S., 3.] 8vo. LOND., [1940]. [Pamph.]
—— Introducing the Christian faith. (1961.) rev. ed. 8vo. LOND., 1970.
—— The narratives of the Passion. [Contemp. Studies in Theol., 1.] 8vo. LOND., 1962. [Pamph.]
—— God, Christ and the world: a study in contemporary theology. (1969.) repr. 8vo. LOND., 1969.
—— Freedom, faith and the future. [Hulsean Lects., 1970.] 8vo. LOND., 1970.
—— Canterbury pilgrim. 8vo. LOND., 1974.
—— Jesus and the living past. [Hale Lects., 1978.] 8vo. OXF., 1980.
Ramsey (Frank Plumpton) Foundations: essays in philosophy, logic, mathematics and economics. Ed. D. H. Mellor. With introds. by D. H. Mellor, L. Mirsky, T. J. Smiley, Richard Stone. [Internat. Lib. of Psychol., Philos., and Scientific Method.] 8vo. LOND. & HENLEY, 1978.
Ramsey (Ian Thomas) *Bp. of Durham.* Models for divine activity. [Zenos Lects., 1966.] 8vo. LOND., 1973.
—— Words about God: the philosophy of religion. [Forum Books.] 8vo. NEW YORK, *etc.*, 1971.
—— *See* Pye (J. H.)
Ramsey (R. W.) Henry Ireton. 8vo. LOND., *etc.*, 1949.
Rankin (D. O.) Portraits from the cross: a meditation manual. 8vo. BOSTON (Mass.), 1978. [Pamph.]
Ransome (Mary) *See* National Portrait Gallery.
Ranston (Harry) The Old Testament wisdom books and their teaching. 8vo. LOND., 1930.
Rapheleng (Franz) *See* Gulik (E. van) and Vervliet (H. D. L.)
Ratcliff (Edward Craddock) *See* Suppt. Alcuin Club. Misc. Publs., 1972.
Rathbone (William) *See* Armstrong (R. A.)
Ratramnus, *d.* 868, *monk of Corbie.* De corpore et sanguine domini. Texte original et notice bibliographique. Éd. renouvelée par J. N. Bakhuizen van den Brink. [Verhandelingen der Koninklijke Nederlandse Akad. van Wetenschappen, Letterkunde, N.R., 87.] 8vo. AMSTERDAM & LOND., 1974.
Raven (C. E.) The cross and the crisis. 8vo. LOND., 1940.
—— Christ and the modern opportunity. Five addresses delivered in McGill Univ., Montreal, Quebec. 8vo. LOND., 1956.
—— *See* Dillistone (F. W.)
Raven (C. E.) and **Heath** (Rachel F.) One called Help: the life and work of Beatrice Hankey. 8vo. LOND., 1937.
Raverat (Gwendolen M.) Period piece: a Cambridge childhood. 8vo. LOND., 1960.
[**Rawlinson** (J.)] Jubilee souvenir of London Road Baptist Church, Portsmouth, 1902-1952. 8vo. [PORTSMOUTH, 1952.] [Pamph.]
[**Rayner** (H. W.)] Fifty years of witness for the Lord in East Ham, 1889-1939: jubilee report of Hope Strict Baptist Chapel, Stafford Road, East Ham, London, E.7. 8vo. CROYDON [printed], [1939]. [Pamph.]
Rayner (Mabel A.) *See* Suppt. Methodist Sacramental Fellowship. M.S.F. Booklets. N.S., 1.
Reade (W. H. V.) Dante's vision of history. [Annual Italian Lect., Brit. Acad., 1939.] 8vo. LOND., [1940]. [Pamph.]
Reader (John) Of schools and schoolmasters: some thoughts on the Quaker contribution to education. [Swarthmore Lect., 1979.] 8vo. LOND., 1979.
Reardon (B. M. G.) From Coleridge to Gore: a century of religious thought in Britain. 8vo. LOND., 1971.
—— Hegel's philosophy of religion. [Lib. of Philos. and Relig.] 8vo. LOND., 1977.
Reason (Joyce) Henry Barrowe (1550-1593) and John Greenwood (-1593). [Heritage Biographies.] 8vo. LOND., 1961. [Pamph.]
—— Robert Browne (1550?-1633) [Heritage Biographies.] 8vo. LOND., 1961. [Pamph.]
Reay (B. G.) The Muggletonians: a study in seventeenth century English sectarianism. 8vo. [SYDNEY, 1976.] [Pamph.]

Record (S. P.)　Proud century: the first hundred years of Taunton School.　8vo. TAUNTON, 1948.
Record Society of Lancashire and Cheshire.　See Suppt.
Recusant History.　See Suppt.
Redfern (Lawrence)　Essential Christianity and the present religious situation. [Religion: its Modern Needs and Problems, 12.]　8vo.　LOND., 1932.
Redgrave (G. R.)　See Bibliographical Soc. Publs., 1973-75.
Redwood (John)　Reason, ridicule and religion: the age of Enlightenment in England, 1660-1750.　8vo.　LOND., 1976.
Rees (D. Benjamin)　Chapels in the valley: a study in the sociology of Welsh Nonconformity.　8vo.　WIRRAL, 1975.
Rees (Frederick A.) *ed.*　Problems of to-morrow: social, moral and religious.　8vo. LOND., 1918.
[Rees (Maureen A.)]　A history of Ashby-de-la-Zouch Baptist Church, founded 1807.　8vo.　[ASHBY-DE-LA-ZOUCH, 1962.]　[Pamph.]
Reese (J. M.)　1 and 2 Thessalonians.　[New Test. Message, 16.]　8vo.　DUBLIN, 1979.
[Reeves (Edith S. W.) *and others.*]　1662-1962: a history of the Baptist Church, Bratton, Wilts.　8vo.　[BRATTON, 1962.]　[Pamph.]
Reeves (Gene) *ed.*　See Brown (Delwin) *and others, ed.*
Reeves (Marjorie E.)　Growing up in a modern society.　[Educational Issues of Today.]　(1946.)　2nd ed.　8vo.　LOND., 1949.
—— Joachim of Fiore and the prophetic future.　8vo.　LOND., 1976.
—— Sheep bell and plough share: the story of two village families [in Bratton, Wilts.]. 8vo.　BRADFORD-ON-AVON, 1978.
Reicke (Bo I.)　See Bible. Commentaries. Anchor Bible, 37.
Reid (James)　Alienation. Rectorial address, Univ. of Glasgow, 28th April, 1972. [Glasgow Univ. Publs.]　8vo.　GLASGOW, 1972.　[Pamph.]
Reid (L. A.)　Meaning in the arts.　[Muirhead Lib. of Philos.]　8vo.　LOND. & NEW YORK, 1969.
Reiling (J.)　See Suppt. Novum Testamentum. Suppts., 37.
Reim (Günter)　Studien zum Alttestamentlichen Hintergrund des Johannesevangeliums.　[Soc. for N.T. Studies, Monograph Ser., 22.]　8vo.　CAMB., 1974.
Reimarus (H. S.)　The goal of Jesus and his disciples. Introd. and trans. by George Wesley Buchanan.　8vo.　LEIDEN, 1970.
Reinach (Adolf)　Was ist Phänomenologie? Vorwort von Hedwig Conrad-Martius. 8vo.　MÜNCHEN, 1951.
Reinink (G. J.)　See Suppt. Corpus Script. Christ. Orient., Subsid., 57; Novum Testamentum.　Suppts., 36.
Rekers (Bernard)　Benito Arias Montano (1527-1598).　[Studies of the Warburg Institute, 33.]　8vo.　LOND. & LEIDEN, 1972.
Religion och Kultur.　See Suppt.
Religious Studies.　See Suppt.
Renaissance and Modern Studies.　See Suppt.
Rendall (Jane)　The origins of the Scottish Enlightenment, 1707-1776.　[History in Depth.]　8vo.　LOND., 1978.
Rendtorff (Rolf)　See Suppt. Zeitschr. für A. T. Wiss. Beihefte, 147.
Rengstorf (K. H.) *ed.*　Das Paulusbild in der neueren deutschen Forschung. In Verbindung mit Ulrich Luck.　[Wege der Forschung, 24.]　8vo.　DARMSTADT, 1964.
Rescher (Nicholas)　The coherence theory of truth.　[Clarendon Lib. of Logic and Philos.]　8vo.　OXF., 1973.
Rétat (Pierre)　Le Dictionnaire de Bayle et la lutte philosophique au XVIII siècle. [Bibliothèque de la Faculté des Lettres de Lyon, 28.]　8vo.　PARIS, 1971.
Reumann (John)　Jesus in the Church's Gospels: modern scholarship and the earliest sources.　8vo.　LOND., 1970.
Reuter (Karl)　Wilhelm Amesius: der führende Theologe der erwachenden reformierten Pietismus.　[Beiträge zur Gesch. u. Lehre der Reform. Kirche, 4.]　8vo. NEUKIRCHEN, 1940.
Reuter (Timothy) *ed.*　The greatest Englishman: essays on St. Boniface and the Church at Crediton.　8vo.　EXETER, 1980.
Réville (Albert)　History of the dogma of the deity of Jesus Christ.　Rev. trans. from the 3rd French ed. of 1904.　8vo.　LOND., 1905.

Revue . . . *See* Suppt.

Reymes (Bullen) 1613-72, *Colonel.* *See* Kaufman (H. A.)

Reynolds, *family of.* *See* Knight (F. F. E.) *ed.*

Reynolds (W. J.) A joyful sound: Christian hymnody. (1963.) 2nd ed. by Milburn Price. 8vo. NEW YORK, 1978.

Ricardo (David) Works and correspondence. Ed. Piero Sraffa with the collab. of M. H. Dobb. (10 vols., 1951-55.) 11. General index. 8vo. CAMB., 1973.

Richards (Edith R.) Private view of a public man: the life of Leyton Richards. 8vo. LOND., 1950.

Richards (Leyton) *See* Richards (E. R.)

Richards (Thomas) Piwritaniaeth a pholitics (1689-1719). Darlith flynyddol, Coleg y Bedyddwyr, Bangor, 1927. 8vo. WRECSAM, 1927.

Richardson (Alan) *See* Dictionaries. Christianity.

Richardson (Robert Douglas) *See* Lietzmann (H.)

Richardson (Roger Charles) Puritanism in North-West England: a regional study of the Diocese of Chester to 1642. 8vo. MANCHESTER & TOTOWA (N.J.), 1972.

—— Puritanism and the ecclesiastical authorities: the case of the Diocese of Chester. 8vo. LOND., [1973]. [Pamph.]

Richmond (James) Ritschl: a reappraisal. A study in systematic theology. 8vo. LOND., *etc.*, 1978.

Richter (Jean Paul Friedrich) [Letters.] Jean Paul und Herder: der Briefwechsel Jean Pauls und Karoline Richters mit Herder und der Herdereschen Familie in den Jahren 1785 bis 1804. Hrsg. Paul Stapf. 8vo. BERN & MÜNCHEN, 1959.

Richter (Michael) *ed.* *See* Suppt. Canterbury and York Soc., 67.

Ridderbos (N. H.) *See* Suppt. Zeitschr. für A. T. Wiss. Beihefte, 117.

Rider (J. S.) United Reformed Church, Whitehorse Street, Baldock. 8vo. BALDOCK, [1976]. [Pamph.]

Riemersma (J. C.) Religious factors in early Dutch capitalism, 1550-1650. [Studies in the Social Sciences, 2.] 8vo. THE HAGUE & PARIS, 1967.

Riesener (Ingrid) *See* Suppt. Zeitschr. für A. T. Wiss. Beihefte, 149.

Ringgren (Helmer) Religions of the ancient Near East. Trans. John Sturdy. 8vo. LOND., 1973.

Riou (Alain) Le monde et l'Église selon Maxime le Confesseur. [Théologie Historique, 22.] 8vo. PARIS, 1973.

Rissi (Mathias) *See* Suppt. Studies in Bibl. Theol., 2nd Ser., 23.

Rist (J. M.) Epicurus: an introduction. 8vo. CAMB., 1972.

—— On the independence of Matthew and Mark. [Soc. for N.T. Studies, Monograph Ser., 32.] 8vo. CAMB., 1978.

[Ritchie (A. M.)] St. George's Place Baptist Church, Canterbury: history and manual, 1948. 8vo. [CANTERBURY, 1948.] [Pamph.]

Ritchie (C. I. A.) The ecclesiastical courts of York. 8vo. ARBROATH, 1956.

—— Frontier parish: an account of the Society for the Propagation of the Gospel and the Anglican Church in America, drawn from the records of the Bishop of London. 8vo. RUTHERFORD (N.J.), *etc.*, 1976.

Ritchie (D. L.) *See* Pringle (A.) *ed.*

Ritschl (Albrecht) *See* Mueller (D. L.); Richmond (J.)

Ritson (Joseph) The romance of Primitive Methodism. [Hartley Lect., 12.] 6th ed. 8vo. LOND., 1911.

Ritter (A. M.) Charisma im Verständnis des Joannes Chrysostomos und seiner Zeit: ein Beitrag zur Erforschung der greichisch-orientalischen Ekklesiologie in der Frühzeit der Reichskirche. [Forschungen zur Kirchen- u. Dogmengesch., 25.] 8vo. GÖTTINGEN, 1972.

Rivington Chapel. Bi-centenary, 1703-1903: souvenir. 8vo. CHORLEY, [1903].

Rizzo (J. J.) *See* Suppt. Analecta Bollandiana. Subsid. Hagiog., 58.

Robbins (C. H. C.) A history of Teignmouth Baptist Church [1865-1965]. 8vo. [TEIGNMOUTH, 1965.] [Pamph.]

Robbins (Keith) John Bright. 8vo. LOND., *etc.*, 1979.

Robert (André) *See* Dictionaries. Biblical.

[Roberts (Benson)] The United Reformed Church, formerly the English Congregational Church, Bridgend: a centenary survey, 1873-1973. 8vo. MAESTEG [printed], [1973]. [Pamph.]

Roberts (Brynley F.) Edward Lhuyd: the making of a scientist. [G. J. Williams Memorial Lect., University Coll., Cardiff, 16 Feb. 1979.] 8vo. CARDIFF, 1980. [Pamph.]
Roberts (Colin H.) Manuscript, society and belief in early Christian Egypt. [Schweich Lects., Brit. Acad., 1977.] 8vo. LOND., 1979.
Roberts (David Everett) Psychotherapy and a Christian view of man. 8vo. NEW YORK, 1950.
Roberts (Eric) *comp.* Stoneycroft century: a souvenir booklet to commemorate the centenary of the Stoneycroft Methodist Church, Liverpool [1868-1968]. 8vo. [LIVERPOOL, 1968.] [Pamph.]
Roberts (George W.) *ed.* Bertrand Russell memorial volume. [Muirhead Lib. of Philos.] 8vo. LOND. & NEW YORK, 1979.
Roberts (Gomer Morgan) *ed.* Hanes Methodistiaeth Galfinaidd Cymru. 2 vols. 8vo. CAERNARFON, 1973-78.
   1. Y deffroad mawr. 1973.
   2. Cynnydd y corff. 1978
Roberts (John) *See* Jones (R. T.)
Roberts (Joseph Kitto) The Mevagissey Independents, 1625-1946. 8vo. TAUNTON, 1946.
Roberts (Richard) *See* Papers for War Time, 2.
Roberts (Samuel) *See* Williams (Glanmor)
[**Roberts** (Thomas W.)] Manchester District Association of Unitarian and Free Christian Churches, 1891-1951: diamond jubilee celebrations. 8vo. [MANCHESTER, 1951.] [Pamph.]
Roberts (Walter J.) The history of the Baptist Church, Wellow, Isle of Wight, 1801-1951. 4to. [NEWPORT, I.o.W., 1951.] [Pamph.]
—— A short history of the Baptists of Newport, Isle of Wight . . . since 1672. Issued in connection with the 150th anniversary of the founding of Castlehold Baptist Church, 1809. 8vo. NEWPORT, I.o.W., [1959]. [Pamph.]
[**Roberts** (William)] The Baptists: their history and claims among the religious denominations of Wales in past ages. A letter from the ministers and messengers of the churches in the Monmouthsire Baptist Association. (1857.) repr. 8vo. LOND., 1953. [Pamph.]
Robertson (D. B.) The religious foundations of Leveller democracy. 8vo. NEW YORK, 1951.
Robertson (E. H.) *See* Bonsall (H. E.) and Robertson (E. H.)
Robertson (John Mackinnon) The dynamics of religion: an essay in English culture history. (1897.) 2nd ed. 8vo. LOND., 1926.
Robertson (William) *See* Black (J. B.)
Robinet (André) Leibniz und wir. [Vortragsreihe der Niedersächsischen Landesregierung zur Förderung der wiss. Forschung in Niedersachsen, 36.] 8vo. GÖTTINGEN, 1967. [Pamph.]
Robinson (F.) History of the Congregational School and Church, Highroad Well, Halifax, 1829-1915. 8vo. HALIFAX, [1915].
Robinson (F. J. G.) *See* Catalogues. *Misc.*
Robinson (Henry Crabb) *See* Schelling (F. W. J. von)
Robinson (James M.) and **Koester** (Helmut) Trajectories through early Christianity. 8vo. PHILADELPHIA, 1971.
Robinson (John) 1575-1625. *See* Martin (R. G.)
Robinson (John A. T.) Liturgy coming to life. (1960.) 2nd ed. (1963.) 2nd imp. 8vo. LOND., 1964.
—— The human face of God. 8vo. LOND., 1973.
—— Redating the New Testament. 8vo. LOND., 1976.
Robinson (N. H. G.) The groundwork of Christian ethics. 8vo. LOND., 1971.
Robinson (Theodore H.) An introduction to the Old Testament. (1948.) repr. 8vo. LOND., 1957.
Robinson (William) The shattered cross: the many churches and the one Church. 8vo. BIRMINGHAM, 1945.
Rockey (Denyse) John Thelwall and the origins of British speech therapy. 4to. BERKHAMSTED [printed], 1979. [Pamph.]
Rodecki (Aleksy) *See* Kawecka-Gryczowa (A.)

Roe (M. F. H.) Letters from afar which are written, in some answer to the rather perplexing question: what is the point, if any, of studying philosophy? 8vo. LOND., 1975.

Roetemeijer (H. J. M.) Christ Church (English Episcopal Church, 1698-1971), Groenburgwal 42, Amsterdam. obl. fol. [AMSTERDAM, 1970.] [Pamph.]

Rogers (Carl R.) Counselling and psychotherapy: newer concepts in practice. 8vo. BOSTON (Mass.), 1942.

Rogers (Clement F.) Astrology in the light of science and religion. 8vo. LOND., 1941.

Rogers (James Guinness) An autobiography. 8vo. LOND., 1903.

Rogerson (J. W.) See Suppt. Zeitschr. für A. T. Wiss. Beihefte, 134.

Rogier (Louis J.) and others, ed. The Christian centuries: a new history of the Catholic Church. 8vo. LOND., 1964-
  5. The Church in a secularised society: Roger Aubert, etc. 1978.

Rolfe (Eugene) The intelligent agnostic's introduction to Christianity. (1959.) new ed. 8vo. LOND., 1963.

Rolle (Richard) of Hampole. See Allen (H. E.)

Romaine (William) The Life, Walk, and Triumph of faith. With an account of his life and work by Peter Toon. 8vo. CAMB. & LOND., 1970.

Romanus, Saint, the hymn writer. Sancti Romani melodi cantica. [Greek text.] Ed. Paul Maas and C. A. Trypanis. 2 vols. 8vo. OXF. [1] & BERLIN [2], 1963-70.
  2. Cantica dubia. 1970.

Rommaynne (P. D.) pseud. And where shall I be? An introd. to the future life. 8vo. LOND. & NEW YORK, 1978.

Roon (A. van) See Suppt. Novum Testamentum. Suppts., 39.

Roper (Alan) See Patrick (J. M.) and Roper (A.)

Roper (Frances Hodgess) The story of the Congregational Church, now the United Reformed Church, in Bognor Regis from 1813 to 1980. 4to. BOGNOR REGIS, [1980]. [Pamph.]

Rordorf (Willy) Sabbat und Sonntag in der Alten Kirche. [Traditio Christiana: Texte u. Kommentare zur patrist. Theol., 2.] 8vo. ZÜRICH, 1972.

Rose (E. A.) The story of Mossley Methodism. 4to. Duplicated. n.p., 1969. [Pamph.]
—— St. Mary's Methodist Church, Handforth, 1872-1972. 8vo. [HANDFORTH, 1972.] [Pamph.]
—— Methodism in Cheshire to 1800. 8vo. WILMSLOW, 1975. [Pamph.]
—— Methodism in Dukinfield. 8vo. Duplicated. [MOTTRAM,] 1978. [Pamph.]
—— ed. See Harrop (S. A.) and Rose (E. A.) ed.

Rose (Edward Elliot) Cases of conscience: alternatives open to Recusants and Puritans under Elizabeth I and James I. 8vo. CAMB., 1975.

Rosendall (B. C.) The eucharistic doctrine of Daniel Waterland: a Roman Catholic study. Dissertation. 8vo. COLLEGEVILLE (Minn.), 1970.

Rosenkreutz (Christian) See Allen (P. M.) and Pietzner (C.) comp.

Rosenstiehl (Jean-Marc) See Bible. Apocrypha. Elijah.

Rosenthal (G. D.) Survival. 8vo. LOND., 1936.

Ross (A. K.) Specimen years in Weech Road and Hoop Lane, 1901 to 1971: All Souls' Unitarian Church, Golders Green. 8vo. Duplicated. [LOND.,] 1975. [Pamph.]

Ross (J. M. E.) William Ross of Cowcaddens: a memoir. 8vo. LOND., 1905.

Ross (William) See Ross (J. M. E.)

Rosten (Leo) ed. Religions in America: a completely revised and up-to-date guide to churches and religious groups in the United States. 8vo. NEW YORK, 1963.

Roth (Cecil) Records of the Western Synagogue, 1761-1932. To which is appended a repr. of Matthias Levy's "The Western Synagogue: some materials for its history" (1897). 8vo. LOND., 1932.
—— Studies in books and booklore: essays in Jewish bibliography and allied subjects. 8vo. FARNBOROUGH, 1972.

Roth (Leon) Foundations. [St. Paul's Lect., Oct. 1961.] 8vo. [LOND., 1961.] [Pamph.]

Rotherham (Thomas) Abp. of York. See Suppt. Canterbury and York Soc., 69.

Rothwell (Harry) See Douglas (D. C.) ed.

Rotondò (Antonio) Calvin and the Italian anti-trinitarians. Trans. John and Anne Tedeschi. [Reformation Essays and Studies, 2.] 8vo. SAINT LOUIS (Mo.), 1968. [Pamph.]
—— Studi e ricerche di storia ereticale italiana del Cinquecento. I. [Pubbl. dell' Instituto di Scienze politiche dell'Univ. di Torino, 31.] 8vo. TORINO, 1974.
Rott (Jean) Correspondance de Martin Bucer: liste alphabétique des correspondants. [Assoc. des Publs. de la Faculté de Théol. Prot. de l'Univ. des Sciences Humaines de Strasbourg, Bull. 1.] 8vo. STRASBOURG, 1977.
Rouquet (James) 1730-76. *See* Suppt. Wesley Hist. Soc. Publs., 8.
Rouschausse (Jean) La vie et l'oeuvre de John Fisher, évêque de Rochester, 1469-1535. [Collection de Babel à Salem, 1.] 8vo. NIEUWKOOP, 1972.
Rousseau (Jean-Jacques) *See* Leigh (R. A.); Lemos (R. M.); Polin (R.)
Rousseau (Philip) Ascetics, authority, and the Church in the age of Jerome and Cassian. [Oxford Historical Monographs.] 8vo. OXF., 1978.
Routley (Erik) Isaac Watts (1674-1748). [Heritage Biographies.] 8vo. LOND., 1961. [Pamph.]
—— Thomas Goodwin (1600-1680). [Heritage Biographies.] 8vo. LOND., 1961. [Pamph.]
[**Rowberry** (D. E.) and **Hunt** (A. R.)] Welling Baptist Church: a brief record of the first 25 years. 8vo. [WELLING, 1964.] [Pamph.]
Rowdon (H. H.) London Bible College: the first twenty-five years. 8vo. WORTHING, 1968.
Rowe (Trevor T.) St. Augustine, pastoral theologian. [Fernley-Hartley Lect., 1974.] 8vo. LOND., 1974.
Rowe (Violet A.) Sir Henry Vane the Younger: a study in political and administrative history. Foreword by Dame Veronica Wedgwood. 8vo. LOND., 1970.
Rowell (D. G.) Hell and the Victorians: a study of the nineteenth-century theological controversies concerning eternal punishment and the future life. 8vo. OXF., 1974.
—— *See* Suppt. Alcuin Club. Collections, 59.
Rowland (Alfred) Open windows, and other sermons. 8vo. LOND., [1903].
—— An independent parson: the autobiography of Alfred Rowland. 8vo. LOND., [1925?].
Rowland (Daniel) *See* Jones (D. J. O.)
Rowland (John) The story of Brighton Unitarian Church. 8vo. LOND., 1972. [Pamph.]
—— The story of Conigre: a short history of Conigre Unitarian Church, Trowbridge. 8vo. TROWBRIDGE, 1975. [Pamph.]
Royal Commission on Historical Manuscripts. *See* Suppt. Historical Manuscripts Commission.
Royal Commission on Historical Monuments. *See* Suppt. Historical Monuments Commission.
Royal Commission on the Church of England and other Religious Bodies in Wales and Monmouthshire. Report.—Minutes of evidence.—Appendices. 6 vols. fol. LOND., 1910-11.
Royal Historical Society. *See* Suppt.
Royal Institute of Philosophy. *See* Suppt. Philosophy.
Royal Institute of Philosophy Lectures. *See* Suppt.
Royden (A. Maude) A threefold cord. 8vo. LOND., 1948.
Rublack (Hans-Christoph) Neuere Forschungen zum Thesenanschlag Luthers. 8vo. MÜNCHEN & FREIBURG, 1970. [Pamph.]
—— Die Einführung der Reformation in Konstanz von den Anfängen bis zum Abschluss, 1531. [Quellen u. Forschungen zur Reformationsgesch., 40] [Veröffent-lich. des Vereins für Kirchengesch. in der Evang. Landeskirche in Baden, 27.] 8vo. GÜTERSLOH & KARLSRUHE, 1971.
—— Die Stadt Würzburg im Bauernkrieg. 8vo. GÜTERSLOH, 1976. [Pamph.]
—— *See* Bucking (J.) and Rublack (H.-C.)
Rudakov (Alexander P.) Ocherki vizantiyskoy kul'tury po dannym grecheskoy agiografii. (1917.) Introd. by Dimitri Obolensky. [Variorum Reprs.] 8vo. LOND., 1970.
Rudberg (S. Y.) *See* Suppt. Texte u. Untersuchungen, 5te. Reihe, 123.

Rudolph (Ebermut) Schulderlebnis und Entschuldung im Bereich säkularer Tiertotung: Religionsgeschichtliche Untersuchung. [Europäische Hochschulschriften, Reihe 23: Theologie, 12.] 8vo. BERN, 1972.

Ruhbach (Gerhard) *ed.* Die Kirche angesichts der konstantinischen Wende. [Wege der Forschung, 306.] 8vo. DARMSTADT, 1976.

Ruinart (Thierri) *See* Mabillon (J.) and Ruinart (T.)

Rumble (A. R.) Onomastic and topographical sources in English local record offices, Sep. 1970: a summary guide. 8vo. NOTTINGHAM, [1974]. [Pamph.]

Rumscheidt (H. Martin) Revelation and theology: an analysis of the Barth-Harnack correspondence of 1923. [Scottish J. of Theol., Monograph Suppt., 1.] 8vo. CAMB., 1972.

Runciman (*Hon. Sir* Steven) Byzantine style and civilization. 8vo. HARMONDSWORTH, 1975.

—— The Byzantine theocracy. [Weil Lects., Cincinnati, 1973.] 8vo. CAMB., 1977.

—— Mistra: Byzantine capital of the Pelopennese. 8vo. LOND., 1980.

Rundle (Bede) Perception, sensation and verification. 8vo. OXF., 1972.

Runes (D. D.) *ed.* *See* Dictionaries. Biography.

Runge (Philipp Otto) *See* Syamken (G.)

Rupp (E. G.) Thomas Müntzer, Hans Huth and the "Gospel of all creatures". 8vo. MANCHESTER, 1961. [Pamph.]

—— Thomas Müntzer: prophet of radical Christianity. 8vo. MANCHESTER, 1966. [Pamph.]

—— 'I seek my brethren': Bishop George Bell and the German Churches. [Mackintosh Lect., Univ. of E. Anglia, 1974.] 8vo. LOND., 1975. [Pamph.]

—— Just men: historical pieces. 8vo. LOND., 1977.

—— [Misc.] Christian spirituality. Essays in honour of Gordon Rupp. Ed. Peter Brooks. 8vo. LOND., 1975.

Rupprecht (Konrad) *See* Suppt. Zeitschr. für A. T. Wiss. Beihefte, 144.

Rushton (J. H.) They kept faith: the history of some Yorkshire Christian congregations including the Pickering and Malton Congregational Churches. fol. *Duplicated.* PICKERING, 1967.

Rusk (R. R.) Doctrines of the great educators. (1918.) 5th ed., rev. by James Scotland. 8vo. [LOND.,] 1979.

Russell (Bertrand A. W.) *3rd Earl. See* Roberts (G. W.) *ed.;* Wickham (H.)

Russell (Conrad S. R.) Parliaments and English politics, 1621-1629. 8vo. OXF., 1979.

—— *ed.* The origins of the English Civil War. [Problems in Focus Ser.] 8vo. LOND., 1973.

Russell (Francis) *2nd Earl of Bedford. See* Byrne (M. St. C.) and Thomson (G. S.)

[Russell (Percy)] A short account of the Congregational Church in Dartmouth founded under the leadership of John Flavell, 1662. 8vo. DARTMOUTH, [1956]. [Pamph.] [Photocopy.]

—— —— [rev. ed.] Flavel Memorial United Reformed Church (formerly Congregational), Dartmouth. 8vo. *Duplicated.* n.p., 1974. [Pamph.]

Ruston (A. R.) A history of lay preaching in the Unitarian movement. 8vo. LOND., 1973. [Pamph.]

—— What is Unitarianism? (1973.) repr. 8vo. LOND., 1974. [Pamph.]

—— Old Presbyterian Meeting House, St. Albans: the story of a building. 8vo. ST. ALBANS, 1979. [Pamph.]

—— Unitarianism in Hertfordshire. 8vo. OXHEY (Herts.) [the author], 1979. [Pamph.]

—— Unitarianism and early Presbyterianism in Hackney. 8vo. OXHEY (Herts.) [the author], 1980. [Pamph.]

Ruston-Harrison (C. W.) *ed. See* Phillimore (W. P. W.) and Ruston-Harrison (C. W.) *ed.*

Rutherford (Mark) *pseud. See* White (William Hale)

Rutland (W. R.) The becoming of God: an outline of the development of man's conception of cosmic process. 8vo. OXF., 1971.

[Ryde (F. M.) *and others.*] Rosslyn Hill Chapel: a short history, 1692-1973. [By F. M. Ryde, W. Meadows and J. Brandon-Jones.] 8vo. LOND., 1974.

Ryder (Dudley F. S.) *3rd Earl of Harrowby. See* Suppt. London University. Inst. of Hist. Research. Bulletin. Special Suppt., 10.

Ryle (Gilbert) Dilemmas. [Tarner Lects., 1953.] (1954.) repr. 8vo. CAMB., 1960.
—— A puzzling element in the notion of thinking. [Annual Philosophical Lect., Brit. Acad., 1958.] 8vo. LOND., [1959]. [Pamph.]
—— The thinking of thoughts. [Univ. of Saskatchewan Lect., 18.] 8vo. [SASKATOON,] 1968. [Pamph.]
—— On thinking. Ed. Konstantin Kolenda. Preface by G. J. Warnock. 8vo. OXF., 1979.
Ryle (J. C.) *Bp. of Liverpool.* See Machray (W. F.)
Rynne (Xavier) *pseud.* Letters from Vatican City: Vatican Council II (first session): background and debates. 8vo. LOND., 1963.
Ryssel (F. H.) *ed.* Protestantismus heute. 8vo. FRANKFURT AM M., 1959.

Sabatier (Pierre) *ed.* See Bible. *Latin.* [Old Latin.]
Sabbatai Sevi. See Scholem (G. G.)
Sabol (Andrew J.) *ed.* See Lewalski (B. K.) and Sabol (A. J.) *ed.*
Sackett (A. B.) See Suppt. Wesley Hist. Soc. Publs., 7, 8.
Sadler (Thomas) The Unitarians of London fifty years ago: reminiscences. 8vo. n.p., 1900.
St. David's, *Diocese of.* Episcopal registers, 1397 to 1518. From the original registers in the diocesan registry of Carmarthen, with a trans. and a general index by R.F. Isaacson. [Cymmrodorion Record Ser., 6.] 2 vols. 8vo. LOND., 1917.
    1. 1397-1407. 1917.
    2. *Not in Library.*
St. John (Henry, *1st Viscount*) 1652-1742. See Smallwood (F. T.)
St. John (Henry) *Viscount Bolingbroke,* 1678-1751. See Dickinson (H. T.)
St. Mark's Review. See Suppt.
Salbstein (M. C. N.) The emancipation of the Jews in Britain: an essay on the preconditions. 8vo. BRIGHTON [printed], 1977.
Sales (John) See Short (E. B.) and Sales (J.)
Salmon (J. H. M.) Society in crisis: France in the sixteenth century. (1975.) repr. 8vo. LOND., 1979.
Salt (H. R.) Gleanings from forgotten fields: being the story of the Berks. Baptist Association, 1652-1907. 8vo. READING, [1907].
Salt (*Sir* Titus) See Suddards (R. W.)
Salter (Alfred) See Brockway A. F.)
Salvation Army. Essays and sketches: the Salvation Army. [Foreword by Bramwell Booth.] 8vo. LOND., 1906.
—— See Sandall (R.)
Samay (Sebastian) Reason revisited: the philosophy of Karl Jaspers. 8vo. DUBLIN & LOND., 1971.
Sampley (J. Paul) 'And the two shall become one flesh': a study of traditions in Ephesians 5: 21-23. [Soc. for N.T. Studies, Monograph Ser., 16.] 8vo. CAMB., 1971.
Sampson (Henry) 1629-1700. See Packard (F.)
Samuel (Herbert L., *1st Viscount*) See Bowle (J.)
Samuel (W. S.) A review of the Jewish colonists in Barbados in the year 1680. 4to. LOND., 1936.
Sandall (Robert) The history of the Salvation Army. 8vo. LOND., 1947-
    6. 1914-1946: Frederick Coutts. 1973.
Sanders (E. P.) Paul and Palestinian Judaism: a comparison of patterns of religion. 8vo. LOND., 1977.
Sanders (J. T.) The New Testament christological hymns: their historical religious background. [Soc. for N.T. Studies, Monograph Ser., 15.] 8vo. CAMB., 1971.
—— Ethics in the New Testament: change and development. 8vo. LOND., 1975.
Sandmel (Samuel) A Jewish understanding of the New Testament. 8vo. CINCINNATI (Ohio), 1957.
—— Philo of Alexandria: an introduction. 8vo. NEW YORK, 1979.
Sangster (Paul) Pity my simplicity: the Evangelical Revival and the religious education of children, 1738-1800. 8vo. LOND., 1963.

Sangster (W. E. R.) God does guide us. (1934.) repr. 8vo. LOND., 1936.
—— The craft of sermon illustration. (1946.) repr. 8vo. LOND., 1950.
—— The approach to preaching. 8vo. LOND., 1951.
—— They met at Calvary. Were you there . . .? 8vo. LOND., 1956.
—— The secret of radiant life. (1957.) 4th imp. 8vo. LOND., 1961.
—— Power in preaching. 8vo. LOND., 1958.
—— Westminster sermons. 2 vols. 8vo. LOND., 1960-61.
   1. At morning worship. 1960.
   2. At fast and festival. 1961.
Sansom (*Sir* G. B.) The Western world and Japan: a study in the interaction of European and Asiatic cultures. (1950.) repr. 8vo. NEW YORK, 1973.
Santayana (George) *See* Wickham (H.)
Santos (Elmar Camilo dos) An expanded Hebrew index for the Hatch-Redpath Concordance to the Septuagint. fol. *Duplicated.* JERUSALEM, [1975?].
Sartre (Jean-Paul) Sketch for a theory of the emotions. Trans. Philip Mairet. Preface by Mary Warnock. 8vo. LOND., 1971.
Sawyer (John F. A.) *See* Suppt. Studies in Bibl. Theol., 2nd Ser., 24.
Saxer (Victor) *See* Suppt. Analecta Bollandiana. Subsid. Hagiog., 57.
Sayers (Dorothy L.) A matter of eternity: selections from the writings of Dorothy L. Sayers, chosen and introd. by Rosamond Kent Sprague. 8vo. GRAND RAPIDS (Mich.), 1973.
Sayles (Alan) 300 years of Nonconformist witness in Writtle. fol. *Duplicated.* [WRITTLE,] 1972. [Pamph.]
Scharf (Kurt) *ed. See* Vogel (H.) [Misc.]
Schechter (Solomon) *See* Bentwich (N.)
Scheler (Max) Der Formalismus in der Ethik und die materiale Wertethik: neuer Versuch der Grundlegung eines ethischen Personalismus. (1913.) 2te. Aufl. 8vo. HALLE A.D. S., 1921.
—— Wesen und Formen der Sympathie: der "Phänomenologie der Sympathiegefühle". (1913.) 3te. Aufl. [Die Sinngesetze des emotionalen Lebens, 1.] 8vo. BONN, 1931.
—— Vom Ewigen im Menschen. (1921.) 3te. Aufl. 8vo. BERLIN, 1933.
—— Die Wissensformen und die Gesellschaft: Probleme einer Soziologie des Wissens. 4to. LEIPZIG, 1926.
—— *See* Chevrolet (J.-P.)
Schelling (F. W. J. von) [Ästhetik.] Schellings Ästhetik in der Überlieferung von Henry Crabb Robinson. [Ed. with an introd. by] Ernst Behler. 8vo. FREIBURG & MÜNCHEN, 1976. [Pamph.]
—— *See* Hartmann (N.)
Schenck (L. B.) The Presbyterian doctrine of children in the Covenant: an historical study of the significance of infant baptism in the Presbyterian Church in America. [Yale Studies in Relig. Education, 12.] 8vo. NEW HAVEN & LOND., 1940.
Schillebeeckx (Edward) Jesus: an experiment in Christology. [Trans. Hubert Hoskins.] 8vo. LOND., 1979.
Schilpp (P. A.) *ed. See* Suppt. Library of Living Philosophers.
Schlatter (Adolf) Der Evangelist Johannes: wie er spricht, denkt und glaubt. Ein Kommentar zum vierten Evangelium. (1930.) 3te. Aufl. 8vo. STUTTGART, 1960.
—— Gottes Gerechtigkeit: ein Kommentar zum Römerbrief. (1935.) 2te. Aufl. Gedächtnisausgabe zum 100. Geburtstag von Adolf Schlatter. 8vo. STUTTGART, 1952.
—— *See* Suppt. Studies in Bibl. Theol., 2nd Ser., 25.
Schleiermacher (Friedrich D. E.) [Two or more works.] Pädagogische Schriften. Unter Mitwirkung von Theodor Schulze, hrsg. von Erich Weniger. [Pädagogische Texte.] 2 vols. in 1. 8vo. DÜSSELDORF & MÜNCHEN, 1957.
—— Kurze Darstellung des theologischen Studiums zum Behuf einleitender Vorlesungen. Hrsg. Heinrich Scholz. [Quellenschriften zur Gesch. des Protestantismus, 10.] (1910.) 4te. Aufl. 8vo. DARMSTADT, n.d.
—— *See* Osborn (A. R.)
Schlenther (B. S.) Scottish influences, especially religious, in colonial America. 8vo. [EDIN, 1976.] [Pamph.]

Schlinck-Lazarraga (Elke) Wiedergeburt schöpferischer Religion im Weltbund für reliöse Freiheit. 1. Geschichte des Weltbundes. 8vo. [NORDERSTEDT, the author, 1975.]

Schmidt (Kurt Dietrich) [Misc.] *See* Kretschmar (G.) and Lohse (B.) *ed.*

Schmidt (Larry) *ed.* George Grant in process: essays and conversations. 8vo. TORONTO, 1978.

Schmidt (Ludwig) *See* Suppt. Zeitschr. für A. T. Wiss. Beihefte, 143.

Schmidt (Martin) John Wesley: a theological biography. 2 vols. in 3. 8vo. LOND., 1962-73.
    2. John Wesley's life mission.
      i. Trans. N. P. Goldhawk. 1971.
      ii. Trans. Denis Inman. 1973.

Schmithals (Walter) Gnosticism in Corinth: an investigation of the letters to the Corinthians. Trans. John E. Steely. 8vo. NASHVILLE (Tenn.), 1971.

Schmidt (Gerhard) The concept of Being in Hegel and Heidegger. [Abhandlungen zur Philos., Psychol. u. Pädagogik, 116.] 8vo. BONN, 1977.

Schmitt (Hans-Christoph) *See* Suppt. Zeitschr. für A. T. Wiss. Beihefte, 154.

Schneller (Ludwig) Tischendorf-Erinnerungen: merkwürdige Geschichte einer verlorenen Handschrift. [Weihnachts-Erinnerungen, 9.] 8vo. LEIPZIG, 1931.

Scholem (G. G.) Major trends in Jewish mysticism. [Hilda Stich Strook Lects., Jewish Inst. of Relig., New York, 1938.] 8vo. JERUSALEM, 1941.

—— Sabbatai Sevi: the mystical messiah, 1626-1676. [Littman Lib. of Jewish Civilization.] 8vo. LOND., 1973.

Schonfield (H. J.) The Passover Plot: new light on the history of Jesus. (1965.) 3rd imp. 8vo. LOND., 1966.

Schoonenberg (Piet) Theologie der Sünde ein theologischer Versuch. [Aus dem niederländischen übersetzt von Hugo Zulauf.] 8vo. EINSIEDELN (Switz.), *etc.*, 1966.

Schoors (Anton) *See* Suppt. Vetus Testamentum. Suppts., 24.

Schopenhauer (Arthur) Gesammelte Briefe. Hrsg. Arthur Hübscher. 8vo. BONN, 1978.

Schramm (Tim) Der Markus-Stoff bei Lukas: eine literarkritische und redaktions-geschichtliche Untersuchung. [Soc. for N.T. Studies, Monograph Ser., 14.] 8vo. CAMB., 1971.

Schrautenbach (Ludwig Carl, *Freiherr von*) *See* Zinzendorf (N. L. von) [Misc.]

Schroeder (W. L.) Science, philosophy and religion. [Religion: its Modern Needs and Problems, 18.] 8vo. LOND., 1933.

Schürer (Emil) The history of the Jewish people in the age of Jesus Christ (175 B.C. -A.D. 135). A new English version, rev. and ed. Geza Vermes, Fergus Millar, Matthew Black. 8vo. EDIN., 1973-
    1. 1973.
    2. 1979.
No more yet published, 1980.

Schürmann (Reiner) Meister Eckhart: mystic and philosopher. Translations with commentary. [Studies in Phenomenol. and Existential Philos.] 8vo. BLOOMING-TON (Ind.) & LOND., 1978.

Schütz (J. H.) Paul and the anatomy of apostolic authority. [Soc. for N.T. Studies, Monograph Ser., 26.] 8vo. CAMB., 1975.

Schulte (Hannelis) *See* Suppt. Zeitschr. für A. T. Wiss. Beihefte, 128.

Schultens (J. J.) *See* Van den Berg (J.)

Schulz (Hermann) *See* Suppt. Zeitschr. für A. T. Wiss. Beihefte, 129.

Schurhammer (G. O.) Francis Xavier: his life, his times. Trans. M. Joseph Costelloe. 8vo. ROME, 1973-
    1. Europe, 1506-1541. 1973.
    2. India, 1541-1545. 1977.
No more yet published, 1980.

Schutte (Anne J.) Pier Paolo Vergerio: the making of an Italian Reformer. [Travaux d'Humanisme et Renaissance, 160.] 4to. GENÈVE, 1977.

Schwartz (Hillel) Knaves, fools, madmen, and that subtile effluvium: a study of the opposition to the French Prophets in England, 1706-1710. [Univ. of Florida Monographs, Social Sciences, 62.] 8vo. GAINESVILLE, 1978.

Schwarz (Werner)   A study in pre-Christian symbolism: Philo, De somnis I, 216-218, and Plutarch, De Iside et Osiride 4 and 77.   4to.   LOND., 1973.   [Pamph.]
—— Humanism and language.   8vo.   [LOND., 1974.]   [Pamph.]
Schweich Lectures.   See Suppt.
Schweitzer (Albert)   The quest of the historical Jesus: a critical study of its progress from Reimarus to Wrede.   [Trans. W. Montgomery.]   (1910.)   3rd ed., with a new introd. by the author.   [Trans. J. R. Coates.]   (1954.)   repr.   8vo.   LOND., 1954.
—— The teaching of reverence for life.   [Trans. Richard and Clara Winston.]   8vo.   LOND., 1966.
—— See Brabazon (J.); Franck (F. S.); Pierhal (J.)
Schweizer (Eduard)   Gemeinde und Gemeindeordnung im Neuen Testament.   [Abhandlung zur Theol. des A. u. N.T., 35.]   (1959.)   2te. Aufl.   8vo.   ZÜRICH, 1962.
—— The good news according to Mark: a commentary on the Gospel.   Trans. Donald H. Madvig   [from Das N.T. Deutsch].   8vo.   LOND., 1971.
—— Jesus.   [Trans. David E. Green.]   8vo.   LOND., 1971.
Schwenckfeld (Caspar)   See Sciegienny (A.)
Sciegienny (André)   Homme charnel, homme spirituel: étude sur la christologie de Caspar Schwenckfeld (1489-1561).   [Veröffentlichungen des Instituts für Europ. Gesch., Mainz, 76: Abteilung für Abendländische Religionsgesch.]   8vo.   WIESBADEN, 1975.
Scots Philosophical Club.   See Suppt. Philosophical Quarterly.
Scott (Charles A. A.)   Words: a brief vocabulary of the New Testament.   8vo.   LOND., 1939.
Scott (Clinton L.)   Promise of Spring: forty meditations.   8vo.   BOSTON (Mass.), 1976.   [Pamph.]
Scott (David V.)   David Proctor, 1861-1923.   8vo.   [COWLEY, printed, 1977.]   [Pamph.]
Scott (Drusilla)   A. D. Lindsay: a biography. With chapters by Tom Lindsay and Dorothy Emmet.   8vo.   OXF., 1971.
Scott (Janet)   What canst thou say? Towards a Quaker theology.   [Swarthmore Lect., 1980.]   8vo.   LOND., 1980.
Scott (Robert) and **Gilmore** (G. W.)   The Church, the people, and the age. Analysis and summary by Clarence Augustine Beckwith.   8vo.   NEW YORK & LOND., 1914.
Scott (Robert B. Y.)   See Bible. Commentaries. Anchor Bible, 18.
Scott (William)   The story of Ashby-de-la-Zouch.   8vo.   ASHBY-DE-LA-ZOUCH, 1907.
Scottish Baptist Yearbook.   See Suppt.
Scottish Journal of Theology.   See Suppt.
Scovel (Carl) ed.   Graces, sung and spoken.   8vo.   BOSTON (Mass.), 1963.   [Pamph.]
Scupoli (Lorenzo)   Unseen warfare: being the Spiritual combat and Path to Paradise, as ed. by Nicodemus of the Holy Mountain and rev. by Theophan the Recluse.   Trans. E. Kadloubovsky and G. E. H. Palmer, with an introd. by H. A. Hodges.   [Classics of the Contemplative Life.]   8vo.   LOND., 1952.
Seaburg (Carl G.) ed.   Great occasions: readings for the celebration of birth, coming-of-age, marriage, and death.   8vo.   BOSTON (Mass.), 1968.
Seaton (William)   See Jones (P. M. S.)
Seaver (P. S.)   The Puritan lectureships: the politics of religious dissent, 1560-1662.   8vo.   STANFORD (Calif.), 1970.
Secretum secretorum.   See Suppt. Early Eng. Text Soc., O.S., 276.
Seed (T. Alexander)   Norfolk Street Wesleyan Chapel, Sheffield: being a history of this famous sanctuary, together with an account of the earlier and later history of Methodism in the town and neighbourhood.   8vo.   LOND., [1907].
Selbie (W. B.)   See Pringle (A.) ed.
Sell (A. P. F.)   Congregationalism at Worplesdon, 1822-1972.   8vo.   [WORPLESDON, 1972.]   [Pamph.]
—— George Burder and the Lichfield Dissenters.   4to.   [KENDAL, printed, 1972.]   [Pamph.]
—— A liberated churchman [Robert Mackintosh].   8vo.   GLASGOW, [1973].   [Pamph.]
—— Nonconformity at Worplesdon.   8vo.   OLD WOKING, [1973].   [Pamph.]

Sell (A. P. F.)—*continued*
—— The social and literary contributions of three Unitarian ministers in nineteenth-century Walsall. 8vo. [LOND.,] 1973. [Pamph.] [Photocopy.]
—— Alfred Dye, minister of the Gospel. 8vo. [LOND.,] 1974. [Pamph.]
—— Some sermons of Gilbert White. 8vo. [EDIN., 1974.] [Pamph.] [Photocopy.]
—— Christian and secular philosophy in Britain at the beginning of the twentieth century: a study of approaches and relationships. 8vo. [DOWNSIDE,] 1975. [Pamph.]
—— Robert Mackintosh: theologian of integrity. [European University Papers, Ser. 23: Theology, 95.] 8vo. BERN (Switz.), 1977.
Sellers (C. C.) *See* Catalogues. *Dickinson Coll.*
Sellers (Ian) The Methodist chapels and preaching places of Liverpool and district (1750-1971). fol. *Duplicated.* [WARRINGTON, the author, 1971.] [Pamph.]
—— Adam Clarke, controversialist: Wesleyanism and the historic faith in the age of Bunting. [Wesley Hist. Soc. Lect., 41, 1975.] fol. *Duplicated.* n.p., 1976. [Pamph.]
—— The life of God in biblical thought and contemporary witness. [Conservative Evangelicals in Methodism, Annual Lect., 4, 1977.] 8vo. SHEFFIELD [printed], 1977. [Pamph.]
—— Nineteenth-century Nonconformity. [Foundations of Modern Hist.] 8vo. LOND., 1977.
—— *ed. See* Briggs (J. H. Y.) and Sellers (I.) *ed.*
Sellin (Ernst) Introduction to the Old Testament. *See* Fohrer (G.)
Selsdon. *Baptist Free Church.* Silver jubilee, 2nd to 9th Nov., 1952. 8vo. [SELSDON, 1952.] [Pamph.]
Sergius, *the Stylite. See* Suppt. Corpus Script. Christ. Orient., Syri, 152-153.
Servetus (Michael) Christianismi restitutio. (1553.) facsim. repr. 8vo. FRANKFURT AM M., 1966.
—— *See* Blazeby (W.); Friedman (J.)
Seton-Watson (R. W.) *See* Papers for War Time, 35.
Setton (K. M.) Europe and the Levant in the Middle Ages and the Renaissance. [Variorum Reprs.] 8vo. LOND., 1974.
Sevenster (J. N.) *See* Suppt. Novum Testamentum. Suppts., 41.
Seventeenth-Century News. *See* Suppt.
Severian, *Bp. of Gabala. See* Lehmann (H. J.)
Severus, *Patriarch of Antioch. See* Chesnut (R. C.); Suppt. Corpus Script. Christ. Orient., Syri, 136-137; Patrologia Orientalis, XXXVI.1, 3, XXXVII.1, XXXVIII.2.
Severus [*ibn al-Mukaffa'*], *Anba, Bp. of Ushmunain. See* Suppt. Corpus Script. Christ. Orient., Arab., 32-35.
Seybold (Klaus) *See* Suppt. Forschungen zur Religion u. Lit., 107.
Shabtai Zevi. *See* Sabbatai Sevi.
Shafto (G. R. H.) The reality of the resurrection. 8vo. LOND., 1930.
Shahîd (Irfan) *See* Suppt. Analecta Bollandiana. Subsid. Hagiog., 48.
Shakespeare (J. H.) *See* Baptist Union of G.B. and Ireland.
Shakespeare (William) *See* Murry (J. M.); Smith (L. P.); Yates (F. A.)
Sharf (Andrew) Byzantine Jewry from Justinian to the Fourth Crusade. [Littman Lib. of Jewish Civilization.] 8vo. LOND., 1971.
Sharpe (Emily) *comp.* Pictures of Unitarian churches, with explanatory remarks. 4to. LOND., 1901.
Sharrock (R. I.) Wordsworth's revolt against literature. 8vo. [OXF., 1953.] [Pamph.]
—— Life and story in The Pilgrim's Progress. [Friends of Dr. Williams's Lib. Lect., 32.] 8vo. LOND., 1978. [Pamph.]
—— *See* Bunyan (J.) [Misc.]
Shaw (J. J.) A brief historical sketch of Bethlehem Church, Newchurch-in-Rossendale. obl. 8vo. WATERFOOT, 1906. [Pamph.]
[Shaw (W. S.)] Ter-centenary, 1653-1953: a short history of the Nantwich Baptist Church. 8vo. [NANTWICH, 1953.] [Pamph.]
Sheard (Michael) The origins and early development of Primitive Methodism in the Manchester area, 1820-1830. [Wesley Hist. Soc., Lancs. and Cheshire Branch, Occ. Publ., 4.] 8vo. *Duplicated.* n.p., 1976. [Pamph.]

Sheffield. *Hillsborough Baptist Church.* Diamond jubilee, 1893-1953. 8vo. [SHEF-FIELD, 1953.] [Pamph.]
Sheffield. *Mount View Methodist Church.* Centenary handbook, 1876-1976. 8vo. [SHEFFIELD, 1976.] [Pamph.]
Sheils (W. J.) The Puritans in the Diocese of Peterborough, 1558-1610. [Publs. of Northants. Record Soc., 30.] 8vo. NORTHAMPTON, 1979.
Sheldon (Gilbert) *Abp. of Canterbury. See* Sutch (V. D.)
Shelley (Jack) The history of the Baptist Church, St. George's Street, Macclesfield, 1873-1973. Pt. 1. The first fifty years. 8vo. [MACCLESFIELD, 1973.] [Pamph.]
Shepherd (William) 1768-1847. *See* Lindon (J. M. A.)
Sheppard (G. T.) *See* Suppt. Zeitschr. für A. T. Wiss. Beihefte, 151.
Sheppard (H. R. L.) God and my neighbour. (1937.) 2nd ed. 8vo. LOND., 1937.
—— [Misc.] Hugh Richard Lawrie Sheppard, 1880-1937. [Tributes by various writers.] 8vo. [LOND., 1937.] [Pamph.]
—— *See* Northcott (R. J.)
Shercliff (W. H.) Gatley United Reformed Church: a short history, 1777-1977. 8vo. [GATLEY,] 1976. [Pamph.]
Sheringham. *Baptist Church.* Opening and dedication of the new church hall in the Holway Road, Apr. 1952. 8vo. [SHERINGHAM, 1952.] [Pamph.]
Sherwin-White (A. N.) *See* Burkill (T. A.)
Sherwood (Polycarp) *See* Dumeige (G.) *ed.*
Sherwood (R. E.) Civil strife in the Midlands, 1642-1651. 8vo. LOND., 1974.
Shiells (Robert) The story of the token as belonging to the sacrament of the Lord's Supper. (1891.) 2nd ed. 8vo. EDIN. & LOND., 1902.
[Shildrick (B. C.)] Sutton Coldfield Baptist Church: a record of fifty years. 8vo. [SUTTON COLDFIELD, 1958.] [Pamph.]
Shillito (Edward) François Coillard, a wayfaring man. 8vo. LOND., 1923.
[—— *ed.*] The mandate: a vision of service. Publ. for the use of ministers. 8vo. LOND., 1920.
Shimmin (F. N.) Permanent values of religion. [Hartley Lect., 16.] 8vo. LOND., 1914.
Shipley (C. E.) *See* Child (R. L.) and Shipley (C. E.)
Shirley (F. J. J.) *See* Edwards (D. L.)
[Short (A. R.)] The principles of Christians called 'Open Brethren'. By a younger Brother. (1913.) 2nd ed. 8vo. GLASGOW, 1913.
Short (E. B.) A respectable society: Bridport, 1593-1835. 8vo. BRADFORD-ON-AVON, 1976.
Short (E. B.) and **Sales** (John) The book of Bridport. 4to. BUCKINGHAM, 1980.
Short (H. L.) *See* Suppt. Unitarian Hist. Soc. Trans. Suppt.
Short (Stephen S.) *See* Suppt. Christian Brethren Research Fellowship, Occ. Papers, 1.
Showler (Karl) A review of the history of the Society of Friends in Kent, 1655 to 1966. 8vo. *Duplicated.* CANTERBURY, 1970. [Pamph.]
Shrubsole (O. A.) *See* Hymns.
[Shutt (W.)] Two hundred years of Christian witness, 1760-1960. [Baptist Chapel, Haggate, Lancs.] 8vo. [HAGGATE, 1960.] [Pamph.]
Sider (R. J.) Andreas Bodenstein von Karlstadt: the development of his thought, 1517-1525. [Studies in Medieval and Reformation Thought, 11.] 8vo. LEIDEN, 1974.
Siderman (E. A.) A saint in Hyde Park: memories of Father Vincent McNabb. 8vo. LOND., 1950.
Silliman (Vincent) *ed. See* Hymns.
Simeon, *the New Theologian. See* Symeon.
Simeon, *Stylites, iun. See* Symeon.
Simeon, *Abp. of Thessalonica. See* Symeon.
Simeon (Charles) *See* Hopkins (H. E.)
Simmonds (Percy G.) For his friends. Letters of 2nd Lt. P. G. Simmonds, of Mansfield College, Oxford, who was killed in action on the Somme, July 1st, 1916. With a foreword by Dr. Selbie. 8vo. OXF., n.d.
[Simon (Marcel) *ed.*] Aspects de l'anglicanisme. Colloque de Strasbourg (14-16 juin 1972). [Bibliothèque des Centres d'Études Supérieures Spécialisés.] 8vo. PARIS, 1974.

Simon (Ulrich E.) Theology of crisis. 8vo. LOND., 1948.
—— Alienation. [Maynard-Chapman Divinity Lect., Westfield Coll., Univ. of London, 14th Mar. 1974.] 8vo. [LOND., 1974.] [Pamph.]
—— Sitting in judgement, 1913-1963: an interpretation of history. 8vo. LOND., 1978.
Simpson, *family of.* See Catalogues. *London. New Coll.*
Simpson (M. A.) John Knox and the troubles begun at Frankfurt. 8vo. WEST LINTON [the author], 1975.
Simpson (Patrick Carnegie) The life of Principal Rainy. 2 vols. 8vo. LOND., 1909.
—— Church principles. 8vo. LOND., (1923).
—— Recollections, mainly ecclesiastical but sometimes human. 8vo. LOND., 1943.
Simpson (W. W.) "The kiss of brotherhood": some reflections on the Jewish-Christian dialogue. [St. Paul's Lect., Oct. 1965.] 8vo. [LOND., 1965.] [Pamph.]
Sims (B. H.) The Dissenting Deputies. [Heritage Biographies.] 8vo. LOND., 1961. [Pamph.]
Sinel (Joseph) The sixth sense: a physical explanation of clairvoyance, telepathy, hypnotism, dreams, and other phenomena usually considered occult. 8vo. LOND., 1927.
Sippell (Theodor) William Dell's Programm einer "lutherischen" Gemeinschaftsbewegung. [Zeitschr. für Theol. u. Kirche, 21, Erg. Heft 3.] 8vo. TÜBINGEN, 1911.
—— Zur Frage nach dem Ursprung des Pietismus. 8vo. TÜBINGEN, 1913. [Pamph.]
—— Zur Vorgeschichte des Quäkertums. Vorwort von Friedrich Loofs. [Studien zur Gesch. des neueren Protestantismus, 12.] 8vo. GIESSEN, 1920.
—— Zur Abendmahlslehre des Anglo-Katholizismus. 8vo. GOTHA, [1935]. [Pamph.]
—— Werdendes Quäkertum. 8vo. STUTTGART, 1937.
Sirks (G. J.) *See* Heering (G. J.) and Sirks (G. J.)
Sixteenth-Century Essays and Studies. *See* Suppt.
Skabalanovich (N. A.) Vizantiiskoe gosudarstvo i tserkov'v XI veke, ot smerti Vasiliia II Bolgaroboitsy do votsareniia Alekseia I Komnina. (The Byzantine state and church in the 11th century, from the death of Basil II, the slayer of the Bulgars, to the accession of Alexius I Comnenus.) (1884). facsim. repr. Introd. by J. M. Hussey. 8vo. FARNBOROUGH, 1972.
Skemp (T. W. W.) After one hundred and fifty years: a short account of Salem Baptist Church, Wood Street, Bilston, June 15 1800-June 15 1950. 8vo. [BILSTON, 1950.] [Pamph.]
—— —— [2nd ed.] One hundred and sixty years...June 15 1800-June 15 1960. 8vo. [BILSTON, 1960.] [Pamph.]
Skinner (A. S.) Adam Smith and the state. 8vo. GLASGOW, 1974 [Pamph.]
Skinner (B. G.) Henry Francis Lyte, Brixham's poet and priest. 8vo. EXETER, 1974.
—— Robert Exon: a biography of Dr. R. C. Mortimer, Bishop of Exeter from 1949-1973. Foreword by Lord Ramsey of Canterbury. 8vo. BOGNOR REGIS, 1979.
Slack (Kenneth) The City Temple: a hundred years. 8vo. LOND., 1974. [Pamph.]
Slader (John) and **Thorne** (R .F. S.) Churches and chapels in Devon. 8vo. [EXETER, 1976.] [Pamph.]
Slosser (G. J.) Christian unity: its history and challenge in all communions, in all lands. With introds. by William Temple and Alfred E. Garvie. 8vo. LOND., 1929.
Slotten (Martha C.) *See* Catalogues. *Dickinson Coll.*
Small (Robert) History of the congregations of the United Presbyterian Church from 1733 to 1900. 2 vols. 8vo. EDIN., 1904.
Smalley (Beryl) The Becket conflict and the schools: a study of intellectuals in politics. [Ford Lects., 1967.] 8vo. OXF., 1973.
Smalley (L. G.) The Baptists in Wokingham: 200 years of Christian witness, 1774-1974. 8vo. WOKINGHAM, [1974]. [Pamph.]
Smalley (S. S.) *ed. See* Moule (C. F. D.) [Misc.]
Smallwood (E. Mary) From pagan protection to Christian oppression. Inaugural lect., Queen's Univ. of Belfast, 2 May 1979. 8vo. BELFAST, [1979]. [Pamph.]
Smallwood (F. T.) Conventicle and school in the vicarage. 8vo. LOND., 1972. [Pamph.]
—— Henry St. John the elder and the Estcourt murder. 4to. *Duplicated.* n.p., 1972. [Pamph.]

SMA 139

Smart (J. J. C.) and **Williams** (B. A. O.) Utilitarianism: for and against. (1973.) repr. 8vo. CAMB., 1976.
Smart (R. Ninian) The phenomenon of religion. [Philos. of Relig. Ser.] 8vo. LOND., 1973.
—— The philosophy of religion. (1970.) repr. [Studies in Philos. and Relig., 6.] 8vo. LOND., 1979.
Smeaton (Oliphant) Principal James Morison: the man and his work. With an appreciation by A. M. Fairbairn. 8vo. EDIN. & LOND., 1902.
Smirnov (P. S.) Istoria Russkago raskola staroobriadchestva. (History of the Russian old-ritualist schism.) (1895.) facsim. repr. 8vo. FARNBOROUGH, 1971.
Smith (Adam) See Skinner (A. S.)
Smith (Alan) Steam and the City: the Committee of Proprietors of the invention for raising water by fire, 1715-1735. 4to. n.p., [1978]. [Pamph.]
Smith (Alan G. R.) ed. See Hurstfield (J.) [Misc.]
Smith (Andrew A.) and **Lawrence** (David) Victoria Road United Reformed Church (formerly Congregational) [Cambridge]: a history of the first hundred years. 8vo. CAMB., [1977]. [Pamph.]
Smith (Arthur Cobden) Chapel Lane Chapel, Bradford, 1719-1919: historical sketch. 8vo. n.p., [1919]. [Pamph.]
Smith (Douglas Bannerman) After 50 years: jubilee of Grimsby Presbyterian Church [1873-1923]. 8vo. HULL, [1924]. [Pamph.]
Smith (Ebenezer) Two centuries of grace: a brief history of the Baptist Church, Waterbeach. 4to. [CAMB.,] 1903. [Pamph.]
Smith (Ernest Alfred) Religion and its social expression. [Religion: its Modern Needs and Problems, 11.] 8vo. LOND., 1932.
Smith (Frank) 1882-1951, Prof. of Education. A history of English elementary education, 1760-1902. 8vo. LOND., 1931.
[**Smith** (Frank) fl. 1977.] Selsdon Baptist Church, 1927-1977. 8vo. [SELSDON, 1977.] [Pamph.]
Smith (Frank Herbert) The story of Ilford (High Road) Baptist Church, 1801-1951. 8vo. ILFORD, [1951]. [Pamph.]
Smith (George Adam) See Smith (Lilian Adam)
Smith (Goldwin) See Gaffney (P. H.) ed.
Smith (H. S.) and others. See Suppt. Egypt Exploration Soc. Memoirs, 48.
Smith (James Sommerville) Miller of Ruchill: the story of a great achievement. With an introd. chapter by D. P. Thomson. 8vo. GLASGOW, [1924].
Smith (Joe William Ashley) Modern history as subject matter for higher education: the contribution of Francis Tallents. 8vo. GENT (Belg.), 1975. [Pamph.]
Smith (John) fl. 1909, of Huncoat, Lancs. A short history of the Huncoat Baptist Church. 8vo. LOND., [1909].
Smith (John Taylor) 1860-1938, Bp. of Sierra Leone. See Whitlow (M.)
Smith (Kathleen L. Carrick) Sonship. 8vo. LOND., 1948. [Pamph.]
Smith (Lilian Adam) George Adam Smith: a personal memoir and family chronicle. 8vo. LOND., 1943.
Smith (Logan Pearsall) Trivia. 8vo. LOND., 1918.
—— More trivia. 8vo. LOND., 1922.
—— Words and idioms: studies in the English language. 8vo. LOND., 1925.
—— Afterthoughts. 8vo. LOND., 1931.
—— All trivia: Trivia (1918); More trivia (1922); Afterthoughts (1931); Last words (1933). (1933.) repr. 8vo. LOND., 1945.
—— On reading Shakespeare. (1933.) 3rd ed. 8vo. LOND., 1945.
—— Reperusals and re-collections. 8vo. LOND., 1936.
—— Unforgotten years. 8vo. LOND., 1938.
—— ed. A treasury of English prose. (1919.) repr. 8vo. LOND., etc., 1943.
—— ed. A treasury of English aphorisms. (1928.) repr. 8vo. LOND., 1943.
—— ed. The golden Shakespeare: an anthology. 8vo. LOND., 1949.
—— See Gathorne-Hardy (R.)
[**Smith** (Margaret I.)] Bristo Baptist Church, Buckingham Terrace, Queensferry Road, Edinburgh: history of the church, 1765-1965. 8vo. [EDIN., 1965.] [Pamph.]
Smith (Morton) Jesus the magician. 8vo. LOND., 1978.
[**Smith** (Philip R. M.)] History of Yardley Hastings Congregational Church. 8vo. BEDFORD [printed], [1972]. [Pamph.]

Smith (R. A.) *ed.* Kings Norton United Reformed Church (Congregational-Presbyterian): 70 years at Watford Road. 4to. [KINGS NORTON,] 1974. [Pamph.]

[**Smith** (Robert Aldrich) *ed.*] The Baptists in King's Lynn: 250th commemoration, 1689-1939. 8vo. [KING'S LYNN, 1939.] [Pamph.]

[**Smith** (Robert Hugh) *comp.*] Landmarks of two hundred years: Chichester Congregational Church. 8vo. [CHICHESTER, 1971.] [Pamph.]

Smith (Rodney) '*Gipsy Smith*'. His life and work, by himself. rev. ed. 8vo. LOND., [1924].

—— *See* Murray (H.)

Smith (Ronald Gregor) *ed.* World come of age: a symposium on Dietrich Bonhoeffer. 8vo. LOND., 1967.

Smith (Samuel) *M.P.* My life-work. 8vo. LOND., 1902.

[**Smith** (Walter Whatley)] Matter, mind and meaning. By Whatley Carington [pseud.]. Preface by H. H. Price. 8vo. LOND., 1949.

Smith (William) 1756-1835, *politician*. *See* Davis (R. W.)

Smith (William Denis Ashley) Joseph Priestley, FRS, LLD (1733-1804), and the 'discovery' of oxygen. 8vo. [LEEDS,] 1975. [Pamph.]

Smyth (Newman) and **Walker** (Williston) *ed.* Approaches towards church unity. 8vo. NEW HAVEN, 1919.

Snaith (N. H.) Notes on the Hebrew text of Jonah. [Study Notes on Bible Books.] 8vo. LOND., 1945.

Sobornost. *See* Suppt.

Sobrino (Jon) Christology at the crossroads: a Latin American approach. [Trans. from the Spanish by John Drury.] 8vo. LOND., 1978.

Société des Bollandistes. *See* Suppt. Analecta Bollandiana.

Société Mabillon. *See* Suppt. Revue Mabillon.

Society for New Testament Studies. *See* Suppt.

Society for Old Testament Study. *See* Suppt.

Society for Promoting Christian Knowledge. *See* Suppt.

Society for Psychical Research. *See* Suppt.

Society for the Promotion of Hellenic Studies. *See* Stevens (P. T.); Suppt. Journal of Hellenic Studies.

Society for the Promotion of Hellenic Studies and **Society for the Promotion of Roman Studies.** Report of a joint meeting held in Oxford, 29th Aug.–5th Sep. 1942. President of the meeting: Prof. Gilbert Murray. 4to. LOND., 1943. [Pamph.]

Society of Biblical Literature. *See* Suppt. Journal of Biblical Literature.

Sociological Yearbook of Religion in Britain. *See* Suppt.

Socrates, *Scholasticus.* *See* Chesnut (G. F.)

Söderblom (Nathan) *Abp. of Upsala.* The mystery of the cross: thoughts for Holy Week and other weeks. Trans. A. G. Hebert. 8vo. LOND., 1933.

Soggin (J. Alberto) Joshua: a commentary. [Trans. from the French by R. A. Wilson.] [Old Test. Lib.] 8vo. LOND., 1972.

Somerset. *Society of Friends. Quarterly Meeting.* [Minutes.] The Somersetshire Quarterly Meeting of the Society of Friends, 1668-1699. Ed. Stephen C. Morland. [Somerset Record Soc., 75.] 8vo. [TAUNTON,] 1978.

Somerset (Edward Seymour, *1st Duke of*) *See* Bush (M. L.)

Sommerville (C. J.) Popular religion in Restoration England. [Univ. of Florida Monographs, Social Sciences, 59.] 8vo. GAINESVILLE, 1977.

Sophronius, *Saint, Patriarch of Jerusalem.* *See* Suppt. Patrologia Orientalis, XXXIX.2.

Sorensen (Reginald W.) *Baron Sorensen of Leytonstone.* Tolpuddle, or "Who's afeared": a democratic episode in three acts. 8vo. LOND., [1928].

—— "Earthquake, wind and fire": conflicting realities and the way to peace. [Alex Wood Memorial Lect., 1958.] 8vo. LOND., 1958. [Pamph.]

—— *See* Catalogues. *House of Lords Record Office.*

Sorrell (Mark) The Peculiar People. 8vo. EXETER, 1979.

South India United Church. *See* Proposed scheme of union.

Southall (Kenneth H.) *ed.* Our Quaker heritage: early meeting houses built prior to 1720 and in use to-day. 4to. LOND., [1974].

Southend-on-Sea. *Park Road Methodist Church.* Centenary, 1870-1970. 4to. SOUTHEND-ON-SEA, 1970. [Pamph.]

Southern (R. W.)   Sir Maurice Powicke, 1879-1963.   [Repr. from Brit. Acad. Proc., 50, 1964.]   8vo.   LOND., [1965].   [Pamph.]

Southey (H. J.)   Congregational church history in Dover, 1600-1925.   8vo.   [DOVER, 1925.]   [Pamph.]

Southgate. *Oakwood Park Free Church (Baptist).*   The Oakwood story, 1935-1960.   8vo.   [LOND., 1960.]   [Pamp,.]

Southwell (Robert) *c.* 1561-95, *S.J.*   The triumphs over death. Together with the Epistle to his father, the Letter to his brother, the Letter to his cousin "W.R.", and a soliloquy. Ed. from the MSS. by John William Trotman.   [Catholic Lib., 8.]   8vo.   LOND., 1914.

—— *See* Janelle (P.)

Sozomen.   *See* Chesnut (G. F.)

Spalding (Ruth J. L.)   The improbable Puritan: a life of Bulstrode Whitelocke, 1605-1675.   8vo.   LOND., 1975.

Spangenberg (August Gottlieb)   *See* Zinzendorf (N. L. von)   [Misc.]

Sparham (G. J.)   The problem of evil.   [Religion: its Modern Needs and Problems, 16.]   8vo.   LOND., 1933.

Sparks (H. F. D.)   On translations of the Bible.   [Ethel M. Wood Lect., 1972.]   8vo.   LOND., 1973.   [Pamph.]

—— *See* Bible. Gospels.   [Harmonies. *English.*]

Speck (W. A.)   Stability and strife: England, 1714-1760.   [New Hist. of England, 6.]   8vo.   LOND., 1977.

Speen. *Baptist Church.*   1813-1963: a brief history of 150 years of Christian witness.   8vo.   [SPEEN, 1963.]   [Pamph.]

Spencer (Frederick A. M.)   The future life: a new interpretation of the Christian doctrine.   8vo.   LOND., 1935.

Spencer (Herbert)   *See* Wiltshire (D.)

Spencer (P. J.)   Lodge Road Church (Unitarian), West Bromwich: its founding and history compiled from church records.   8vo.   *Duplicated.*   n.p., 1952.   [Pamph.]

—— —— [rev. ed.]   1875-1975.   8vo.   [WEST BROMWICH, 1975.]   [Pamph.]

Spencer (Sidney)   The meaning and value of religion.   [Religion: its Modern Needs and Problems, 13.]   8vo.   LOND., 1932.

Spender (J. A.)   *See* Harris (H. W.)

Spener (Philip Jacob)   *See* Weigelt (H.)

Spenser (Edmund)   *See* Yates (F. A.)

Sperber (Alexander) *ed.*   *See* Bible. *Aramaic.*

Speyer (Wolfgang)   Die literarische Fälschung in heidnischen und christlichen Altertum: ein Versuch ihrer Deutung.   [Handbuch der Altertumswiss., I, 2.]   8vo.   MÜNCHEN, 1971.

Spidlik (Thomas)   Grégoire de Nazianze: introd. à l'étude de sa doctrine spirituelle   [Orientalia Christiana Analecta, 189.]   8vo.   ROMA, 1971.

Spielman (John P.)   *See* Miller (S. J. T.) and Spielman (J. P.)

Spiers (Maurice)   *See* Suppt. Chetham Soc., 3rd Ser., 23.

Spinks (B. D.)   The original form of the Anaphora of the Apostles: a suggestion in the light of Maronite Sharar.   8vo.   [ROME, 1977.]   [Pamph.]

Spinola (Cristobal Rojas y)   *See* Miller (S. J. T.) and Spielman (J. P.)

Sprigg (William)   *See* Greaves (R. L.)

Spriggs (D. G.)   *See* Suppt. Studies in Bibl. Theol., 2nd Ser., 30.

Sprunger (Keith La Verne)   The learned Doctor William Ames: Dutch backgrounds of English and American Puritanism.   URBANA (Ill.), *etc.*, 1972.

—— Other pilgrims in Leiden: Hugh Goodyear and the English Reformed Church.   8vo.   [BERNE (Ind.),] 1972.   [Pamph.]

—— The Dutch career of Thomas Hooker.   8vo.   [PORTLAND (Me.),] 1973.   [Pamph.]

Spufford (H. Margaret)   The schooling of the peasantry in Cambridgeshire, 1575-1700.   4to.   [READING,] 1970.   [Pamph.]

—— Contrasting communities: English villagers in the sixteenth and seventeenth centuries.   8vo.   CAMB., 1974.

Spurgeon (Charles Haddon)   *See* Pearce (G. J. M.)

Spurgeon (Thomas)   *See* Fullerton (W. Y.)

Spurr (F. C.)   Death and the life beyond in the light of modern religious thought and experience. (1913.)   new ed.   8vo.   LOND., 1926.

Spurr (F. C.)—*continued*
—— —— [Another ed.] The life hereafter in the light of modern religious life and experience. 8vo. LOND., [1934].
Squibb (G. D.) *ed. See* Suppt. Harleian Soc. Publs., 117.
Stack (C. M.) *See* Gray-Stack (C. M.)
[Stacpoole (Alberic)] The making of a monastic historian: Dom David Knowles, 1896-1940. [Offpr. from The Ampleforth Journal.] 3 pts. in 1. 8vo. [MARKET WEIGHTON, 1975.] [Pamph.]
Stankiewicz (W. J.) The wars of religion and their impact. 8vo. LOND., 1953. [Pamph.]
—— The Huguenot question. 8vo. LOND., 1954. [Pamph.]
—— The Edict of Nantes in the light of mediaeval political theory. 8vo. LOND., 1955. [Pamph.]
—— The Huguenot downfall: the influence of Richelieu's policy and doctrine. 4to. PHILADELPHIA, 1955. [Pamph.]
—— Intoleranz im Frankreich des XVI. Jahrhunderts. 8vo. LECK (W. Ger.), 1959. [Pamph.]
—— [Articles on "Huguenots" and "Wars of religion" from the New Catholic Encyclopaedia.] 4to. [NEW YORK, 1967?] [Pamph.]
—— Relativism: thoughts and aphorisms. 4to. WEST CHESTERFIELD (N.H.), 1972.
Stanley (John) The church in the hop garden: a chatty account of the Longworth-Coate Baptist Meeting, Berks. and Oxfordshire (ante 1481-1935), and its ministers. 8vo. LOND., [1934].
Stansbach. *Baptist Church.* One hundred years of witness at Stansbach Baptist Church. 8vo. [STANSBACH, 1963.] [Pamph.]
Stanton (G. N.) Jesus of Nazareth in New Testament preaching. [Soc. for N.T. Studies, Monograph Ser., 27.] 8vo. CAMB., 1974.
—— Interpreting the New Testament today. Inaugural lect., Chair of N.T. Studies, Univ. of London, King's Coll., 14 Nov. 1978. 8vo. [LOND., 1979]. [Pamph.]
Staples (Laurence) Washington Unitarianism: a rich heritage. 8vo. WASHINGTON, D.C., 1970.
Starr (Edward C.) *ed.* A Baptist bibliography: being a register of printed material by and about Baptists, including works written against the Baptists. 25 vols. 8vo. [1] & 4to. [2-25]. ROCHESTER (N.Y.), *etc.*, 1947-76.
Stead (G. C.) Divine substance. 8vo. OXF., 1977.
Stead (Harold A. D.) Great is thy faithfulness: a short history of Matson Baptist Church, 1952-1977. 8vo. [MATSON, 1977.] [Pamph.]
Stead (Harry G.) The education of a community today and tomorrow. 8vo. BICKLEY (Kent), 1942.
Steadman (J. M.) Epic and tragic structure in Paradise Lost. 8vo. CHICAGO & LOND., 1976.
Stearne (John) A confirmation and discovery of witch craft. (1648.) facsim. repr. 8vo. EXETER, 1973. [Pamph.]
Stearns (R. P.) and **Brawner** (D. H.) New England church "relations" and continuity in early Congregational history. 8vo. WORCESTER (Mass.), 1965. [Pamph.]
Steck (O. H.) *See* Suppt. Forschungen zur Religion u. Lit., 115.
Steel (D. J.) Sources for Nonconformist genealogy and family history. [National Index of Parish Registers, 2.] 8vo. CHICHESTER, 1973.
Steere (Douglas V.) God's irregular: Arthur Shearly Cripps: a Rhodesian epic. 8vo. LOND., 1973.
Steiner (Rudolf) Cosmic memory: prehistory of Earth and Man. Trans. Karl E. Zimmer. 8vo. ENGLEWOOD (N.J.), 1959.
—— *See* Allen (P. M.) *comp.*
Steinmetz (Johann Adam) *See* Kawerau (P.)
Stell (C. F.) Architects of Dissent: some Nonconformist patrons and their architects. [Friends of Dr. Williams's Lib. Lect., 30.] 8vo. LOND., 1976. [Pamph.]
Stella (Aldo) Dall'anabattismo al socianesimo nel Cinquecento veneto. Ricerche storiche. 8vo. PADOVA, 1967.
—— Anabattismo e antitrinitarismo in Italia nel XVI secolo. Nuove ricerche storiche. 8vo. PADOVA, 1969.

Stelling-Michaud (Sven) and **Stelling-Michaud** (Suzanne) *ed.* Le livre du Recteur de l'Académie de Genève (1559-1878). [Travaux d'Humanisme et Renaissance.] 6 vols. 4to. GENÈVE, 1959-80.
   3. Notices biographiques des étudiants. D-G. 1972.
   4. —— H-M. 1975.
   5. —— N-S. 1976.
   6. —— T-Z. 1980.
Stendahl (Krister) Paul among Jews and Gentiles, and other essays. 8vo. LOND., 1977.
Stenhousemuir. *Universalist Church.* Jubilee of the Universalist Church, Stenhousemuir, Larbet, Scotland, 1867-1917. 8vo. GLASGOW [printed], 1917. [Pamph.]
Stephen, *Bp. of Heracleopolis Magna. See* Suppt. Corpus Script. Christ. Orient., Copt., 39-40.
Stephen (*Sir* Leslie) Mausoleum Book. Introd. by Alan Bell. 8vo. OXF., 1977.
Stephens (W. Peter) The Holy Spirit in the theology of Martin Bucer. 8vo. CAMB., 1970.
Sternacki (Sebastian) *See* Kawecka-Gryczowa (A.)
Stevens (P. T.) The Society for the Promotion of Hellenic Studies, 1879-1979: a historical sketch. 8vo. OXF. [printed], [1979]. [Pamph.]
Stewart (James Stuart) A man in Christ: the vital elements of St. Paul's religion. (1935.) repr. 8vo. LOND., 1947.
—— Thine is the kingdom. 8vo. EDIN., 1956.
—— The wind of the Spirit. 8vo. LOND., 1968.
Stewart (M. A.) *ed. See* Suppt. Philosophical Books.
[**Stewart** (W. S.)] Early history of the Presbyterian Church of England, Oldham [1883-1909]. 8vo. OLDHAM, [1909]. [Pamph.]
Stewart (William A.C.) Quakers and education, as seen in their schools in England. 8vo. LOND., 1953.
Stillingfleet (Edward) *Bp. of Worcester. See* Carroll (R. T.)
Stoddart (Jane T.) My harvest of the years. 8vo. LOND., 1938.
Stoeckle (Bernhard) *ed. See* Dictionaries. Christianity.
Stoeffler (F. Ernest) German Pietism during the eighteenth century. [Studies in the Hist. of Religions., 24.] 8vo. LEIDEN, 1973.
Stone (Lawrence) The causes of the English Revolution, 1529-1642. 8vo. LOND., 1972.
Stonebridge (Elsie R.) and **Stonebridge** (Lilian M.) Gleanings from history over three hundred years, tracing the line of our descent from Philip James, born 1664. 4to. BEDFORD, 1970. [Pamph.]
Stonier (Geoffrey) Isaac Watts and preaching. 8vo. EDIN., 1974. [Pamph.]
Stony Stratford. *Baptist Church.* 1657-1957: three centuries of worship, work and witness. 8vo. NORTHAMPTON, 1957. [Pamph.]
[**Stout** (E. G.) *and others.*] Northfleet Congregational Church, Dover Road, 1850-1950: centenary booklet. obl. 8vo. GRAVESEND [printed], [1950]. [Pamph.]
Strachan (C. G.) The Pentecostal theology of Edward Irving. 8vo. LOND., 1973.
Strachey (Ray) Frances Willard: her life and work. Introd. by Lady Henry Somerset. 8vo. LOND., 1912.
Strachey (Richard P. F.) A Strachey child. 8vo. OXF., 1979.
Straeten (Joseph van der) *See* Suppt. Analecta Bollandiana. Subsid. Hagiog., 50, 56.
Stratos (A. N.) Byzantium in the seventh century. Trans. M. Ogilvie-Grant [1]; H. T. Hionides [2+]. 8vo. AMSTERDAM, 1968-
   2. 634-641. 1972.
   3. 642-668. 1975.
   4. 668-685. 1978.
Strauss (David Friedrich) *See* Harris (H.)
Strauss (Gerald) Luther's house of learning: indoctrination of the young in the German Reformation. 8vo. BALTIMORE & LOND., 1978.
Strawson (P. F.) Introduction to logical theory. (1952.) repr. 8vo. LOND., 1963.
Strawson (William) Jesus and the future life. [Fernley Lects., 1959.] (1959.) 2nd ed. 8vo. LOND., 1970.
Strecker (Georg) *See* Bauer (W.)

Street (C. J.)   Thomas Asline Ward and Upper Chapel, Sheffield: the Sunday School centenary volume.   8vo.   SHEFFIELD, 1910.
Street (M. Jennie) *ed.*   *See* Chaplin (W. K.) and Street (M. J.) *ed.*
Streeter (B. H.)   *See* Papers for War Time, 20.
Strict Baptist Historical Society.   *See* Suppt.
Stroebel (August)   *See* Suppt. Zeitschr. für A. T. Wiss. Beihefte, 145; Zeitschr. für N. T. Wiss. Beihefte, 40.
Strong (Josiah)   Our country. (1891.) Ed. Jurgen Herbst.   [John Harvard Lib.]   8vo.   CAMB. (Mass.), 1963.
Strong (T. B.) *Bp. of Oxford.*   The miraculous in Gospels and creeds.   8vo.   LOND., 1914.   [Pamph.]
Struthers (J. P.)   [Misc.]   Life and letters of John Paterson Struthers, late Minister of Greenock Reformed Presbyterian Church.   Ed. Annie L. Struthers. 8vo.   LOND., [1918].
Stubbe (Henry) 1632-76.   An account of the rise and progress of Mahometanism, with the life of Mahomet and a vindication of him and his religion from the calumnies of the Christians. Ed. with an introd. and an appendix by Hafiz Mahmud Khan Shairani.   (1911.)   2nd imp.   8vo.   LAHORE, 1954.
—— *See* Holt (P. M.); Nicastro (O.)
Stubbs (John) 1541?-90.   Gaping gulf, with letters and other relevant documents. Ed. Lloyd E. Berry.   [Folger Documents of Tudor and Stuart Civilization.]   8vo.   CHARLOTTESVILLE (Va.), 1968.
Studdert-Kennedy (G. A.)   [Selections.]   The best of G. A. Studdert Kennedy (Woodbine Willie), selected from his writings by a friend.   8vo.   LOND., 1947.
—— The hardest part.   8vo.   LOND., 1918.
—— Food for the fed-up.   8vo.   LOND., [1921].
—— The wicket gate, or Plain bread. (1923.)   repr.   8vo.   LOND., 1935.
—— The warrior, the woman and the Christ: a study of the leadership of Christ. (1928.)   repr.   8vo.   LOND., 1930.
—— The new man in Christ.   Ed. by the Dean of Worcester   [W. M. Ede]. (1932.) repr.   8vo.   LOND., 1935.
Students' Pentecostal Fellowship.   *See* Suppt. Pentecostal.
Studia et Acta Ecclesiastica.   *See* Bartha (T.) *ed.; Bucsay (M.) and others.*
Studia Evangelica.   *See* Suppt. Texte u. Untersuchungen, 103, 112.
Studia Patristica.   *See* Suppt. Texte u. Untersuchungen, 108, 115-117.
Studies in Biblical Theology.   *See* Suppt.
Studies in Church History.   *See* Suppt.
Studies in Theology.   *See* Suppt. Duckworth Studies in Theology.
Studiorum Novi Testamenti Societas.   *See* Suppt. New Testament Studies.
Stuhlmacher (Peter)   Vom Verstehen des Neuen Testaments: eine Hermeneutik. [Grundrisse zum N.T., 6.]   8vo.   GÖTTINGEN, 1979.
Stunt (T. C. F.)   *See* Suppt. Christian Brethren Research Fellowship. Occ. Papers, 3.
Subsidia Hagiographica.   *See* Suppt. Analecta Bollandiana.
Suddards (R. W.)   Titus of Salts.   8vo.   BRADFORD, 1976.   [Pamph.]
Sulivan (Elizabeth)   *See* Suppt. Royal Hist. Soc. Camden 4th Ser., 23.
Sulivan (Lawrence)   *See* Suppt. Royal Hist. Soc. Camden 4th Ser., 23.
Sumner (Mary E.)   *See* Porter (M.) *and others.*
Sunday School Association.   *See* Broadbent (A.)
Sunday School Union.   *See* Groser (W. H.)
Sunderland (J. T.)   Three centuries and a half of Unitarianism in Hungary.   8vo.   BOSTON (Mass.), 1907.   [Pamph.]
Sundkler (B. G. M.)   Bantu prophets in South Africa. (1948.) 2nd ed.   8vo.   LOND., 1961.
Supek (Rudi) and **Bošnjak** (Branko) *ed.*   Jugoslawien denkt anders: Marxismus und Kritik des etatistischen Sozialismus.   [Europäische Perspektiven.]   8vo.   WIEN, etc., 1971.
Suppan (Klaus)   Die Ehelehre Martin Luthers: theologische und rechtshistorische Aspekte des reformatorischen Eherverständnisses.   8vo.   SALZBURG & MÜNCHEN, 1971.
Surtees Society.   *See* Suppt.
Survey of London.   *See* Suppt. Greater London Council.
Suso (Heinrich)   *See* Deutsche Mystiker, 1.

Sussex Congregational Union and Home Missionary Society. Manual for 1923, with reports for 1922. 8vo. n.p., [1923]. [Pamph.]

Sutch (V. D.) Gilbert Sheldon, architect of Anglican survival, 1640-1675. [Internat. Archives of the Hist. of Ideas, Ser. Minor, 12.] 8vo. THE HAGUE, 1973.

Sutherland (Gillian) *See* Suppt. Historical Assn. Gen. Ser., 76.

Sutherland (Nicola M.) The massacre of St. Bartholomew and the European conflict, 1559-1572. 8vo. LOND., 1973.

—— The Huguenot struggle for recognition. 8vo. NEW HAVEN & LOND., 1980.

Sutterby (Janet) "Saints below"; a history of the Baptist Church meeting at the Bridge Street Chapel, Banbury. 8vo. [BANBURY,] 1973. [Pamph.]

Sutton. *Baptist Church.* Glimpses of the past [1884-1934]. obl. 8vo. [SUTTON, 1934.] [Pamph.]

Sutton (Joseph) St. George's Place Baptist Church, Canterbury: 'Its beginnings and growth'. 8vo. [CANTERBURY,] 1973. [Pamph.]

Swale (W. E.) Three hundred years of Dissent: a brief history of the Unitarian Church in Lancaster. 4to. *Duplicated.* [LANCASTER,] 1971. [Pamph.]

Swanston (H. F. G.) Ideas of order: Anglicans and the renewal of theological method in the middle years of the nineteenth century. 8vo. ASSEN, 1974.

Swart (K. W.) *See* Suppt. Historical Assn. Gen. Ser., 94.

Swarthmore Lectures. *See* Suppt.

Swedenborg (Emanuel) *See* Van Dusen (W. M.)

Swift (Jonathan) *See* Ehrenpreis (I.)

Swift (R. C.) In every generation: a brief history of the Methodist churches in Nottingham, 1764-1978. 8vo. n.p., 1979. [Pamph.]

Swift (W. F.) Methodism in Scotland: the first hundred years. [Wesley Hist. Soc. Lect., 13, 1947.] 8vo. LOND., 1947.

Swinburne (Richard) The coherence of theism. [Clarendon Lib. of Logic and Philos.] 8vo. OXF., 1977.

—— The existence of God. [Wilde Lects., 1976-77.] 8vo. OXF., 1979.

Syamken (Georg) Die "Tageszeiten" von Philipp Otto Runge und "The Book of Job" von William Blake. 4to. [HAMBURG,] 1975. [Pamph.]

Sydenham. *Baptist Church.* A hundred years: the history of Sydenham Baptist Church, 1856-1956. 8vo. [LOND., 1956.] [Pamph.]

Sydenham (George) *comp.* Source material for the history of Suffolk Congregationalism. 8vo. IPSWICH, 1973. [Pamph.]

Sykes (Norman) The Church of England and non-episcopal churches in the sixteenth and seventeenth centuries: an essay towards an historical interpretation of the Anglican tradition from Whitgift to Wake. [Theology Occ. Papers, N.S., 11.] 8vo. LOND., 1948. [Pamph.]

—— *See* Bezzant (J. S.)

Sykes (S. W.) *ed.* Karl Barth: studies of his theological method. 8vo. OXF., 1979.

Sykes (S. W.) and **Clayton** (J. P.) *ed.* Christ, faith and history: Cambridge studies in Christology. 8vo. CAMB., 1972.

Syme (*Sir* Ronald) Emperors and biography: studies in the Historia Augusta. 8vo. OXF., 1971.

Symeon, *the New Theologian.* Hymnes. Introd., texte critique et notes par Johannes Koder. Trad. par Joseph Parmelle et Louis Neyrand. [Sources Chrétiennes, 156, 174, 196.] 3 vols. 8vo. PARIS, 1969-73.
 2. Hymnes 16-40. 1971.
 3. Hymnes 41-58. 1973.

—— *See* Völker (W.)

Symeon, *Saint, Stylites, iun,* 521-592. *See* Suppt. Analecta Bollandiana. Subsid. Hagiog., 32.

Symeon, *Abp. of Thessalonica.* Politico-historical works (1416/17 to 1429). Critical Greek text with introd. and commentary by David Balfour. [Wiener Byzant. Studien, 13.] 8vo. WIEN, 1979.

Symonds (Joshua) *See* Tibbutt (H. G.)

Synodicon. *See* Suppt. Corpus Script. Christ. Orient., Syri, 161-164.

Tachau (Peter) *See* Forschungen zur Religion u. Lit., 105.

Taeger (Fritz) Charisma: Studien zur Geschichte des antiken Herrscherkultes. 2 vols. 8vo. STUTTGART, 1957-60.

Tagore (*Sir* Rabindranath) *See* Pearson (W. W.)
Talbot (E. S.) *Bp. of Winchester*. *See* Papers for War Time, 25.
Tallents (Francis) *See* Smith (J. W. A.)
Tannehill (R. C.) *See* Suppt. Zeitschr. für N. T. Wiss. Beihefte, 40.
Tanner (John) Lucius Cary, Viscount Falkland, cavalier and catalyst. [Royal Stuart Papers, 5.] 8vo. ILFORD, 1974. [Pamph.]
Tanner (L. E.) Westminster Abbey: the library and muniment room. [Westminster Papers, 1.] (1933). 2nd ed. 8vo. OXF. & LOND., 1935. [Pamph.]
Tapiero (Judith K.) *See* Suppt. Jewish Hist. Soc. Publs., 1974.
Tapley-Soper (Gwendolyn E) Thomas Benet, M.A., Reformation martyr of Exeter, and Master Dusgate, Fellow of Corpus Christi College, Cambridge. (Read at Exeter, 25th June, 1931.) 8vo. n.p., [1931]. [Pamph.]
Tapp (R. B.) Religion among the Unitarian Universalists: converts in the stepfathers' house. [Quantitative Studies in Social Relations.] 8vo. NEW YORK & LOND., 1973.
[Tarbet (William)] Homilies and teachings doctrinal and practical. By the author of Pastoral ministries and teachings. 8vo. LOND., 1901.
Tarrant (Dorothy) Recollections. Address given to the London Unitarian Club, 1967. 8vo. [LOND., 1967.] [Pamph.]
Tate (*Sir* Henry) *See* Jones (T.)
Tate (W. E.) A. F. Leach as a historian of Yorkshire education. [St. Anthony's Hall Publs., 23.] 8vo. YORK, 1963. [Pamph.]
Tauler (Johann) *See* Deutsche Mystiker, 4.
Tavard (G. H.) The seventeenth-century tradition: a study in Recusant thought. [Studies in the Hist. of Christian Thought, 16.] 8vo. LEIDEN, 1978.
Tavener (W. B.) The challenge of humanism. [Religion: its Modern Needs and Problems, 19.] 8vo. LOND., 1933.
—— The path of humanism. Ed. Francis Terry. 8vo. LOND., 1968.
Tawney (R. H.) Commonplace Book. Ed. and with an introd. by J. M. Winter and D. M. Joslin. [Economic Hist. Rev. Suppt., 5.] 8vo. CAMB., 1972.
—— History and society. Ed. and with an introd. by J. M. Winter. 8vo. LOND., *etc.*, 1978.
[Tayler (H. S.) *ed.*] Dukinfield Old Chapel Sunday School: centenary souvenir, 1900. 8vo. ASHTON-UNDER-LYNE, 1901.
Taylor (Clare) British and American abolitionists: an episode in Transatlantic understanding. 8vo. EDIN., 1974.
Taylor (Frederick H.) Chingford Congregational Church: the first seventy years (1888-1957). 8vo. [CHINGFORD, 1957.]
Taylor (Hudson) *See* Taylor (Howard) and Taylor (M. Geraldine)
Taylor (Howard) and **Taylor** (M. Geraldine) Hudson Taylor in early years: the growth of a soul. Introd. by D. E. Hoste. (1911.) repr. 8vo. LOND., 1927.
—— Hudson Taylor and the China Inland Mission: the growth of a work of God. (1918.) repr. 8vo. LOND., 1927.
Taylor (Jane) Prose and poetry. Introd. by F. V. Barry. 8vo. LOND., 1925.
Taylor (Jeremy) *See* Suppt. Alcuin Club. Collections, 61.
Taylor (John) 1580-1653, *the Water Poet*. *See* Notestein (W.)
Taylor (John H.) L.C.U. story. 8vo. [SOUTHAMPTON, printed,] 1972. [Pamph.]
Taylor (John R.) God loves like that! The theology of James Denney. [Preacher's Lib.] 8vo. LOND., 1962.
Taylor (John V.) The go-between God: the Holy Spirit and the Christian mission. (1972.) 2nd imp. 8vo. LOND., 1973.
Taylor (M. Geraldine) Behind the ranges: [James Outram] Fraser of Lisuland, S. W. China. 8vo. LOND., [1944].
—— *See* Taylor (Howard) and Taylor (M. Geraldine)
[Taylor (T. A.)] Chesterfield Baptist Church: centenary, 1861-1961. 8vo. [CHESTERFIELD, 1961.]
Taylor (Vincent) The Passion narrative of St. Luke: a critical and historical investigation. Ed. Owen E. Evans. [Soc. for N.T. Studies, Monograph Ser., 19.] 8vo. CAMB., 1972.
Taylor (William) An abridged version of the History of Billericay Congregational Church. 8vo. [BILLERICAY, *c.* 1970.] [Pamph.]
—— Calling the generations: a history of the Independent Protestant Dissenters of Billericay (1672-1972). 8vo. [BILLERICAY, 1976.]

Teilhard de Chardin (Pierre) The making of a mind: letters from a soldier-priest, 1914-1919. Trans. René Hague. 8vo. LOND., 1965.
—— Man's place in nature: the human zoological group. Trans. René Hague. 8vo. LOND., 1966.
—— The vision of the past. Trans. J. M. Cohen. 8vo. LOND., 1966.
—— Science and Christ. Trans. René Hague. 8vo. LOND., 1968.
—— [Misc.] Teilhard de Chardin album. Designed and ed. by Jeanne Mortier and Marie-Louise Aboux from the publs. and letters of Pierre Teilhard de Chardin, and from papers preserved at the Fondation Teilhard de Chardin. [Trans. from the French.] 4to. LOND., 1966.
Temkin (S. D.) Bertram B. Benas: the life and times of a Jewish Victorian. Memorial lect., 7 June 1978. 8vo. ALBANY (N.Y.), 1978. [Pamph.]
Temple (William) *Abp. of Canterbury.* Christ's revelation of God. Three lectures. (1925.) 2nd ed. (1929.) repr. [Religion and Life Books.] 8vo. LOND., 1934.
—— The idea of immortality in relation to religion and ethics. [Drew Lect., 1931.] 8vo. LOND., 1932. [Pamph.]
—— One Lord, one people. 8vo. LOND., 1941. [Pamph.]
—— *ed. See* Papers for War Time.
—— *See* Craig (R.); Dark (S.)
Tener (R. H.) The writings of Richard Holt Hutton: a check-list of identifications. 4to. AMHERST (Mass.), 1972. [Pamph.]
—— R. H. Hutton: some attributions. 4to. AMERST (Mass.), 1973. [Pamph.]
—— R. H. Hutton's editorial career. 3 pts. 4to. TORONTO, 1974-75. [Pamphs.]
—— Walter Bagehot: some new attributions. 8vo. [CHARLOTTESVILLE (Va.),] 1976. [Pamph.]
Tertullian. [Works. *Latin.*] Opera. [Corpus Christianorum, Ser. Latina, 1-2.] 2 vols. 8vo. TURNHOUT, 1953-54.
2. Opera montanistica. 1954.
—— [Adv. Marcionem. *Latin and English.*] Adversus Marcionem. Ed. and Trans. Ernest Evans. [Oxford Early Christian Texts.] 2 vols. 8vo. OXF., 1972.
—— *See* Barnes (T. D.)
Texte und Untersuchungen zur Geschichte der altchristlichen Literatur. *See* Suppt.
Thackray (Edgar) The revelation of God in nature and man. 8vo. LOND., 1916.
Thatcher (Adrian) The ontology of Paul Tillich. [Oxford Theological Monographs.] 8vo. OXF., 1978.
Thecla, *Saint. See* Suppt. Analecta Bollandiana. Subsid. Hagiog., 62.
Thelwall (John) 1764-1834, *reformer. See* Rockey (D.)
Theodora, *Empress of the East. See* Browning (R.)
Theodore, *Saint, Archimandrite of Sykeon. See* Suppt. Analecta Bollandiana. Subsid. Hagiog., 48.
Theodoret, *Bp. of Cyrus.* Eranistes. Critical text and prolegomena by Gerard H. Ettlinger. 8vo. OXF., 1975.
——*See* Ashby (G. W. E. C.); Canivet (P.); Chesnut (G. F.); Koch (G.)
Theodorus, *Teganistes. See* Cameron (A. D. E.)
Theological Collections. *See* Suppt. Society for Promoting Christian Knowledge.
Theologische Literaturzeitung. *See* Suppt.
Theologische Rundschau. *See* Suppt.
Theology. *See* Suppt.
Theology Today. *See* Suppt.
Theoria to Theory. *See* Suppt.
Theresa, *Saint, of Avila. See* Peers (E. A.)
Therrien (Gérard) Le discernement dans las écrits pauliniens. [Études Bibliques.] 8vo. PARIS, 1973.
Thibaudet (Albert) Trente ans de vie française. 3. Le bergsonisme. 8vo. PARIS, 1923.
Thibon (Gustave) *See* Perrin (J. M.) and Thibon (G.)
Thiele (Walter) *ed. See* Bible. *Latin.* [Old Latin.]
Thielicke (Helmut) Fragen des Christentums an die moderne Welt: Untersuchungen zur geistigen und religiösen Krise des Abendlandes. 8vo. TÜBINGEN, 1948.
—— Theologie der Anfechtung. 8vo. TÜBINGEN, 1949.

Thode (Henry)   Franz von Assisi und die Anfänge der Kunst der Renaissance in Italien. (1885.)   4te.   Aufl.   8vo.   WIEN, 1934.

Thomas (Daniel John)   A short history of the Monmouthshire English Baptist Association, written for its centenary, 1957.   8vo.   [NEWPORT (Mon.), the author, 1957.]   [Pamph.]

Thomas (David Oswald)   Richard Price, 1723-91.   8vo.   LOND., 1972.   [Pamph.]

—— Richard Price and America (1723-91).   8vo.   ABERYSTWYTH [the author], 1975.   [Pamph.]

—— Richard Price, 1723-1791.   [In Welsh and English.]   8vo.   [CARDIFF,] 1976.

—— The honest mind: the thought and work of Richard Price.   8vo.   OXF., 1977.

—— ed.   See Suppt. Price-Priestley Newsletter.

Thomas (Dylan Marlais)   Deaths and entrances: poems by Dylan Thomas. (1946.) 3rd imp.   12mo.   LOND., 1949.

Thomas (Edward George)   Centenary souvenir of Heptonstall Slack Baptist Church, 1807-1907. With an introd. chapter on Baptist pioneering.   8vo.   LOND.,   [1907].

Thomas (H. Arnold)   [Misc.]   Arnold Thomas of Bristol. Collected papers and addresses. With a memoir by Nathaniel Micklem.   8vo.   LOND., 1925.

Thomas (John) and **Porteus** (C. A.)   Memorials of Lowther Street Congregational Church, Carlisle, 1786-1936.   8vo.   CARLISLE, 1936.   [Pamph.]

Thomas (John Heywood)   Logic and metaphysics in Luther's eucharistic theology. 8vo.   NOTTINGHAM, 1979.   [Pamph.]

Thomas (Joshua)   See Nuttall (G. F.)

Thomas (Keith V.)   Religion and the decline of magic: studies in popular beliefs in sixteenth and seventeenth century England.   8vo.   LOND., 1971.

—— ed.   See Hill (C.)   [Misc.]

Thomas (Muriel) comp.   Hersden, 1929-1979: fifty years of Methodism in a Kentish mining village.   8vo.   Duplicated.   CANTERBURY, 1979.   [Pamph.]

Thomas (Owen C.)   Attitudes toward other religions: some Christian interpretations. [Forum Books.]   8vo.   LOND., 1969.

Thomis (M. I.)   Old Nottingham.   8vo.   NEWTON ABBOT, 1968.

Thompson (Alexander Hamilton)   The ground plan of the English parish church. [Cambridge Manuals of Science and Lit.]   (1911.)   repr.   8vo.   CAMB., 1913.

—— See Douglas (D. C.)

Thompson (Craig R.)   [Misc.]   See DeMolen (R. L.) ed.

Thompson (David M.)   Let sects and parties fall: a short history of the Association of Churches of Christ in Great Britain and Ireland.   8vo.   BIRMINGHAM, 1980.

—— ed.   Nonconformity in the nineteenth century.   [Birth of Modern Britain Ser.] 8vo.   LOND., 1972.

Thompson (G. H. P.)   See Bible. Commentaries. New Clarendon.

Thompson (H. L.)   The Church of St. Mary the Virgin, Oxford, in its relation to some famous events of English history.   8vo.   [LOND.,] 1903.

Thompson (K. M.) comp.   Bloodie rebellion: Leicestershire and Rutland in the Civil War, 1642-1660.   [Facsims. of contemp. documents with introd. notes, annotations, and some transcriptions.]   [Leics. Museum Publs., 15.]   fol.   (Loose sheets in folder.)   LEICESTER, 1979.

Thompson (Kenneth F.)   Whitehead's philosophy of religion.   [Studies in Philos., 20.]   8vo.   THE HAGUE & PARIS, 1971.

Thompson (Mary L.) ed.   Stopping places: 1974 UUA meditation manual. By Unitarian Universalist women writers.   8vo.   BOSTON (Mass.), 1974.   [Pamph.]

Thompson (Phyllis)   Climbing on track: a biography of Fred Mitchell. (1953.)   repr. 8vo.   LOND., 1954.

Thompson (Ralph Wardlaw)   See Pringle (A.) ed.

Thompson (Richard Walker)   Benjamin Ingham (the Yorkshire evangelist) and the Inghamites.   8vo.   KENDAL, 1958.

Thompson (Thomas L.)   See Suppt. Zeitschr. für A. T. Wiss. Beihefte, 133.

Thomson (D. P.)   The Beadle, yesterday and today.   8vo.   CRIEFF, 1971.

Thomson (Gladys Scott)   See Byrne (M. St. C.) and Thomson (G. S.)

Thomson (J. Arthur)   See Papers for War Time, 24.

Thorne (R. F. S.)   The last Bible Christians: their church in Devon in 1907.   8vo. n.p., [1975].   [Pamph.]

Thorne (R. F. S.)—*continued*

—— Hocking: or the tales of two brothers. A catalogue of the works of the Hockings (Joseph, Silas and Salome) in the collection of Michael E. Thorne. 4to. *Duplicated.* EXETER, 1978. [Pamph.]

—— *See* Slader (J.) and Thorne (R. F. S.)

Thornton Heath. *St. John's Congregational Church.* Renewed for the twentieth century: the story of St. John's Congregational Church, Thornton Heath. 8vo. n.p., 1967. [Pamph.]

Thornwell (James H.) *See* Huh (S. G.)

Thorpe (W. H.) Animal nature and human nature. [Based on Gifford Lects., 1969-71.] 8vo. LOND., 1974.

Thrapston. *Baptist Church.* Thrapston and its Baptist Church: an institution of historical interest and present day value. 8vo. [THRAPSTON, 1938.] [Pamph.]

Thuillier (Vincent) *See* Mabillon (J.) and Ruinart (T.)

Tibbutt (H. G.) Early Nonconformity in Huntingdonshire. 3. St. Neots. 8vo. [HUNTINGDON,] 1970. [Pamph.]

——Bibliography of the published writings of H. G. Tibbutt. fol. *Duplicated.* [BEDFORD, the author, 1971.] [Pamph.]

—— Joshua Symonds, an eighteenth-century Bedford Dissenting minister. 8vo. [BEDFORD, 1978.] [Pamph.]

[——] Stevington Baptist Church, founded 1655. 8vo. [STEVINGTON,] 1979. [Pamph.]

—— *ed.* Some early Nonconformist church books. [Bedfordshire Historical Record Soc., 51.] 8vo. [BEDFORD,] 1972.

Tilborg (Sjef van) *See* Van Tilborg (S.)

Tillich (Paul J.) Das Dämonische: ein Beitrag zur Sinndeutung der Geschichte. [Sammlung gemeinverständlicher Vorträge u. Schriften aus dem Gebiet der Theol. u. Religionsgesch., 119.] 8vo. TÜBINGEN, 1926. [Pamph.]

—— Die Theologie des Kairos und die gegenwärtige geistige Lage: ein offener Brief an Emanuel Hirsch. (1934.) repr. 8vo. STUTTGART, [1978]. [Pamph.]

—— The courage to be. [Dwight H. Terry Lects., Yale Univ., 1952.] (1952.) repr. 8vo. WELWYN, 1961.

—— Christianity and the encounter of the world religions. [Bampton Lects. in America, 14, 1961.] (1963.) repr. 8vo. NEW YORK & LOND., 1966.

—— The eternal now. Sermons. 8vo. LOND., 1963.

— Morality and beyond. (1964.) repr. [Fontana Lib. of Theol. and Philos.] 8vo. LOND., 1969.

—— The future of religions. [Four lectures, with tributes to Tillich.] Ed. Jerald C. Brauer. 8vo. NEW YORK, 1966.

—— On the boundary: an autobiographical sketch. [Trans. from a rev. ed. of pt. 1 of The Interpretation of History (1936).] Introd. by J. Heywood Thomas. 8vo. LOND., 1967.

—— [Misc.] Im memoriam Paul Tillich, 1886-1965: Nachrufe.—Ansprache Paul Tillichs auf der "Convocation Pacem in Terris". New York, Feb. 1965. 8vo. STUTTGART, 1965. [Pamph.]

—— *See* Thatcher (A.)

Tims (Margaret) Jane Addams of Hull House, 1860-1935: a centenary study. 8vo. LOND., 1961.

Tin (Pe Maung) Buddhist devotion and meditation: an objective description and study. 8vo. LOND., 1964.

Tinling (J. F. B.) The promise of life, or revelation of conditional immortality. (1881.) 2nd ed. 8vo. LOND., [1903].

Tinne, *family of.* *See* Dentz (F. O.)

Tischendorf (L. F. C.) *See* Schneller (L.)

[Tizard (Hilda M.)] The story of our church. [Bosham United Reformed Church, formerly Congregational.] 4to. *Duplicated.* [BOSHAM, 1974.] [Pamph.]

Tizard (L. J.) [Misc.] Facing life and death. A volume in commemoration of the late Rev. Leslie J. Tizard. Ed. Harry Guntrip. 8vo. LOND., 1959.

Todd (William) New light on Genesis: the narrative explained against its geographical, historical and social background. 8vo. LOND., 1978.

Tolmie (Murray) The triumph of the saints: the separate churches of London, 1616-1649. 8vo. CAMB., 1977.

Tomkins (M.) *See* Harrod (J.) and Tomkins (M.)

Tompson (R. S.) Classics or charity? The dilemma of the 18th century grammar school 8vo. MANCHESTER, 1971.

Took (J. F.) Towards an interpretation of the Fiore. 8vo. CAMB. (Mass.), 1979. [Pamph.]

Toon (Peter) God's statesman: the life and work of John Owen, pastor, educator, theologian. 8vo. EXETER, 1971.
—— Der englische Puritanismus. 8vo. MÜNCHEN, [1972]. [Pamph.]
—— Puritans and Calvinism. 8vo. SWENGEL (Pa.), 1973
—— Evangelical theology, 1833-1856: a response to Tractarianism. [Marshalls Theol. Lib.] 8vo. LOND., 1979.
—— *See* Owen (J.); Romaine (W.)

Tornikès (Georges) and **Tornikès** (Dèmètrios) Lettres et discours. Introd., texte, analyses, trad. et notes par Jean Darrouzès. [Le Monde Byzantin.] 4to. PARIS, 1970.

Torrance (T. F.) Space, time and incarnation. (1969.) repr. 8vo. OXF., 1978.
—— Space, time and resurrection. 8vo. EDIN., 1976.

Torrey (R. A.) *ed.* *See* Fundamentals.

Towers (L. T.) John Bunyan (1628-1698). [Heritage Biographies.] 8vo. LOND., 1961. [Pamph.]

Toynbee (Arnold J.) Constantine Porphyrogenitus and his world. 8vo. OXF., 1973.

Toynbee (Arnold J.) and **Ikeda** (Daisaku) Choose life: a dialogue. Ed. Richard L. Gage. 8vo. OXF., 1976.

Toynbee (Margaret R.) and **Young** (Peter) Cropredy Bridge, 1644: the campaign and the battle. 8vo. KINETON, 1970.

Toynbee (T. Philip) Christians, then and now. [Essex Hall Lect., 1979.] 8vo. LOND., 1979. [Pamph.]

Toyne (A. C.) Religious teaching in schools: a plea for a revision of the syllabus. 8vo. WALLINGTON, 1944.

Tracy (James D.) Erasmus: the growth of a mind. [Travaux d'Humanisme et Renaissance, 126.] 4to. GENÈVE, 1972.
—— The politics of Erasmus: a pacifist intellectual and his political milieu. 8vo. TORONTO, 1979.

Trafodion Cymdeithas Hanes Bedyddwyr Cymru. *See* Suppt.

Traherne (Thomas) Centuries. (1908.) [Preface by H. M. Margolioth, introd. by Hilda Vaughan.] (1960.) repr. 8vo. LOND., 1963.

Transactions of. . . *See* Suppt.

Traskey (J. P.) Milton Abbey: a Dorset monastery in the Middle Ages. 8vo. TISBURY, 1978.

[Treen (H.) *and others.*] Bishop's Hull, 1877-1977. 8vo. [BISHOP'S HULL,] 1977. [Pamph.]

Treharne (R. F.) *comp.* Documents of the baronial movement of reform and rebellion, 1258-1267. Ed. I. J. Sanders. [Oxford Medieval Texts.] 8vo. OXF., 1973..

[Trenchard (John)] An argument shewing that a standing army is inconsistent with a free government. (1697.) facsim. repr. 8vo. EXETER, 1971. [Pamph.]

Treu (Erwin) Die Bildnisse des Erasmus von Rotterdam. 8vo. BASEL, 1959.

Trevelyan (George Macaulay) Grey of Fallodon, being the life of Sir Edward Grey, afterwards Viscount Grey of Fallodon. (1937.) repr. 8vo. LOND., *etc.*, 1937.
—— *See* Trevelyan (Mary C.)

Trevelyan (Mary C.) *Mrs. J. R. H. Moorman.* George Macaulay Trevelyan: a memoir, by his daughter. 8vo. LOND., 1980.

Trevor (Meriol) Apostle of Rome: a life of Philip Neri, 1515-1595. 8vo. LOND., 1966.
—— Pope John [XXIII]. 8vo. LOND., 1967.

Trevor-Roper (H. R.) Queen Elizabeth's first historian: William Camden and the beginnings of English 'civil history'. [Neale Lect. in Eng. Hist., 1971.] 8vo. LOND., 1971. [Pamph.]
—— *See* Fogle (F. R.) and Trevor-Roper (H. R.)

Trillmich (Werner) and **Buchner** (Rudolf) *ed.* Quellen des 9. und 11. Jahrhunderts zur Geschichte der hamburgischen Kirche und des Reiches. [Ausgewählte Quellen zur Deutschen Gesch. des Mittelalters, 11.] (1961.) 2te. Aufl. 8vo. DARMSTADT, 1968.

Trinterud (L. J.) *ed.* Elizabethan Puritanism. [Lib. of Protestant Thought.] 8vo. NEW YORK, 1971.
—— *See* Hudson (W. S.) and Trinterud (L. J.)
Trites (Allison A.) The New Testament concept of witness. [Soc. for N.T. Studies, Monograph Ser., 31.] 8vo. CAMB., 1977.
Trocmé (Étienne) Jesus and his contemporaries. [Trans. R. A. Wilson.] 8vo. LOND., 1973.
Trosse (George) 1631-1713. Life, written by himself, and published posthumously according to his order in 1714. Ed. A. W. Brink. 4to. MONTREAL & LOND., 1974.
Tubbs (E. J.) The visual Hebrew grammar lexicon. fol. HERTFORD, 1963.
—— Visual Arabic grammar-lexicon. 4to. LOND., 1972.
Tucker (Josiah) *Dean of Gloucester*. Reflections on the expediency of a law for the naturalization of foreign Protestants. In two parts. (1751-52.) facsim. repr. 8vo. FARNBOROUGH, 1969.
Tucker (Norman) Royalist Major-General Sir John Owen. 8vo. COLWYN BAY, 1963.
—— *ed. See* Young (P.) and Tucker (N.) *ed.*
Tucker (L. L.) Puritan protagonist: President Thomas Clap of Yale College. 8vo. CHAPEL HILL (N.C.), 1962.
Tübingen. *Universitätsbibliothek. Theologische Abteilung. See* Suppt. Mitteilungen u. Neuerwerbungen; Zeitschrifteninhaltsdienst Theologie.
Tukker (C. A.) De Classis Dordrecht van 1573 tot 1609: bijdrage tot de kennis van in- en extern leven van de Gereformeerde Kerk in de periode van haar organisering. [Leidse Historische Reeks, 10.] 8vo. LEIDEN, 1965.
Turner (J. Horsefall) Idle Chapel Independent Sunday School: the centenary memorial. 8vo. BINGLEY [printed], 1907.
Turner-Smith (N. A.) Living stones: the building of Immanuel Congregational Church, Southbourne, 1910-1965. 4to. Duplicated. [SOUTHBOURNE, 1965.]
Turtas (Raimondo) L'attività e la politica missionaria della direzione della London Missionary Society, 1795-1820. With an English résumé. [Analecta Gregoriana, 182: Ser. Facultatis Historiae Eccles., B.30.] 8vo. ROMA, 1971.
Tuthill (W. B.) The cathedral church of England. [Essays on Architectural Art, 2.] 8vo. NEW YORK, 1923.
Twinn (Kenneth) *See* Catalogues. *Dr. Williams's Lib.*
Tyacke (N. R. N.) An unnoticed work by Samuel Rawson Gardiner. 8vo. [LOND., 1974.] [Pamph.]
—— Wroth, Cecil and the Parliamentary session of 1604. 8vo. [LOND.,] 1977. [Pamph.]
—— *ed. See* Hurstfield (J.) [Misc.]
Tyndale (William) *See* Greensalde (S. L.); More (*Sir* T.)
Tyson (Gerald P.) Joseph Johnson: a liberal publisher. 8vo. IOWA CITY, 1979.
Tytler (D. A.) *See* Cope (G. F.) *and others.*

Ullmann (Walter) The future of medieval history. Inaugural lect., Univ. of Cambridge, 6 Nov. 1972. 8vo. CAMB., 1973. [Pamph.]
Underdown (David) Pride's purge: politics in the Puritan revolution. 8vo. OXF., 1971.
—— Somerset in the Civil War and Interregnum. 8vo. NEWTON ABBOT, 1973.
Underhill (Evelyn) The house of the soul. (1929.) 2nd ed. 8vo. LOND., 1933.
—— The inside of life. [Broadcast address, Dec. 13, 1931.] (1932.) repr. 8vo. LOND., 1932. [Pamph.]
—— The mystery of sacrifice: a meditation on the liturgy. 8vo. LOND., 1938.
—— Abba: meditations based on the Lord's Prayer. 8vo. LOND., 1940.
—— *ed. See* Cloud of unknowing.
—— *See* Armstrong (C. J. R.)
Underwood (Paul A.) The Kariye Djami. 4 vols. fol. LOND., 1967-75.
    4. Studies in the art of the Kariye Djami and its intellectual background. 1975.
Underwood (Ted Leroy) Quakers and the Royal Society of London in the seventeenth century. 8vo. [LOND., 1976.] [Pamph.]
Unitarian and Free Christian Churches. *See* Suppt. General Assembly of Unitarian and Free Christian Churches.

Unitarian Brotherhood Church. *Lagos Branch.* A brief history of the Unitarian Brotherhood Church in Nigeria. 8vo. [LAGOS, 1969.] [Pamph.]

Unitarian Historical Society. *See* Suppt.

Unitarian Historical Society [of America]. *See* Suppt.

Unitarian Information Department. *See* Suppt. Chalice.

Unitarian Universalist Association. The Free Church in a changing world. The reports of the Commissions to the churches and fellowships of the U.U.A. 8vo. BOSTON (Mass.), 1963.

—— Report of the Committee on Goals. 4to. [BOSTON (Mass.), 1967.] [Pamph.]

—— *See* Suppt.

United Bible Societies. *See* Suppt. Bible Translator.

United Church of Canada. *See* Beaton (K. J.)

United Church of Northern India. *See* Plan of church union.

United Reformed Church. *Reports.* Non-violent action: a Christian appraisal. A report commissioned for the U.R.C. [John Johansen-Berg, convener.] 8vo. LOND., 1973.

United Reformed Church History Society. *See* Suppt.

United Reformed Church Year Book *See* Suppt.

Universalist Historical Society. *See* Suppt.

Unnik (W. C. van) *See* Suppt. Novum Testamentum. Suppts., 29, 47-48.

[Unsworth (Anna)] A brief history of and guide to Great Meeting, Leicester. fol. [ff.2.] *Duplicated.* LEICESTER, [1970].

Upminster. *Baptist Church.* 1935-1956: a story of God's leading. 8vo. [UPMINSTER, 1956.] [Pamph.]

Urch (W. H.) The place of spiritual gifts in Pentecostal churches. Two Bible Studies given at the 1954 Christmas Convention in the Ulster Temple, Belfast. 8vo. LOND., 1955. [Pamph.]

Urwick (E. J.) *See* Papers for War Time, 14.

Urwin (E. C.) Henry Carter, C.B.E.: a memoir. 8vo. LOND., 1955.

—— *See* MacLachlan (L.)

Usher (Roland G.) The reconstruction of the English Church. (1910.) facsim. repr. 2 vols. 8vo. FARNBOROUGH, 1969.

Valdés (Juan de) *See* Nieto (J. C.)

Valentine (Peter) *See* Noon (F. E.) and Valentine (P.)

Valentine (T. F.) Concern for the ministry: the story of the Particular Baptist Fund, 1717-1967. 8vo. TEDDINGTON, [1967].

Van den Berg (Johannes) John Wesley's contacten met Nederland. 8vo. [THE HAGUE, 1971.] [Pamph.]

—— Oplossing der kerk in der maatschappij? Modernen, ethischen en de toekomstvisie van Richard Rothe. 8vo. [KAMPEN, 1975.] [Pamph.]

—— Een Leids pleidooi voor verdraagzaamheid: het optreden van Jan Jacob Schultens in de zaak-Van der Os. Rede. 8vo. LEIDEN, 1976. [Pamph.]

—— Eighteenth century Dutch translations of the works of some British latitudinarian and enlightened theologians. 8vo. ['s GRAVENHAGE, 1979.] [Pamph.]

—— "Letterkennis" en "Geestelijke kennis": een theologenstrijd in de achttiende eeuw over de verstaanbaarheid van de Schrift. 8vo. [THE HAGUE, 1980.] [Pamph.]

Van den Berg (Johannes) and **Dooren** (J. P. van) *ed.* Pietismus und Reveil. Referate der internationalen Tagung: der Pietismus in den Niederlanden und seine internationalen Beziehungen Zeist 18.-22. Juni 1974. [Kerkhistorische Bijdragen, 7.] 8vo. LEIDEN, 1978.

Van der Kemp (J. T.) *See* Martin (A. D.)

Van der Straeten (Joseph) *See* Straeten (J. van der)

Van Dieten (J. L.) *See* Dieten (J. L. van)

Van Dusen (W. M.) The presence of other worlds: the psychological/spiritual findings of Emanuel Swedenborg. 8vo. NEW YORK, *etc.*, 1974.

Vane (*Sir* Henry) *the younger. See* Rowe (V. A.)

Van Leeuwen (A. T.) *See* Leeuwen (A. T. van)

Van Roon (A.) *See* Roon (A. van)

Vansina (Jan) Oral tradition: a study in historical methodology. Trans. H. M. Wright. 8vo. LOND., 1965.

Van Tilborg (Sjef) The Jewish leaders in Matthew. 8vo. LEIDEN, 1972.

Van Unnik (W. C.)   *See* Unnik (W. C. van)
Varga (Béla)   Dávid Ferenc és az Unitárius vallas.   8vo.   BUDAPEST, 1979.
Varley (Henry) 1835-1912.   *See* Varley (Henry) 1859-1933.
Varley (Henry) 1859-1933.   Henry Varley's life-story. By his son.   8vo.   LOND. & GLASGOW, [1913].
Varley (Joan)   A Bedfordshire clergyman of the Reform era and his bishop   [Timothy Matthews and John Kaye, Bishop of Lincoln].   8vo.   [BEDFORD, 1978.]   [Pamph.]
Varrentrapp (C.)   Landgraf Philipp von Hessen und die Universität Marburg.   [Marburger Akademische Reden, 1905, 11.]   8vo.   MARBURG, 1904.   [Pamph.]
Vaughan (Henry) *Silurist.*   *See* Lewalski (B. K.) and Sabol (A. J.) *ed.*
Vaughan (P. H.)   The meaning of 'b mâ' in the Old Testament: a study of etymological, textual and archaeological evidence.   [Soc. for O.T. Study, Monograph Ser., 3.]   8vo.   CAMB., 1974.
Vaux (Roland de)   Archaeology and the Dead Sea Scrolls.   [Schweich Lects., Brit. Acad., 1959.] (1961.)   rev. ed.   [Trans. David Bourke.]   8vo.   LOND., 1973.
—— Histoire ancienne d'Israël: des origines à l'installation en Canaan.   [Études Bibliques.]   8vo.   PARIS, 1971.
—— *See* Discoveries in the Judaean Desert.
Ven (Paul van den)   *See* Suppt. Analecta Bollandiana. Subsid. Hagiog., 32.
Ventris (Michael) and **Chadwick** (John)   Evidence for Greek dialect in the Mycenaean archives.   4to.   [LOND.,] 1953.   [Pamph.]
Verburgt (J. W.)   The Pilgrim Fathers in Leiden, Holland. (1955.)   2nd ed.   8vo.   LEIDEN, 1970.   [Pamph.]
Vergerio (Pier Paolo)   *See* Schutte (A. J.)
Verheule (Anthoine F.) *ed.*   *See* Suppt. Novum Testamentum. Suppts., 50.
Vermes (Geza)   Jesus the Jew: a historian's reading of the Gospels.   8vo.   LOND., 1973.
Vernant (Jean-Pierre)   *See* Detienne (M.) and Vernant (J.-P.)
Verner (Beryl A.) *comp.*   Huguenots in South Africa: a bibliography.   8vo.   CAPE TOWN, 1967.   [Pamph.]
Vervliet (H. D. L.)   *See* Gulik (E. van) and Vervliet (H. D. L.)
Vesey (Godfrey N. A.) *ed.*   *See* Suppt. Royal Inst. of Philos. Lects., 9-11.
Vessey (D. W. T.)   The trial and execution of Mary, Queen of Scots in contemporary literature.   [Royal Stuart Papers, 3.]   8vo.   ILFORD, 1973.   [Pamph.]
Vetus Testamentum.   *See* Suppt.
Vickers (Hilary)   *See* Vickers (J. A.) and Vickers (H.)
Vickers (John A.)   Thomas Coke, apostle of Methodism.   8vo.   LOND., 1969.
—— The story of Canterbury Methodism (1750-1961): St. Peter's Methodist Church, Canterbury. (1961.)   repr.   8vo.   [CANTERBURY, 1970.]   [Pamph.]
Vickers (John A.) and **Vickers** (Hilary)   Methodism in a cathedral city: Southgate Methodist Church, Chichester, 1877-1977.   8vo.   [CHICHESTER,] 1977.   [Pamph.]
Vickers (John A.) and **Young** (Betty)   A Methodist guide to London and the South-East.   8vo.   BOGNOR REGIS, 1980.   [Pamph.]
Victoria History of the Counties of England.   *See* Suppt.
Victorinus (C. Marius) *Afer.*   [Works. *Latin.*]   *See* Suppt. Corpus Script. Eccles. Lat., 83.
—— Traités théologiques sur la Trinité.   [Sources Chrétiennes, 68-69.]   2 vols.   8vo.   PARIS, 1960.
    1.   Texte établi par Paul Henry. Introd., trad. et Notes par Pierre Hadot.
    2.   Commentaire par Pierre Hadot.
—— *See* Hadot (P.)
Vidler (A. R.)   Christian belief. A course of open lectures, Univ. of Cambridge.   8vo.   LOND., 1950.
—— Scenes from a clerical life: an autobiography.   8vo.   LOND., 1977.
Vielhauer (Philipp)   Aufsätze zum Neuen Testament.   [Theologische Bücherei, 31.]   8vo.   MÜNCHEN, 1965.
Vigiliae Christianae.   *See* Suppt.
Vinay (Valdo)   Ecclesiologica ed etica politica in Giovanni Calvino.   [Biblioteca di Cultura Religiosa, 22.]   8vo.   BRESCIA, 1973.
Vincent (E. R. P.)   Re-reading the Divine Comedy.   [Annual Italian Lect., Brit. Acad., 1945.]   8vo.   LOND., 1946.   [Pamph.]
Vincent de Paul, *Saint.*   *See* McCormack (J.) and Condon (K.); Mahoney (A. G.)

Viney (Basil)   The revelation of God in nature and humanity.   [Religion: its Modern Needs and Problems, 4.]   8vo.   LOND., 1931.
—— God, commonwealth and afterlife.   [Uncensored Avowals, 4.]   8vo.   LOND., [1938.].
—— I am sure: the autobiography of a theistic parson.   8vo.   LOND., 1975.
Visser 't Hooft (W. A.) *ed.*   Holländische Kirchendokumente: der Kampf der holländischen Kirche um die Geltung der göttlichen Gebote im Staatsleben.   8vo.   ZOLLIKON & ZÜRICH, 1944.
Vizantijskij Vremennik.   *See* Suppt.
Völker (Walther)   Praxis und Theoria bei Symeon dem Neuen Theologen: ein Beitrag zur byzantinischen Mystik.   4to.   WIESBADEN, 1974.
—— *ed.*   Quellen zur Geschichte der christlichen Gnosis.   [Sammlung Ausgewählter Kirchen- u. Dogmengesch.   Quellenschriften, N.F., 5.]   8vo.   TÜBINGEN, 1932.
Vööbus (Arthur)   *See* Suppt. Corpus Script. Christ. Orient., Subsid., 38-40, 45, 56.
Voet (Gisbert) 1589-1679.   Inaugurele rede over Godzaligheid te verbinden met de wetenschap. (1634.) Latijnse tekst opnieuw uitgegeven met Nederlandse vertaling, inleiding en toelichtingen door Dr. Aart de Groot.   8vo.   KAMPEN, 1978.
—— *See* Duker (A. C.)
Vogel (Heinrich)   [Misc.]   Vom Herrengeheimnis der Wahrheit. Festschirft fur Heinrich Vogel.   Hrsg. Kurt Scharf.   8vo.   BERLIN & STUTTGART, 1962.
Vollmar (Paul)   Die liturgischen Anschauungen des Ignaz Heinrich von Wessenberg (1774-1860).   Dissertation.   8vo.   ZÜRICH, 1971.
Vollmer (Jochen)   *See* Suppt. Zeitschr. für A. T. Wiss. Beihefte, 119.
Voltaire (F. M. A. de)   *See* Black (J. B.); Lauer (R. Z.)
Von Glasenapp (Helmuth)   *See* Glasenapp (H. von)
Von Ivánka (Endre)   *See* Ivánka (E. von)
Von Rad (Gerhard)   *See* Rad (G. von)
Vooght (Paul de)   *See* De Vooght (Paul)
Vox Evangelica.   *See* Suppt.
Voysey (Charles)   Religion for all mankind, based on facts which are never in dispute. [Rev. ed. of his Mystery of pain, death and sin (1878).]   8vo.   LOND., 1903.
—— "Do we believe?" Six sermons.   8vo.   LOND., 1905.   [Pamph.]
—— Life after death: an enquiry into the grounds of hope for it.   8vo.   LOND., 1905. [Pamph.]
—— Lectures on the theistic faith and its foundations, and on the Bible.   8vo.   LOND., 1910.   [Pamph.]
Vryonis (Speros)   The decline of medieval Hellenism in Asia Minor and the process of Islamization from the eleventh through the fifteenth century.   8vo.   BERKELEY (Calif.), *etc.*, 1971.

[W. (C. P.)]   Baptist Church, Loughton, Stony Stratford: centenary services; brief history, 1831-1931.   8vo.   [LOUGHTON, 1931.]   [Pamph.]
Waddington (C. H.)   *See* Kenny (A. J. P.) *and others.*
[Waddington (Norah)]   The first ninety years: Clarendon Park Congregational Church, Leicester.   8vo.   n.p., [1976].   [Pamph.]
Waddy (F. F.)   A history of Northampton General Hospital, 1743 to 1948: two hundred and five years as a voluntary hospital.   8vo.   NORTHAMPTON, 1974.
Wade (W. L.)   West Park Congregational Church (Queen Street Memorial): tercentenary, 1672-1972.   8vo.   LEEDS, 1972.   [Pamph.]
Wadsworth (K. W.)   The Yorkshire Congregational Union and Home Missionary Society, 1872-1972.   4to.   n.p., [1973].   [Pamph.]
Wagner (*Sir* Anthony R.)   *See* Suppt. Harleian Soc. Publs., 111-112.
Wagner (Georg)   Der Ursprung der Chrysostomsliturgie.   [Liturgiewiss. Quellen u. Forschungen, 59.]   8vo.   MÜNSTER IN W., 1973.
Wagner (Oskar)   Mutterkirche vieler Länder: Geschichte der evangelischen Kirche im Herzogtum Teschen, 1545-1918/20.   [Studien u. Texte zur Kirchengesch. u. Gesch., 1. Reihe, IV/1-2.]   8vo.   WIEN, *etc.*, 1978.
Wagner (Volter)   *See* Suppt. Zeitschr. für A. T. Wiss. Beihefte, 127.
Wainwright (Geoffrey) *ed.*   *See* Jones (Cheslyn P. M.) *and others, ed.*
Wakefield (G. S.)   Methodist devotion: the spiritual life in the Methodist tradition, 1791-1945.   [Wesley Hist. Soc. Lect., 32, 1966.]   8vo.   LOND., 1966.
Walatta Petros, *Saint.*   *See* Suppt. Corpus Script. Christ. Orient., Aethiop., 61.

Walker (C. M.) A short history of the Baptist cause in Altrincham, 1872-1972. 8vo. [ALTRINCHAM, 1972.] [Pamph.]

Walker (David Grant) *ed.* A history of the Church in Wales. 8vo. PENARTH, 1976.

—— *ed. See* Jones (O. W.) and Walker (D. G.) *ed.*

Walker (Edmund T. F.) *See* Little (F. G.) and Walker (E. T. F.)

Walker (Eric C.) William Dell, master Puritan. 8vo. CAMB., 1970.

[**Walker** (George E.) *and others.*] Willaston School, 1900-1937. [By G. E. Walker, H. J. McLachlan and Kenneth Gill Smith.] 4to. *Duplicated.* n.p., 1973.

Walker (Willison) *ed. See* Smyth (N.) and Walker (W.) *ed.*

Wallace (I. H.) The brotherhood movement at Patricroft. 4to. *Duplicated.* ECCLES, 1971.

Walling (E. B.) Leigh-on-Sea Baptists: their diamond jubilee story, 1893 to 1953. 8vo. LOND., 1953. [Pamph.]

Wallis (P. J.) *See* Catalogues. *Misc.*

Wallis (R. T.) Neoplatonism. [Classical Life and Letters.] 8vo. LOND., 1972.

Walpole (G. H. S.) *Bp. of Edinburgh.* Waiting. 8vo. LOND., [1925].

Walsh (F. W.) Love, order, progress: Auguste Comte and the religion of humanity. 8vo. LOND., 1913. [Pamph.]

—— —— [Another ed.] With a criticism by Rev. L. G. Berrington and a rejoinder by Mr. Walsh. 8vo. LIVERPOOL, 1913. [Pamph.]

Walsh (H. H.) The Christian Church in Canada. 8vo. TORONTO, 1956.

Walsh (Walter) Free religious addresses. Nos. 38-55, 101-121, 179-200, 252-275, 325-345. Pamphs. in 5 vols. 8vo. [LOND., 191-]-1930.

—— The endless quest: spoken reviews of men and books. [Free Religious Lib.] 8vo. LOND., 1920.

—— The republic of God. [Free Religious Lib.] 8vo. LOND., 1921.

—— Jesus: war or peace? in the light of modern criticism. 8vo., [1924].

—— "Lift up your hearts": a hundred aspirations towards peace and goodwill. 8vo. LOND., 1929.

—— Twenty dialogues on universal religion between seeker and finder. 8vo. LOND., 1930.

Walsh (William H.) Kant's criticism of metaphysics. 8vo. EDIN., 1975.

Walter (Christopher) L'iconographie des conciles dans la tradition byzantine. Préface par André Grabar. [Archives de l'Orient Chrétien, 13.] 8vo. PARIS, 1970.

Walters (Peter) *formerly Katz.* The text of the Septuagint: its corruptions and their emendation. Ed. D. W. Gooding. 8vo. CAMB., 1973.

[**Walton** (D. S.)] Monton Methodist Church, Eccles: 75th chapel anniversary, 1899-1974. 8vo. [ECCLES, 1974.] [Pamph.]

Walz (H. H.) *ed. See* Dictionaries. Christianity.

Wand (J. W. C.) *See* Suppt. Alcuin Club. Misc. Publs., 1973.

Wanke (Gunther) *See* Suppt. Zeitschr. für A. T. Wiss. Beihefte, 122.

Warburton (John) Mercies of a covenant God: being an account of some of the Lord's dealings in providence and grace with John Warburton, minister of the Gospel, Trowbridge. (1837.) Together with an account of the author's last days. [By his son, John Warburton of Southill.] (1857.) repr. [With preface and notes by Geoffrey Williams.] 8vo. SWENGEL (Pa.), 1964.

Ward (Keith) The development of Kant's view of ethics. 8vo. OXF., 1972.

Ward (Thomas Asline) *See* Street (C. J.)

Ward (W. R.) Theology, sociology and politics: the German Protestant social conscience, 1890-1933. [Univ. of Durham Publs.] 8vo. BERNE (Switz.), *etc.*, 1979.

Warfield (B. B.) Counterfeit miracles. (1918.) repr. 8vo. LOND., 1972.

—— Perfectionism. Ed. Samuel G. Craig. (1958.) repr. 8vo. PHILADELPHIA, 1967.

Wark (K. R.) *See* Suppt. Chetham Soc., 3rd Ser., 19.

[**Warmington** (B. H.) *and others.*] One hundred years, 1861-1961: Redland Park Congregational Church, Bristol. 8vo. [BRISTOL, 1961.] [Pamph.]

[**Warne** (Arthur) Church and society in eighteenth-century Devon. 8vo. NEWTON ABBOT, 1969.

Warne (R. B.) Godistencism: a study of the concept of personal survival within the framework of biological evolution. 8vo. TOTTINGTON (Lancs.) [the author], 1959.

[**Warner** (A. J.) Through the centuries, 1707-1947: Beechen Grove Baptist Church, Watford. 8vo. [WATFORD, 1947.] [Pamph.]

Warnock (G. J.)　Berkeley. (1953.)　repr.　8vo.　HARMONDSWORTH, 1969.

Warren (Max A. C.)　The whole church: an Anglican consideration of the South India church union scheme.　8vo.　LOND., [1943].　[Pamph.]

Warschauer (Joseph)　Is immortality a dream?　[Deansgage Lects.]　8vo.　MAN-CHESTER, [1913].　[Pamph.]

Watcyn-Williams (Morgan)　Creative fellowship: an outline of the history of Calvinistic Methodism in Wales.　8vo.　CAERNARVON, [c. 1935].

Waterland (Daniel)　See Rosendall (B. C.)

Watkins (Owen C.)　The Puritan experience.　8vo.　LOND., 1972.

Watson (Ambrose C.)　A history of religious Dissent and Nonconformity in Ashford, Kent.　[Ashford History Ser., 2.]　fol.　Duplicated.　ASHFORD, 1979.　[Pamph.]

Watson (Bernard)　A hundred years' war: the Salvation Army, 1865-1965.　8vo.　LOND., 1964.

[Watson (Richard)]　West Street Baptist Church, Rochdale, 1773-1923: souvenir of the 150th anniversary.　8vo.　ROCHDALE, [1923].　[Pamph.]

Watters (W. R.)　See Suppt. Zeitschr. für A. T. Wiss. Beihefte, 138.

Watts (David R.)　A history of the Hertfordshire Baptists.　8vo.　[STEVENAGE, printed,] 1978.　[Pamph.]

——　Rural mission work in Hertfordshire: a case study of the work of the Hertfordshire Baptist Union.　fol.　Duplicated.　n.p., 1979.　[Pamph.]

——　Why were there so many Baptist chapels in Tring?　fol.　n.p., [1979].　[Pamph.] [Photocopy.]

Watts (Isaac)　Divine songs attempted in easy language for the use of children.　Facsim. reprs. of the first ed. of 1715 and an illus. ed. of c.1840, with an introd. and bibliog. by J. H. P. Pafford.　[Juvenile Lib.]　8vo.　OXF., 1971.

——　See Fountain (D. G.); Hoyles (J.); Routley (E.); Stonier (G.)

Watts (Michael R.)　The Dissenters.　8vo.　OXF.

　　1.　From the Reformation to the French Revolution.　1978.

　　2.　Not yet published, 1980.

Watts (Trevor)　The story of Beilihalog.　4to.　Duplicated.　n.p., [1972?].　[Pamph.]

——　See Catalogues. Trevor Jones Lib.

Weatherby (H. L.)　Cardinal Newman in his age: his place in English theology and literature.　8vo.　NASHVILLE (Tenn.), 1973.

Weatherhead (Leslie D.)　After death: a popular statement of the modern Christian view of life beyond the grave. (1923.)　6th imp.　8vo.　LOND., 1937.

——　The transforming friendship: a book about Jesus and ourselves. (1928.)　8th imp. 8vo.　LOND., 1930.

——　Psychology in service of the soul. (1929.)　repr.　8vo.　LOND., 1938.

——　His life and ours: the significance for us of the life of Jesus.　8vo.　LOND., 1932.

——　How can I find God? (1933.)　repr.　8vo.　LOND., 1933.

——　Why do men suffer? (1935.)　2nd ed.　8vo.　LOND., 1935.

——　A shepherd remembers: a devotional study of the twenty-third Psalm. (1937.) new ed.　8vo.　LOND., 1960.

——　This is the victory.　8vo.　LOND., 1940.

——　In quest of a kingdom.　8vo.　LOND., 1943.

——　A plain man looks at the Cross: an attempt to explain in simple language for the modern man the significance of the death of Christ.　8vo.　LOND., 1945.

——　Prescription for anxiety.　8vo.　LOND., 1956.

——　Key next door, and other City Temple sermons.　8vo.　LOND., 1960.

——　Wounded spirits.　8vo.　LOND., 1962.

Webb (Clement C. J.)　The contribution of Christianity to ethics.　[Stephanos Nirmalendu Ghosh Lects., 1930-31.]　8vo.　CALCUTTA, 1932.

Webb (Sidney) and **Webb** (Beatrice)　See Hamilton (M. A.)

Webster (Alexander)　Memories of ministry.　8vo.　LOND. & ABERDEEN, 1913.

Webster (Charles)　The great instauration: science, medicine and reform, 1626-1660. 8vo.　LOND., 1975.

——　ed.　The intellectual revolution of the seventeenth century.　[Past and Present Ser.]　8vo.　LOND., 1974.

Webster (Graham)　The Roman Imperial Army of the first and second centuries A.D. (1969.)　2nd ed.　8vo.　LOND., 1979.

Weder (Hans)　See Suppt. Forschungen zur Religion u. Lit., 120.

Weeks (Courtenay C.) Alcohol and human life. Being partly a revision of "Alcohol and the human body" by Sir Victor Horsley and Dr. Mary Sturge. Foreword by Sir Thomas Barlow. (1929.) 2nd ed. 8vo. LOND., 1938.
Weeks (W. R.) A hundred years and more: the history of Faversham Baptist Church. Ed. A. F. Munden. [Faversham Papers, 14.] 4to. *Duplicated.* FAVERSHAM, 1977. [Pamph.]
Wegg (Jervis) Richard Pace: a Tudor diplomatist. 8vo. LOND., 1932.
Weigelt (Horst) Pietismus-Studien. I. Der spener-hallische Pietismus. [Arbeiten zur Theologie, II. Reihe, 4.] 8vo. STUTTGART, 1965.
—— Sebastian Franck und die lutherische Reformation. [Schriften des Vereins für Reformationsgesch., 186, Jg. 77.] 8vo. GÜTERSLOH, 1972.
Weigh House Quarterly. *See* Suppt. King's Weigh House Monthly.
Weil (Simone) The need for roots: prelude to a declaration of duties towards mankind. [Trans. A. F. Wills.] Preface by T. S. Eliot. 8vo. LOND., 1952.
—— Letter to a priest. [Trans. A. F. Wills.] 8vo. LOND., 1953.
—— *See* Perrin (J. M.) and Thibon (G.); Pétrement (S.)
Weimar (Peter) *See* Suppt. Zeitschr. für A. T. Wiss. Beihefte, 146.
Weinberg (J. R.) Ockham, Descartes, and Hume: self-knowledge, substance, and causality. 8vo. MADISON (Wis.), 1977.
[Weinrich (Lorenz) *ed.*] Toleranz und Brüderlichkeit: 30 Jahre Gesellschaft für christlich-jüdische Zusammenarbeit in Berlin. 8vo. BERLIN, 1979.
Weippert (Helga) *See* Suppt. Zeitschr. für A. T. Wiss. Beihefte, 132.
Weippert (Manfred) *See* Suppt. Studies in Bibl. Theol., 2nd Ser., 21.
Weiser (Artur) *ed.* *See* Bible. O.T. Commentaries. Das A. T. Deutsch.
Weitzman (M. P.) How useful is the logarithmic type/token ratio? 8vo. LOND., 1971. [Pamph.]
—— *See* Bermant (C.) and Weitzman (M. P.)
Welch (Charles Edwin) The downfall of Bishop Williams. 8vo. LEICESTER, 1965. [Pamph.]
—— Dissenters' Meeting-houses in Plymouth, 1852-1939. 8vo. [TORQUAY, 1967.] [Pamph.]
—— Nonconformist trust deeds. 4to. [LOND., 1968.] [Pamph.]
—— The early Methodists and their records. 4to. [LOND., 1971.] [Pamph.]
—— William Barton, hymnwriter. 8vo. [LOND.,] 1971. [Pamph.]
—— Lady Huntingdon and Spa Fields Chapel. 8vo. [LOND., 1972]. [Pamph.]
—— Lady Huntington's [*sic*] Plans. 8vo. [LOND., 1975.] [Pamph.]
—— *ed.* Two Calvinistic Methodist chapels, 1743-1811: the London Tabernacle and Spa Fields Chapel. [London Record Soc., 11.] 8vo. [LEICESTER,] 1975.
Welch (Charles Henry) Hell, or "Pure from the blood of all men." 8vo. LOND., [192-?]. [Pamph.]
—— An autobiography. 8vo. LOND., 1960.
Welch (Claude) Protestant thought in the nineteenth century. 8vo. NEW HAVEN & LOND.
  1. 1799-1870. (1972.) repr. 1974.
  2. *Not yet published*, 1980.
Wells (Clarke) The strangeness of this business: a meditation manual for 1976, Ash Wednesday to Easter. 8vo. BOSTON (Mass.), 1975. [Pamph.]
Wells (G. A.) Did Jesus exist? 8vo. LOND., 1975
—— Goethe and the development of science, 1750-1900. [Science in Hist., 5.] 8vo. ALPHEN A/D RIJN, 1978.
Wendland (Heinz-Dietrich) Die Kirche in der modernen Gesellschaft: Entscheidungsfragen für das kirchliche Handeln im Zeitalter der Massenwelt. 8vo. HAMBURG, 1956.
Wentworth (Thomas) *1st Earl of Strafford*, and **Wentworth** (*Sir* William) *See* Suppt. Royal Hist. Soc. Camden 4th Ser., 12.
Werblowsky (R. J. Z.) Beyond tradition and modernity: changing religions in a changing world. [Jordan Lects. in Comparative Relig., 11, 1974.] 8vo. LOND., 1976.
Wernle (Paul) Der evangelische Glaube nach den Hauptschriften der Reformatoren. 1. Luther. 8vo. TÜBINGEN, 1918.
Wesley (Charles) *See* Suppt. Methodist Sacramental Fellowship. M.S.F. Booklets. Wesley Reprs., 1.

Wesley (John) [Journal. Selections.] John Wesley in Wales, 1739-1790: entries from his journal and diary relating to Wales. Ed. with an introd. by A. H. Williams. 8vo. CARDIFF, 1971.
—— *See* Clarkson (G. E.); Ford (J.); Schmidt (M.); Van den Berg (J.); Williams (A. H.); Suppt. Methodist Sacramental Fellowship, M.S.F. Booklets, Wesley Reprs.
Wesley Historical Society. *See* Suppt.
Wesleyan Methodist Church. *Local Preachers' Connexional Committee.* Compendium of rules and regulations relating to local preachers. 8vo. LOND., 1902. [Pamph.]
Wessenberg (Ignaz Heinrich von) *See* Vollmar (P.)
West (C. C.) Communism and the theologians: study of an encounter. 8vo. LOND., 1958.
West (W. M. S.) John Hooper and the origins of Puritanism. Dissertation der theol. Fakultät der Univ. Zürich. Teildruck. 8vo. n.p., [priv. printed], 1955. [Pamph.]
West (W. P.) Tottenham Baptist Church, 1827-1952. 8vo. [LOND., 1952.] [Pamph.]
Westermann (Claus) *See* Suppt. Forschungen zur Religion u. Lit., 116.
Weston (Agnes) My life among the bluejackets. (1909.) rev. ed. (1915.) repr. 8vo. LOND., 1918.
Weston School of Theology (*formerly* Weston College), Mass. *See* Suppt. New Testament Abstracts.
Whale (J. H.) One Church, one Lord. 8vo. LOND., 1979.
Whedbee (J. W.) Isaiah and Wisdom. 8vo. NASHVILLE (Tenn.) & NEW YORK, 1971.
Wheeler (B. R.) Alfred Henry Baynes, J. P. [Brief Biographies of Leading Laymen, 5.] 8vo. LOND., [194-]. [Pamph.]
Wheeler (*Sir* R. E. Mortimer) The British Academy, 1949-1968. 8vo. LOND., 1970.
Wheldon (Thomas Jones) *See* Williams (D. D.)
Where are the dead? [Articles by various writers.] 8vo. LOND., 1928.
Whitaker (E. C.) *See* Suppt. Alcuin Club. Collections.
Whitaker (William) Steps to the religious life. [Religion: its Modern Needs and Problems, 10.] 8vo. LOND., 1932.
Whitby (G. S.) *ed.* *See* Pearce-Higgins (J. D.) and Whitby (G. S.) *ed.*
White (Alan R.) *ed.* The philosophy of action. (1968.) repr. [Oxford Readings in Philos.] 8vo. OXF., 1977.
White (B. R.) The doctrine of the church in the Particular Baptist Confession of 1644. 8vo. OXF., 1968. [Pamph.]
—— The English Separatist tradition: from the Marian martyrs to the PilgrimFathers. [Oxford Theological Monographs.] 8vo. OXF., 1971.
—— Hanserd Knollys and Radical Dissent in the 17th century. [Friends of Dr. Williams's Lib. Lect., 31.] 8vo. LOND., 1977.
—— *See* John (J. M.) *ed.;* Suppt. Baptist Historical Soc. Publs.
White (B. R.) and **Fancutt** (Walter) The story of Andover Baptist Church, 1824-1974: a short history. 8vo. ANDOVER, [1974]. [Pamph.]
White (Gilbert) *See* Sell (A. P. F.)
White (James) *ed.* My Clonmel scrap book. 2nd ed. 8vo. DUNDALK, n.d.
White (Thomas) 1593-1676, *R.C. priest.* The grounds of obedience and government. 2nd ed. (1655.) facsim. repr. 8vo. FARNBOROUGH, 1968.
White (William Hale) '*Mark Rutherford*'. Letters to three friends. 8vo. LOND., 1924.
White (Winifred M.) Six Weeks Meeting, 1671-1971: three hundred years of Quaker responsibility. 8vo. LOND., 1971.
Whitefield (George) Letters, 1734-1742. [Works, vol 1. (1771) with suppts.] facsim. repr. 8vo. EDIN., 1976.
—— *See* Belden (A. D.); Dallimore (A. A.)
Whitehead (A. N.) *See* Wickham (H.)
Whitehead (Thomas) Illustrated guide to Nidderdale, and a history of its Congregational churches. 8vo. [KEIGHLEY, 1932.]
Whitelocke (Bulstrode) *See* Spalding (R. J. L.)
Whitfield (J. T.) *comp.* Highfield Congregational Church, Rock Ferry, Birkenhead: a record of a hundred years, 1870-1970. 8vo. [BIRKENHEAD, 1970.] [Pamph.]

Whiting (Arthur)   *See* Loveridge (S. M.) and Whiting (A.)

Whitley (Charles F.)   *See* Suppt. Zeitschr. für A. T. Wiss. Beihefte, 148.

Whitlow (Maurice)   J. Taylor Smith: everybody's bishop. 8vo. LOND., 1938.

Whitney (Janet)   Geraldine S. Cadbury, 1865-1941: a biography. 8vo. LOND., 1948.

Whitting (Philip)   Byzantium: an introduction. 8vo. OXF., 1971.

Whittington (R. R.)   Doddington Congregational Church, Whitchurch. 4to. SHREWSBURY, 1961. [Pamph.]

Whybray (R. N.)   The heavenly counsellor in Isaiah XL. 13-14: a study of the sources of the theology of Deutero-Isaiah. [Soc. for O.T. Study, Monograph Ser., 1.] 8vo. CAMB., 1971.

—— *See* Bible. Commentaries. New Century Bible; Suppt. Zeitschr. für A. T. Wiss. Beihefte, 135.

Wickenden (Hubert)   A short history of Park Baptist Church, Brentford, 1855-1955. 8vo. [LOND., 1955.] [Pamph.]

Wicker (Colin H.)   *comp.* Unitarian (Williamson Memorial) Church, Dundee. [List of church records.] 4to. *Duplicated.* DUNDEE, 1980. [Pamph.]

Wickert (Ulrich)   *See* Suppt. Zeitschr. für N.T. Wiss. Beihefte, 41.

Wickham (Harvey)   The unrealists: William James, Bergson, Santayana, Einstein, Bertrand Russell, John Dewey, Alexander and Whitehead. 8vo. LOND., 1931.

Wicks (G. H.)   Bristol's heathen neighbours: the story of the Bristol Itinerant Society, 1811-1911. 8vo. [BRISTOL, 1911]

Wicks (W. O.)   A desirable object: the story of the first 150 years of Stroud Baptist Church. obl. 8vo. [STROUD, 1975.] [Pamph.]

Widmer (Charles)   Gabriel Marcel et le théisme existentiel. Thèse. 8vo. PARIS, 1972.

Widows' Fund, *Lancashire and Cheshire.*   Rules of the Association, established in 1764, for the benefit of widows and orphans of Protestant Dissenting ministers, and of ministers themselves. 8vo. n.p., 1925. [Pamph.]

—— *See* Catalogues. *Manchester Central Lib. Archives Dept.*

Wigfield (W. M.)   Ecclesiastica, the Book of Remembrance of the Independent congregations of Axminster and Chard, and their part in the Monmouth rebellion. 8vo. [TAUNTON, 1975.] [Pamph.]

—— Quakers in Chard. 4to. [TAUNTON, 1978.] [Pamph.]

Wigley (Thomas)   Religion's part in modern life: a psychological approach. [Address to the Soc. for the Study of Religions, 14th Feb. 1945.] 8vo. [LOND., 1945.] [Pamph.]

Wigmore-Beddoes (D. G.)   Yesterday's radicals: a study of the affinity between Unitarianism and Broad Church Anglicanism in the nineteenth century. 8vo. CAMB. & LOND., 1971.

—— A religion that thinks: a psychological study. The psychology of Unitarianism. [Ulster Unitarian Christian Assn. Lect., 1969.] 8vo. BELFAST, 1972. [Pamph.]

Wigston. *Congregational Church.*   Tercentenary, 1666-1966. obl. 8vo. [WIGSTON, 1965.] [Pamph.]

Wikgren (Allen P.)   [Misc.]   *See* Suppt. Novum Testamentum. Suppts., 33.

Wiles (G. P.)   Paul's intercessory prayers: the significance of the intercessory prayer passages in the letters of St. Paul. [Soc. for N.T. Studies, Monograph Ser., 24.] 8vo. CAMB., 1974.

Wiles (M. F.)   Looking into the sun. Inaugural lect., Chair of Christian Doctrine, Univ. of London, King's Coll., 16 Jan. 1968. 8vo. [LOND.,] 1969. [Pamph.]

—— The remaking of Christian doctrine. [Hulsean Lects., 1973.] 8vo. LOND., 1974.

—— Faith, doubt and theology. Maynard-Chapman Divinity Lect., Westfield Coll., Univ. of London, 30 Apr. 1975. 8vo. [LOND., 1975.] [Pamph.]

Wilken (R. L.)   Judaism and the early Christian mind: a study of Cyril of Alexandria's exegesis and theology. [Yale Publs. in Religion, 15.] 8vo. NEW HAVEN & LOND., 1971.

Wilkinson (John T.)   William Clowes, 1780-1851. 8vo. LOND., 1951.

—— Arthur Samuel Peake: a biography. 8vo. LOND., 1971.

Willan (T. S.)   *See* Suppt. Chetham Soc., 3rd Ser., 27.

Willard (Frances Elizabeth) 1839-98. *See* Strachey (R.)

Willey (Basil)   Samuel Taylor Coleridge. 8vo. LOND., 1972.

Willi (Thomas) *See* Suppt. Forschungen zur Religion u. Lit., 106.
William, *of Hoo.* The letter-book of William of Hoo, sacrist of Bury St. Edmunds, 1280-1294. Ed. Antonia Gransden. [Suffolk Records Soc., 5.] 8vo. [IPSWICH,] 1963.
William, *of Moerbeke, Abp. of Corinth. See* Suppt. Corpus Philos. Medii Aevi. Aristoteles Latinus. Opera, VI, XXXI.
William, *of Ockham. See* Ockham (William)
William, *of Saint-Thierry.* Exposé sur le Cantique des cantiques. Texte latin, introd. et notes de J.-M. Déchanet. Trad. française de M. Dumontier. [Sources Chrétiennes, 82.] 8vo. PARIS, 1962.
William and Mary Quarterly. *See* Suppt.
Williams (A. H.) John Wesley a Chymru. [Darlithiau Amgueddfa'r Hen Gapel, Tre'r-ddôl, 1.] 8vo. TRE'R-DDÔL, 1969. [Pamph.]
Williams (*Mrs.* A. J. Bailey) The story of the West Hill Road Unitarian Church, Bournemouth, 1882-1962. 8vo. BOURNEMOUTH, [1962]. [Pamph.]
Williams (Bernard A. O.) *See* Smart (J. J. C.) and Williams (B. A. O.)
Williams (Bill) The making of Manchester Jewry, 1740-1875. 8vo. MANCHESTER, 1976.
Williams (Charles W. S.) Thomas Cranmer of Canterbury. [The Canterbury Play, 1936.] 8vo. OXF. & LOND., 1936.
—— The image of the City, and other essays. Selected by Anne Ridler, with a critical introd. 8vo. LOND., 1958.
—— *See* Hadfield (A. M.)
Williams (D. D.) Cofiant Thomas Jones Wheldon. Ynghyda rhai o'i ysgrifau a'i bregethau. 8vo. CAERNARFON, 1925.
Williams (Daniel Day) The spirit and the forms of love. [Lib. of Constructive Theol.] 8vo. LOND., 1968.
Williams (David) *ed. See* Jones (I. G.) and Williams (D.) *ed.*
Williams (E. T.) *ed. See* Dictionaries. Biography.
Williams (*Sir* George) 1821-1905, *founder of the Y.M.C.A. See* Binfield (J. C. G.); Williams (J. E. H.)
Williams (George) Harpenden Congregational Church: the record of a hundred years, 1822-1922. 8vo. [HARPENDEN, 1922.] [Pamph.]
Williams (George Huntston) American universalism: a bicentennial historical essay. [J. of the Universalist Historical Soc., 9, 1971.] 8vo. BOSTON (Mass.), 1971.
[Williams (Glanmor)] Samuel Roberts, Llanbrynmair. 8vo. CARDIFF, 1950.
—— *See* John (J. M.) *ed.*
Williams (Huw Llewelyn) Yr emyn yn gwasanaeth crefyddol. [Darlith Davies, 1972.] 8vo. CAERNARFON, 1973. [Pamph.]
—— *ed.* Braslun o hanes Methodistiaeth Galfinaidd Môn, 1935-1970. 8vo. n.p., 1977.
Williams (*Sir* Ifor) Lectures on early Welsh poetry. 8vo. DUBLIN, 1944. [Pamph.]
Williams (J. E. Hodder) The life of Sir George Williams. 8vo. LOND., 1906.
Williams (J. Gwyn) Witchcraft in seventeenth-century Flintshire. Pt. 1. 8vo. [PRESTATYN, 1976.] [Pamph.]
Williams (John) *c.*1582-1650, *Abp. of York. See* Welch (C. E.)
Williams (John Tudno) Aspects of the life and work of C. H. Dodd. 8vo. [LOND., 1975.] [Pamph.]
Williams (Neville John) John Foxe the martyrologist: his life and times. [Friends of Dr. Williams's Lib. Lect., 29.] 8vo. LOND., 1975. [Pamph.]
Williams (Owen) *comp. See* Catalogues. *Denbighshire County Lib.*
Williams (Penry) The Tudor regime. 8vo. OXF., 1979.
Williams (Samuel) John Penry, 1563-1593. 8vo. CARDIFF, 1955.
[Williams (Thomas Minns)] A short history of Old King Street Baptist Church, Bristol. 8vo. [BRISTOL, 1956.] [Pamph.]
Williams (Thomas Rhondda) Shall we understand the Bible. 2nd ed. (1902.) repr. 8vo. LOND., 1909.
—— Three years of war: what now? Delivered at Union Church, Brighton, Aug. 5th, 1917. 8vo. BRIGHTON, [1917]. [Pamph.]
[Williams (William Henry)] 1808-1958: Bethesda Baptist Church, Narberth. 8vo. NARBERTH, 1958. [Pamph.]

Williamson (Benedict) The Bridgettine order: its foundress, history and spirit. 8vo. LOND., 1922.

Williamson (David) Sir John Kirk: the life story of the children's friend. 8vo. LOND., [1922].

Williamson (George) Milton and others. 8vo. CHICAGO, 1965.

Williamson (George Charles) Lady Anne Clifford, Countess of Dorset, Pembroke and Montgomery, 1590-1676: her life, letters and work, extracted from all the original documents available. 4to. KENDAL, 1922.

Willi-Plein (Ina) *See* Suppt. Zeitschr. für A. T. Wiss. Beihefte, 123.

Wills (A. W.) The history of Argyle Congregational Church, Bath, 1781 to 1938. 8vo. [BATH, 1938.]

Wilmslow. Norcliffe Chapel, Styal.—Dean Row Chapel, Wilmslow. 8vo. [WILMSLOW, 195-.] [Pamph.]

Wilson (Bryan R.) Religion in secular society. (1966.) repr. 8vo. HARMONDSWORTH, 1969.

—— Religious sects: a sociological study. [World University Lib.] 8vo. LOND., 1970.

—— Magic and the millen[n]ium. (1973.) repr. 8vo. ST. ALBANS, 1975.

—— Contemporary transformations of religion. [Riddell Memorial Lects., 45, 1974.] 8vo. OXF., 1976.

Wilson (C. W.) Mount Pleasant Chapel, Northampton: history, 1873-1973. 8vo. [NORTHAMPTON, 1973.] [Pamph.]

Wilson (Colin) The occult. 8vo. LOND., 1971.

Wilson (Edward Meryon) Richard Leake's Plague sermons, 1599. 8vo. KENDAL, 1975. [Pamph.]

Wilson (Ellen Gibson) The loyal blacks. 8vo. NEW YORK, 1976.

—— John Clarkson and the African adventure. 8vo. LOND. & BASINGSTOKE, 1980.

Wilson (Henry Joseph) *See* Catalogues. *Sheffield Univ. Lib.*

Wilson (John H. S.) Emotion and object. 8vo. CAMB., 1972.

Wilson (Kenneth B.) Making sense of it: an essay in philosophical theology. [Fernley-Hartley Lect., 1973.] 8vo. LOND., 1973.

Wilson (P. Whitwell) Liberty and religion: a reply to certain bishops. 8vo. LOND., 1906.

Wilson (Stephen G.) The Gentiles and the Gentile mission in Luke-Acts. [Soc. for N.T. Studies, Monograph Ser., 23.] 8vo. CAMB., 1973.

Wilson (Thomas) *Bp. of Sodor and Man. See* Ziegler (A. B.)

Wilson (William E.) Quaker and evangelical. [Rendel Harris Lect., 1948.] 8vo. LOND., 1949. [Pamph.]

—— Essential Christianity. 8vo. LOND., 1952.

Wiltshire (David) The social and political thought of Herbert Spencer. [Oxford Historical Monographs.] 8vo. OXF., 1978.

Wind (Edgar) Pagan mysteries in the Renaissance. 4to. LOND., 1958.

Wingfield-Stratford (Esmé C.) King Charles and the conspirators. 8vo. LOND., 1937.

Winkler (G. B.) Erasmus von Rotterdam und die Einleitungsschriften zum Neuen Testament: formale Strukturen und theologischer Sinn. [Reformationsgesch. Studien u. Texte, 108.] 8vo. MÜNSTER IN W., 1974.

Winnett (A. R.) Peter Browne: provost, bishop, metaphysician. [Church Historical Ser., 95.] 8vo. LOND., 1974.

Winnington-Ingram (A. F.) *Bp. of London.* Fifty years' work in London, 1889-1939. 8vo. LOND., 1940.

Winstanley (D. A.) The University of Cambridge in the eighteenth century. 8vo. CAMB., 1922.

—— Unreformed Cambridge: a study of certain aspects of the University in the eighteenth century. 8vo. CAMB., 1935.

—— Early Victorian Cambridge. 8vo. CAMB., 1940.

Winstanley (Gerrard) Works. With an appendix of documents relating to the Digger movement. Ed. with an introd. by George H. Sabine. 8vo. ITHACA (N.Y.), 1941.

—— *See* Greaves (R. L.); Hill (C.)

Wintersteen (P. B.) Christology in American Unitarianism: an anthology of outstanding nineteenth and twentieth century Unitarian theologians, with commentary and historical background. 8vo. BOSTON (Mass.), 1977.

Winterton (W. H.) Harvest of the years: autobiography. 8vo. BIRMINGHAM, 1969.
Wintler (Robert) Das Geistproblem in seiner Bedeutung für die Prinzipienfragen der systematischen Theologie der Gegenwart. 8vo. GÖTTINGEN, 1926. [Pamph.]
Wisdom (A. J. T. D.) Problems of mind and matter. (1934.) repr. 8vo. CAMB., 1963.
Wiseman (Alexander) The Bible and the immortality of man. 8vo. LOND., [1929].
Wiseman (D. J.) *ed.* Peoples of Old Testament times. Ed. for the Soc. for O.T. Study. 8vo. OXF., 1973.
Wiseman (P. J.) Clues to creation in Genesis. Foreword by D. J. Wiseman. 8vo. LOND., 1977.
Wishaw. *Baptist Church.* One Lord, one faith, one baptism: centenary, 1871-1971. 8vo. [WISHAW, 1971.] [Pamph.]
Wissowa (Georg) *ed. See* Dictionaries. Classical.
Witard (G. Doris) The history of Braintree Baptist Church, Essex. 8vo. LOND., 1955.
—— Bibles in barrels: a history of Essex Baptists. 8vo. SOUTHEND-ON-SEA [printed], [1962].
Withycombe (Elizabeth G.) *See* Ghosh (J. C.) and Withcombe (E. G.)
Wittgenstein (Ludwig) Philosophical grammar. Pt. 1. The proposition and its sense. Pt. 2. On logic and mathematics. Ed. Rush Rhees. Trans. Anthony Kenny. 8vo. OXF., 1974.
—— Remarks on colour. Ed. G. E. M. Anscombe. Trans. Linda L. McAlister and Margaret Schättle. (1977.) repr. 8vo. OXF., 1978.
—— Lectures, Cambridge, 1930-1932. From the notes of John King and Desmond Lee. Ed. Desmond Lee. 8vo. OXF., 1980.
—— *See* Ambrose (A.) and Lazerowitz (M.) *ed.;* Copi (I. M.) and Beard (R. W.) *ed.;* Hudson (W. D.); Suppt. Royal Inst. of Philos. Lects., 7.
Wolff (H. W.) Frieden ohne Ende: Jesaja 7, 1-17 und 9, 1-6 ausgelegt. [Biblische Studien, 35.] 8vo. NEUKIRCHEN, 1962.
Wolff (R. P.) *ed.* Kant: a collection of critical essays. [Modern Studies in Philos.] 8vo. LOND., *etc.*, 1968.
Wolfson (H. A.) Studies in the history of philosophy and religion. Ed. Isadore Twersky and George H. Williams. 2 vols. 8vo. CAMB., (Mass.), 1973-77.
Wolin (S. S.) Hobbes and the epic tradition of political theory. [Clark Lib. Seminar Papers, 1968.] 8vo. LOS ANGELES, 1970. [Pamph.]
Wolter (Michael) *See* Suppt. Zeitschr. für N. T. Wiss. Beihefte, 43.
Wolterstorff (Nicholas) On universals: an essay in ontology. 8vo. CHICAGO & LOND., 1970.
Wood (Alfred C.) Nottinghamshire in the Civil War. (1937.) facsim. repr. With a new foreword by K.S.S. Train. 8vo. EAST ARDSLEY, 1971.
Wood (Herbert G.) The truth and error of communism. 8vo. LOND., 1933.
Wood (J. Duncan) The World Council of Churches. 8vo. LOND., 1972. [Pamph.]
Wood (Joseph) Church needs and conference ideals. A paper read before the National Conference of Presbyterian, Unitarian, Liberal Christian and other non-subscribing churches, held in Liverpool, Apr. 21-24, 1903. 8vo. BIRMINGHAM, [1903]. [Pamph.]
Woodbridge. *Quay Congregational Church.* 1651-1951: tercentenary celebrations, July 14th-22nd, 1951. 8vo. [WOODBRIDGE, 1951.] [Pamph.]
Wood Green. *Unitarian Society.* Annual reports. [2nd-21st.] 20 pts. in 1 vol. 8vo. [WOOD GREEN, 1891-] 1910.
Woodhams (R.) Christ the Saviour of all. 8vo. LOND., [1923].
Woodhead (*Sir* G. Sims) [Misc.] In memoriam Sir George Sims Woodhead, K.B.E., 1855-1921. [Memorial notices, collected by Harriett E. Woodhead.] 8vo. EDIN. [priv. printed], 1923.
Woodland (Christine) *See* Suppt. Royal Hist. Soc. Guides and Handbooks. Suppt. Ser., 1.
[Woods (S. R.)] King Edward Street Chapel, Macclesfield: historical notes. 8vo. [s.sh.fold.] *Duplicated.* n.p., 1977.
Woodward (*Sir* E. L.) Towards a new learning. A public lecture, Univ. of Oxford. 8vo. LOND., 1947. [Pamph.]
Woodward (John) *See* Levine (J. M.)
Woodward (Mary) *See* Porter (M.) *and others.*

Woodworth (R. S.) Contemporary schools of psychology. (1931.) 8th ed. 8vo. LOND., 1951.

Woof (R. S.) The Wordsworth circle: studies of twelve members of Wordsworth's circle of friends. 8vo. GRASMERE, 1979. [Pamph.]

Woolf (Virginia) *See* Forster (E. M.)

Woolhouse (R. S.) Locke's philosophy of science and knowledge: a consideration of some aspects of 'An essay concerning human understanding'. 8vo. OXF., 1971.

[**Woollard** (J. S.)] Osmaston Road Baptist Church, Derby: history of the church from its inception in 1827. 8vo. [DERBY, 1962.] [Pamph.]

Woolman (John) *See* Suppt. Friends' Hist. Soc. Journal. Suppt. 32.

Woolrych (A. H.) Oliver Cromwell. [Clarendon Biographies, 2.] 8vo. OXF., 1964.

Worden (Blair) The Rump Parliament, 1648-1653. 8vo. CAMB., 1974.

Wordsworth (William) Prose works. Ed. W. J. B. Owen and Jane Worthington Smyser. 3 vols. 8vo. OXF., 1974.

—— *See* Clutterbuck (N.) *ed.;* Prickett (S.); Sharrock (R. I.); Woof (R. S.)

Wordsworth (William) and **Wordsworth** (Dorothy) Letters. Ed. Ernest de Selincourt. (1935-39.) 2nd ed., rev. and ed. Alan G. Hill. 8vo. OXF.
4[mispr. as 3]. The later years. 1. 1821-28. 1978.
5. —— 2. 1829-34. 1979.

World Council of Churches. *See* Bell (G. K. A.); Suppt. Ecumenical Review.

Worsfold (J. E.) A history of the charismatic movements in New Zealand, including a Pentecostal perspective and a breviate of the Catholic Apostolic Church in Great Britain. 8vo. n.p., 1974.

Wrede (William) *See* Suppt. Studies in Bibl. Theol., 2nd Ser., 25.

Wren, *family of.* *See* Wren (C.)

Wren (Christopher) 1675-1747, *son of Sir Christopher Wren.* Parentalia: or, memoirs of the family of the Wrens. (1750.) facsim. repr. fol. FARNBOROUGH, 1965.

Wright (Conrad) The beginnings of Unitarianism in America. (1955.) repr. 8vo. HAMDEN (Conn.), 1976.

—— The liberal Christians: essays on American Unitarian history. 8vo. BOSTON (Mass.), 1970.

—— *ed.* A stream of light: a sesquicentennial history of American Unitarianism. 8vo. BOSTON (Mass.), 1975.

Wright (Esmond) *See* Suppt. Historical Assn. Gen. Ser., 87.

Wright (Georg Henrik von) Explanation and understanding. [Internat. Lib. of Philos. and Scientific Method.] 8vo. LOND., 1971.

Wright (George Herbert) Immortality in the poets of to-day. [Drew Lect., 1930.] 8vo. LOND., [1930].

[**Wright** (Trevor W.)] A short history of the United Free Church, High Street, Tring, 1750-1950. 8vo. [TRING, 1950.] [Pamph.]

Wrightson (Keith) and **Levine** (David) Poverty and piety in an English village: Terling, 1525-1700. [Studies in Social Discontinuity.] 8vo. NEW YORK, *etc.*, 1979.

Wrigley (E. A.) Population: private choice and public policy. [Essex Hall Lect., 1972.] 8vo. LOND., 1972. [Pamph.]

Wrigley (Hugh) "Yet there is room": the story of "Reheboth" Baptist Chapel [Cliftonville, Margate], 1914-1974. RAMSGATE [printed], [1974]. [Pamph.]

Wroth (*Sir* Robert) *See* Tyacke (N. R. N.)

Würthwein (Ernst) *See* Bible. O.T. Commentaries. Handbuch zum A.T. I,18.

Wulfstan, *Saint, Bp. of Worcester. See* Suppt. Early Eng. Text Soc., O.S., 266.

[**Wykes** (D. L.)] Belper Unitarian Chapel: founded 1689, built 1788. 8vo. DERBY, 1978. [Pamph.]

Wylam. *Methodist Church.* Centenary, 1876-1976. 8vo. [WYLAM, 1976.] [Pamph.]

Wyvill (Christopher) *See* Dinwiddy (J. R.)

Yadin (Yigael) Hazor. With a chapter on Israelite Megiddo. [Schweich Lects., Brit. Acad., 1970.] 8vo. LOND., 1972.

Yarnold (Edward) *S. J., ed. See* Jones (Cheslyn P. M.) *and others, ed.*

Yates (Frances A.) The art of memory. 8vo. LOND., 1966.

—— Theatre of the world. 8vo. LOND. 1969.

—— The Rosicrucian enlightenment. 8vo. LOND. & BOSTON (Mass.), 1972.

Yates (Frances A.)—*continued*
—— Shakespeare's last plays: a new approach. 8vo. LOND., 1975.
—— Elizabethan Neoplatonism reconsidered: Spenser and Francesco Giorgi. [Soc. for Renaissance Studies, Annual Lect., 1977.] 8vo. LOND., 1977. [Pamph.]
—— The occult philosophy in the Elizabethan age. 8vo. LOND., *etc.*, 1979.
Yates (J. T.) A brief account of the history of Bamford Chapel from 1801-1976. 8vo. ROCHDALE [printed], [1976]. [Pamph.]
Yearbook of the General Assembly of Unitarian and Free Christian Churches. *See* Suppt. General Assembly of Unitarian and Free Christian Churches.
Yeo (Stephen) Religion and voluntary organisations in crisis. [Croom Helm Social Hist. Ser.] 8vo. LOND., 1976.
Yeovil. *South Street Baptist Church.* In celebration of the completion of the organ and building scheme, 1956. 4to. [YEOVIL, 1956.] [Pamph.]
Yepes (Diego de) *Bp. of Tarazona.* Historia particular de la persecucion de Inglaterra. (1599.) facsim. repr. Introd. by D. M. Rogers. 8vo. FARNBOROUGH, 1971.
Yevele (Henry) *See* Harvey (J. H.)
Yoder (J. H.) Täufertum und Reformation im Gespräch: Dogmengeschichtliche Untersuchung der frühen Gespräche zwischen Schweizerischen Täufern und Reformatoren. [Basler Studien zur hist. u. syst. Theol., 13.] 8vo. ZÜRICH, 1968.
—— The politics of Jesus: vicit Agnus Noster. (1972.) repr. 8vo. GRAND RAPIDS (Mich.), 1973.
Yoná (Yacob Abraham) The Judeo-Spanish ballad chapbooks. Ed. Samuel G. Armistead and Joseph H. Silverman. [Folk Lit. of the Sephardic Jews, 1.] 8vo. BERKELEY (Calif.), *etc.*, 1971.
Yorkshire Congregational Year Book. *See* Suppt.
Young (Betty) *See* Vickers (J. A.) and Young (B.)
Young (Brigham) *See* Hirshson (S. P.)
Young (Dinsdale T.) *See* Murray (H.)
Young (Edward) 1683-1765, *poet.* Correspondence. Ed. Henry Pettit. 8vo. OXF., 1971.
Young (G. H.) A short history of Harlow Baptist Church, 1662-1962. (1941.) Ed. and with extra material by J. W. Barker. 8vo. HARLOW, 1962. [Pamph.]
Young (George M.) Charles I and Cromwell: an essay. 8vo. LOND., 1935.
Young (Harry) The Duke Street story, 1870-1970: a hundred years of Christian witness in the Duke Street Baptist Church, Richmond. 8vo. LOND., 1970.
Young (Kenneth) Chapel: the joyous days and prayerful nights of the Nonconformists in their heyday, circa 1850-1950. 8vo. LOND., 1972.
Young (Peter) Oliver Cromwell and his times. [Makers of Britain.] 8vo. LOND., 1962.
—— Marston Moor, 1644: the campaign and the battle. 8vo. KINETON, 1970.
—— *See* Burne (A. H.) and Young (P.); Toynbee (M. R.) and Young (P.)
Young (Peter) and **Emberton** (Wilfrid) The Cavalier army: its organisation and everyday life. 8vo. LOND., 1974.
Young (Peter) and **Tucker** (Norman) *ed.* Richard Atkyns [Vindication, 1669], ed. Peter Young.—John Gwyn [Memoirs, 1679-82], ed. Norman Tucker. [Military Memoirs: The Civil War.] 8vo. LOND., 1967.
Young (Robert) Freedom, responsibility and God. [Lib. of Philos. and Relig.] 8vo. LOND., 1975.
Young Men's Christian Association. In the midst of the years: a brief chronicle of London Central Y.M.C.A. from its beginning in the City of London in 1844. 8vo. [LOND.,] 1955. [Pamph.]
Youngs (Frederic A.) *See* Suppt. Royal Hist. Soc. Guides and Handbooks, 10.
Yule (George) Continental patterns and the Reformation in England and Scotland. 8vo. [EDIN.,] 1969. [Pamph.]
—— In what way should we understand the causes of the Reformation? 8vo. MELBOURNE, 1971. [Pamph.]

Zaehner (R. C.) Concordant discord: the interdependence of faiths. [Gifford Lects., 1967-69.] 8vo. OXF., 1970.
—— Which God is dead? [Friends of Dr. Williams's Lib. Lect., 28.] 8vo. LOND., 1974. [Pamph.]
Zahrnt (Heinz) What kind of God? A question of faith. 8vo. LOND., 1971.

Za-Johannes, *of Kebran.* *See* Suppt. Corpus Script. Christ. Orient., Aethiop., 64-65.
Zar'a Buruk. *See* Suppt. Corpus Script. Christ. Orient., Aethiop., 72.
Zehrer (Karl) Die Beziehungen zwischen dem hallischen Pietismus und dem frühen Methodismus. 8vo. [BIELEFELD (W. Ger.), 1975.] [Pamph.] [Photocopy.]
Zeitlin (Solomon) *ed.* *See* Bible. Apocrypha. Judith.
Zeitschrift für... *See* Suppt.
Zeitschriften Inhaltsdienst Theologie. *See* Suppt.
Zeller (Winifred) *ed.* Der Protestantismus des 17. Jahrhunderts. [Klassiker des Protestantismus, 5.] 8vo. BREMEN, 1962.
Ziegler (A. B.) Thomas Wilson, Bischof von Sodor und Man, 1663-1755: ein Beitrag zur Geschichte der englischen Literatur des 18. Jahrhunderts. [Seges: Philol. u. lit. Studien u. Texte, 15.] 8vo. FREIBURG (Schweiz), 1972.
Ziesler (J. A.) The meaning of righteousness in Paul: a linguistic and theological enquiry. [Soc. for N.T. Studies, Monograph Ser., 20.] 8vo. CAMB., 1972.
Zimmels (H. J.) Ashkenazim and Sephardim. [Jews' Coll. Publs., N.S., 2.] (1958.) repr. 8vo. LOND., 1969.
Zimmer (Hermann) A fraudulent testament devalues the Bahai religion into political Shogism. Trans. Jeannine Blackwell. Rev. by Karen Gasser and Gordon Campbell. 8vo. WAIBLINGEN & STUTTGART, 1973.
Zimmerli (Walther) Der Mensch und seine Hoffnung im Alten Testament. 8vo. GÖTTINGEN, 1968.
—— Ezechiel. [Biblischer Kommentar, A.T., 13.] 2 vols. 8vo. NEUKIRCHEN-VLUYN, 1969.
  1. 1-24.
  2. 25-48.
—— *See* Suppt. Studies in Bibl. Theol., 2nd Ser., 20.
Zinzendorf (Nikolaus Ludwig, *Graf von*) Ergänzungsbände zu den Hauptschriften. Hrsg. Erich Beyreuther und Gerhard Meyer. 12 vols. 8vo. HILDESHEIM, 1964-66.
  7-9. Büdingische Sammlung. 3 vols. 1965-66.
  10. *Not in Library.*
  11-12. Freywillige Nachlese (Kleine Schr.). 2 vols. 1972.
—— Nine public lectures on important subjects in religion preached in Fetter Lane Chapel in London in the year 1746. Trans. and ed. George W. Forrell. 8vo. IOWA CITY, 1973.
—— [Misc.] Materialien und Dokumente. [Facsim. reprs.] Hrsg. Erich Beyreuther, Gerhard Meyer und Amedeo Molnár. 8vo., *etc.* HILDESHEIM & NEW YORK.
  Reihe 1. Quellen und Darstellungen zur Geschichte der böhmischen Brüder-Unität.
    1. Jan Hus: Dat bokeken van deme repe.—De uthlegghinge ouer den louen. Aus dem Tschech. ins Niederdeutsche übertragen von Johann von Lübeck. (1480.) 1971.
    5. Peter Cheltschizki: Das Netz des Glaubens. Aus dem Alttschech. ins Deutsche übertragen von Carl Vogl. (1924.) 1970.
  No more in Library.
  Reihe 2. N. L. von Zinzendorf: Leben und Werk in Quellen und Darstellungen.
    1-8. August Gottlieb Spangenberg: Leben des Herrn Nicholaus Ludwig Grafen und Herrn von Zinzendorf und Pottendorf. (1773-75.) 8 vols. in 4. 1971.
    9. Ludwig Carl Freiherr von Schrautenbach: Der Graf von Zinzendorf und die Brüdergemeine seiner Zeit. Hrsg. F. W. Kölbing. (1871.) 1972.
    10. Johann Albrecht Bengel: Abriss der so genannten Brüdergemeine. (1751.) 1972.
  No more in Library.
"Zoe" Brotherhood of Theologians. *ed.* A sign of God: Orthodoxy 1964. A pan-Orthodox symposium. 8vo. ATHENS, 1964.
Zoványi (Jenő) A reformáczió egyháza. Irta és a "Budapesti Dávid Ferencz-Egylet" 1908 decz. 12-én tartott ülésén felolvasta Zoványi Jenő. 8vo. SÁROSPATAK, 1909. [Pamph.]
—— Kisebb dolgozatok a magyar protestantismus történetének köréből. 8vo. SAROSPATAK, 1901.
Zsigmond (Ferenc) *comp.* A Debreceni Református Kollégium története 1538(?)-1938. DEBRECEN, 1937.
Zsindely (Endre) *ed.* *See* Gäbler (U.) and Zsindely (E.) *ed.*
Zwingli (Huldreich) *See* Potter (G. R.)

SUPPLEMENT

PERIODICALS, PUBLICATIONS OF SOCIETIES
CONNECTED SERIES, ETC.

In specifying the Library's holdings, the following symbols have been used:

+   after volume number and date. The Library has a complete series from the volume and date specified.

—   between volume numbers and between dates. The Library has a complete series between the limits specified.

...   after volume number and date (or between volume numbers and between dates). The Library has an incomplete series within the limits specified.

/   between dates. The year specified began in one calendar year and ended in the other.

[ ]   Information enclosed in square brackets is not found on the title page but is supplied from elsewhere.

Supplement to the Catalogue

Periodicals, Publications of Societies, Connected Series, etc.

Alcuin Club. COLLECTIONS. 8vo. LOND., *etc.* 1+ 1899+

53. The Anglican Ordinal: its history and development from the Reformation to the present day: P. F. Bradshaw. 1971.
54. The liturgy of comprehension, 1689: an abortive attempt to revise the Book of Common Prayer: T. J. Fawcett. 1973.
55. Martin Bucer and the Book of Common Prayer: E. C. Whitaker. 1974.
56. The ministry of healing in the Church of England: an ecumenical-liturgical study: C. W. Gusmer. 1974.

57. Eucharist and Holy Spirit: the eucharistic epiclesis in twentieth century theology (1900-1966): J. H. McKenna. 1975.
58. Eucharist and institution narrative: a study in the Roman and Anglican traditions of the consecration of the eucharist from the eighth to the twentieth centuries: R. F. Buxton. 1976.
59. The liturgy of Christian burial: an introductory survey of the historical development of Christian burial rites: Geoffrey Rowell. 1977.
60. Confirmation then and now: J. D. C. Fisher. 1978.
61. Jeremy Taylor, liturgist (1613-1667): H. B. Porter. 1979.

—— MANUALS. 8vo. LOND. 1+ 1978+

1. The Eucharist: Michael Perham. 1978.

—— MISCELLANEOUS PUBLICATIONS. [Pamphs.] 8vo. LOND.

1972. Edward Craddock Ratcliff, 1896-1967: a bibliography of his published works. [Comp. A. H. Couratin and D. H. Tripp.]
1973. Anglican eucharistic theology in the twentieth century: William Wand.
1974. The new Roman mass and the Anglican Series Three: J. D. Crighton.
1975. The Alcuin Club and its publications: an annotated bibliography, 1897-1974: P. J. Jagger.

1975. The fulness of Christian initiation: J. D. C. Fisher.
1977. The art of worship: Eric Kemp.
1978. The origins of the daily office: P. F. Bradshaw.
1979. Notes on the new rites of initiation: J. D. C. Fisher.
1980. Percy Dearmer and the English Hymnal: M. P. Draper.

American Congregational Association. *See* Bulletin of the Congregational Library.

American Journal of Semitic Languages and Literature. *See* Journal of Near Eastern Studies.

American Journal of Theology. *See* Journal of Religion.

American Schools of Oriental Research. *See* Biblical Archaeologist.

American Society of Church History. *See* Church History.

Analecta Bollandiana. (Société des Bollandistes.) 8vo. PARIS & BRUXELLES. 1+ 1882+

—— SUBSIDIA HAGIOGRAPHICA. 8vo. BRUXELLES. 1, 4, 6-10, 12+ 1886 . . . 1910, 1911+

32. La vie ancienne de S. Syméon Stylite le jeune (521-592): P. van den Ven. 2 vols. 1962-70.
48. Vie de Théodore de Sykéôn, A.-J. Festugière. 1970.
49. The martyrs of Najrân: new documents: I. Shahîd. 1971.
50. Les manuscrits hagiographiques d'Arras et de Boulogne-sur-Mer: J. van der Straeten. 1971.
51. Recherches et documents d'hagiographie byzantine: F. Halkin. 1971.
52. Recherches d'hagiographie latine: B. de Gaiffier. 1971.
53. Historia monachorum in Aegypto: A.-J. Festugière. 1971.
54. Chronologie des lettres de S. Cyprien: le dossier de la persécution de Dèce: L. Duquenne. 1972.
55. Légendes greques de "Martyres romaines": ed. F. Halkin. 1973.

56. Les manuscrits hagiographiques de Charleville, Verdun et Saint-Mihiel: J. van der Straeten. 1974.
57. Le dossier vézelien de Marie Madeleine: invention et translation des reliques en 1265-1267. Contribution à l'histoire de culte de la sainte à Vézelay à l'apogée du moyen âge: V. Saxer. 1975.
58. The Encomium of Gregory Nazianzen by Nicetas the Paphlagonian: J. J. Rizzo. 1976.
59. Les homélies festales d'Hésychius de Jerusalem: M. Aubineau. I. 1978.
60. Douze récits byzantins sur Saint Jean Chrysostome: F. Halkin. 1977.
61. Recueil d'hagiographie: B. de Gaiffier. 1977.
62. Vie et miracles de Sainte Thècle: G. Dagron et M. Dupré La Tour. 1978.

Anglican Theological Review. 8vo. EVANSTON (Ill.). 49+ 1967+

Anglo-Catholic Congress. REPORTS. 8vo. LOND. 1-6. 1920, 1923, 1927, 1930, 1933, 1948.

Annual Journal of the Universalist Historical Society. *See* Universalist Historical Society.

Aquarius: AN ANNUAL RELIGIO-CULTURAL REVIEW. (Servite Priory, Benburb, Co. Tyrone.) 4to. BENBURB. nos. 4-7. 1971-74. [*Formerly* Everyman.]

Arbeiten zur Neutestamentlichen Textforschung. 8vo. BERLIN. 1-3, 5. 1963-69, 1972. [*No more in Library.*]

5. Die alten Übersetzung des Neuen Testaments die Kirchenväterzitate und Lektionare: hrsg. K. Aland. 1972.

Archives de la France Monastique. *See* Revue Mabillon.

Archivum Franciscanum Historicum. 8vo. QUARACCHI, *etc.* 1+ 1908+

—— Indices tomorum 1-50 (1908-1957). 1960.

Aristotelian Society. PROCEEDINGS. N.S. 8vo. LOND. 1+ 1901+

—— —— Synoptic index. [I.] 1900-   —— —— —— II. 1950-1959. 1961.
1949.   1954.   —— —— —— III. 1960-1969. 1975.

—— SUPPLEMENTARY VOLUMES. 8vo. LOND. [1-49], TISBURY [50+].
1+   1918+

43. Symposia read at the joint session   48. —— 12-14 July 1974.   1974.
    of the Aristotelian Society and the   49. —— 18-20 July 1975.   1975.
    Mind Association, 11-13 July 1969.   50. —— 9-11 July 1976.   1976.
                              1969.   51. —— 8-10 July 1977.   1977.
44. —— 10-12 July 1970.   1970.   52. —— 7-9 July 1978.   1978.
45. —— 9-11 July 1971.   1971.   53. —— 13-15 July 1979.   1979.
46. —— 7-9 July 1972.   1972.   54. —— 11-13 July 1980.   1980.
47. —— 13-15 July 1973.   1973.

Arthur Stanley Eddington Memorial Lectures. 8vo. CAMB. 1-25.
1948-72.

24. Korner (S.): Abstraction in science   25. Hick (J. H.): Biology and the soul.
    and morals.   1971.   1972.

Association de l'Orient Chrétien. See Patrologia Orientalis.

Association of British Theological and Philosophical Libraries.
See Bulletin of the Association of British Theological and Philosophical Libraries.

Bampton Lectures. 8vo. LOND. 1780+

1968. Dillistone (F. W.): Traditional   1974. Baelz (P. R.): The forgotten
    symbols and the contemporary   dream: experience, hope and God.
    world.   1973.   1975.
1972. Gutteridge (R. J. C.): Open thy   1976. Lampe (G. W. H.): God as
    mouth for the dumb! The German   Spirit.   1977.
    Evangelical Church and the Jews,   1978. Peacocke (A. R.): Creation and
    1879-1950.   1976.   the world of science.   1979.

Baptist Handbook. (Baptist Union of Great Britain and Ireland.) 8vo.
LOND. 1871, 1875-76, 1884-1972.
[*Wanting* 1913, 1920.]
[*Contd. as* Baptist Union Directory *and* Baptist Union Handbook.]

Baptist Historical Society. TRANSACTIONS. See Baptist Quarterly.

—— PUBLICATIONS.
1971-74. Association records of the Particular Baptists of England,
    Wales and Ireland to 1660: ed. B. R. White. 8vo. LOND. 1-3.

1. South Wales and the Midlands.
        [1971.]
2. The West Country and Ireland.
        [1973.]
3. The Abingdon Association. 1974.

—— —— —— Indexes, comp. K. W. H. Howard. 4to. [Typescript.]
1976.

Baptist Quarterly: INCORPORATING THE TRANSACTIONS OF THE BAPTIST HISTORICAL SOCIETY. 8vo. LOND. N.S. 1+ 1922/23+
[*Formerly* Transactions of the Baptist Historical Society.]
—— Cumulative index. 1-10 [1922-41].
1970.
—— —— 11-20 [1942-64]. 1976.

Baptist Union (of Great Britain and Ireland).
DIRECTORY. 8vo. LOND. 1973/74+ [Annual.]
HANDBOOK. 8vo. LOND. 1973/78+ [Publ. every five years.]
[*Formerly* Baptist Handbook.]

Baptist Union of Scotland. *See* Scottish Baptist Yearbook.

Bible Translator: A QUARTERLY PUBLISHED BY THE UNITED BIBLE SOCIETIES.
8vo. LOND. 9+ 1958+

Biblica: COMMENTARII EDITI CURA PONTIFICI INSTITUTI BIBLICI. 8vo.
ROMA. 32+ 1951+
—— ELENCHUS BIBLIOGRAPHICUS BIBLICUS. 8vo. ROMA. 49+ 1969+
[1-48 *incl. in* Biblica.]

Biblical Archaeologist. (American Schools of Oriental Research.)
8vo. NEW HAVEN, CAMBRIDGE (Mass.). 1-38. 1938-75.
fol. ANN ARBOR. 39+ 1976+

Biblical Research: PAPERS OF THE CHICAGO SOCIETY OF BIBLICAL RE-SEARCH. 8vo. AMSTERDAM [1-3], CHICAGO [4+]. 1+ 1958+

Bibliographical Society. TRANSACTIONS. *See* Library.
—— PUBLICATIONS. 4to. LOND. 1895+

1971. English music printing, 1553-1700: D. W. Krummel. 1975.
1973-75. A short-title catalogue of books printed in England, Scotland, & Ireland, and of English books printed abroad, 1475-1640. First

comp. by A. W. Pollard & G. R. Redgrave. Second ed., rev. & enl., begun by W. A. Jackson & F. S. Ferguson, completed by K. F. Pantzer. Vol. 2. I-Z. 1976.

—— ILLUSTRATED MONOGRAPHS. 4to. LOND.

22/22a. English woodcuts, 1480-1535: Edward Hodnett. (1935.) [Repr. with additions and corrections.]
1973.

Bibliographie de la Philosophie: BULLETIN TRIMESTRIEL. (Institut International de Philosophie.) [Added English t.p.] 8vo. PARIS.
4+ 1957+

Biographical Studies. *See* Recusant History.

Bodleian Library Record. 8vo. OXF. 1-10, no. 2. 1938-79.
[*Formerly* Bodleian Quarterly Record.]

Bollandist Fathers (i.e. Société des Bollandistes). *See* Analecta Bollandiana.

British Academy. PROCEEDINGS. 8vo. LOND. 15+ 1929+

British Institute of Philosophy.   *See* Philosophy.

British Journal for the Philosophy of Science. 8vo. EDIN. 1+ 1950+

British Journal of Aesthetics. 8vo. LOND. 1-14, no. 2. 1960-74.

British School of Archaeology in Jerusalem. *See* Palestine Exploration Quarterly.

Bulletin of the American Congregational Association. *See* Bulletin of the Congregational Library.

Bulletin of the Association of British Theological and Philosophical Libraries. 4to. *Duplicated.* LOND. 1-23. 1956-66.
—— N.S. 8vo. EDIN. 1+ 1974+

Bulletin of the Congregational Library. (American Congregational Association.) 8vo. BOSTON (Mass.). 9, no. 2+ 1958+
[*Formerly* Bulletin of the American Congregational Association.]

Bulletin of the Institute of Historical Research. *See* London University. Institute of Historical Research. Bulletin.

Bulletin of the John Rylands (University) Library. 8vo. MANCHESTER. 1+ 1903+
[*Title lengthened* 1972.]

Byzantina Chronica.   *See* Vizantijskij Vremennik.

Byzantinische Zeitschrift. 8vo. LEIPZIG, *etc.* 1-9, 12, 17-42, pt.1, 49+ 1892-1900, 1903, 1908-42, 1956+

Byzantinoslavica. 8vo. PRAGUE. 1+ 1929+
[*Wanting* 5-7, 13, pt. 1, 20, pt. 1.]

Byzantion: REVUE INTERNATIONALE DES ÉTUDES BYZANTINES. 8vo. PARIS, *etc.* [1-5], BRUXELLES [6+]. 1+ 1924+

Camden Society.   *See* Royal Historical Society.

Canterbury and York Society. 8vo. LOND. [1-29], OXF. [30-55, 57], TORQUAY [56, 58+]. 1+ 1905+

58. Diocese of Salisbury. The registers of Roger Martival, 1315-1330. II (2nd half). 1972.
63. Diocese of Exeter. The register of Edmund Lacy, 1420-1455. IV. 1971.
66. —— v. 1972.
67. Canterbury professions ed. Michael Richter. 1973.
68. Diocese of Salisbury. The registers of Roger Martival, 1315-1330. IV. 1975.

69. Diocese of York. The register of Thomas Rotherham, 1480-1500. I. 1976.
70-71. Diocese of York. The register of William Melton, 1317-1340. I-II. 1977-78.

Catholic Record Society.   *See* Recusant History.

C.B.R.F. *See* Christian Brethren Research Fellowship.

Chalice. (Unitarian Information Dept.) fol. LOND. Nos. 2-5. Autumn 1966-Summer 1968. [*Ceased.*]

Charles Lamb Bulletin: THE JOURNAL OF THE CHARLES LAMB SOCIETY. 4to. LOND. N.S. 1+ 1973+

Cheshire. *See* Record Society of Lancashire and Cheshire.

Chetham Society. Remains. 8vo. MANCHESTER. THIRD SERIES. 1+ 1949+

19. Elizabethan recusancy in Cheshire: K. R. Wark. 1971.
20. The Lancashire textile industry in the sixteenth century: N. Lowe. 1972.
21. The early records of the Bankes family at Winstanley: ed. J. Bankes and E. Kerridge. 1973
22. Provision for the relief of the poor in Manchester, 1754-1826: G. B. Hindle. 1975.
23. Victoria Park, Manchester: a nineteenth century suburb in its social and administrative context: M. Spiers. 1976.
24. The encouragement of the fine arts in Lancashire, 1760-1860: C. P. Darcy. 1976.
25. The Lancashire gentry and the Great Rebellion, 1640-60: B. G. Blackwood. 1978.
26. Methodist secessions: the origins of Free Methodism in three Lancashire towns: Manchester, Rochdale, Liverpool: D. A. Gowland. 1979.
27. Elizabethan Manchester: T. S. Willan. 1980.

Chicago Society of Biblical Research. *See* Biblical Research.

Christian Brethren Research Fellowship. JOURNAL. 4to. *Duplicated.* 1-5. May 1963-Jun. 1964. 8vo. PINNER [10-26], EXETER [27+]. 7, 10-30. Feb. 1965, Dec. 1965-1980.
—— OCCASIONAL PAPERS. 8vo. BRISTOL [1], PINNER [2-5], EXETER [6-7]. 1-7. 1965-78.

1. The ministry of the Word: S. S. Short. 1965.
2. Prophetic developments, with particular reference to the early Brethren movement: F. R. Coad. 1966.
3. Early Brethren and the Society of Friends: T. C. F. Stunt. 1971.
4. The role of women in the New Testament church: L. Birney. 1971.
5. Women and the Gospel: an essay on the scriptural authority for the ministry of women in the church: Joyce Harper. 1974.
6. Brethren missionary work in Mysore State: K. J. Newton. 1975.
7. Christianity and the mentally handicapped: a short introd. and bibliography: M. Miles. 1978.

Christian Irishman: THE JOURNAL/OFFICIAL MAGAZINE OF THE IRISH MISSION OF THE PRESBYTERIAN CHURCH IN IRELAND. 8vo. BELFAST. 65, no. 773-95, no. 7 [=no. 1136]. May 1947-Jul./Aug. 1978. [*Subtitle varies.*]

Christianity Today. fol. WASHINGTON (D.C.). 1, no. 1 . . . 20, no. 9. Oct. 1956 . . . Jan. 1976.

Church History. (American Society of Church History,) 8vo. BERNE (Indiana) [1-38], CHICAGO [39+]. 1+ 1932+ [Vols. 1-26 photographic repr.]

Church Quarterly. 8vo. LOND. 1, no. 1-4, no. 1. Jul. 1968-Jul. 1971.
[*Incorporating the* Church Quarterly Review *and the* London Quarterly and Holborn Review.]
[*Ceased publication* 1971.]

Churchman: A QUARTERLY JOURNAL OF ANGLICAN THEOLOGY. 8vo.
LOND. 66, no. 2 . . . 87, no. 4. Jun. 1952 . . . Winter 1973.

Clarendon Library of Logic and Philosophy. 8vo. OXF. 1973 . . .

The coherence theory of truth: N. Rescher. 1973.
The nature of necessity: A. Plantinga. 1974.
Relative identity: N. Griffin. 1977.

The coherence of theism: R. Swinburne. 1977.
Divine commands and moral requirements: P. L. Quinn. 1978.

Cofiadur (Y): CYLCHGRAWN CYMDEITHAS HANES ANNIBYNWYR CYMRU.
8vo. WRECSAM, LLANDYSUL, ABERTAWE. 1 . . . 1923 . . .

College of the Bible Quarterly. *See* Lexington Theological Quarterly.

Communio Viatorum: A THEOLOGICAL QUARTERLY. 8vo. PRAGUE.
7+ 1964+

Congregational Historical Society. TRANSACTIONS. 8vo. LOND. 1-21,
pt. 4. 1901-1972.
[*Contd. in* United Reformed Church History Society Journal.]

Congregational Year Book. 8vo. LOND. 1846-1972.
[*Wanting* 1913, 1927, 1961, 1962, 1964/65.]
[*Contd. in* United Reformed Church Year Book.]

Corpus Philosophorum Medii Aevi. ARISTOTELES LATINUS. Opera.
8vo. LEIDEN, *etc.*

VI.1-3. De Sophisticis Elenchis. Translatio Boethii, fragmenta translationis Iacobi, et recensio Guillelmi de Moerbeke. 1975.
XXV.2 Metaphysica. Lib. I-X, XII-XIV. Translatio anonyma sive 'Media'. 1976.
XXVI.1-3. Ethica Nicomachea.
1. Praefatio: R. A. Gauthier. 1974.
2. Translatio antiquissima libr. II-III sive 'Ethica Vetus', et translationis antiquioris quae supersunt sive 'Ethica Nova', 'Horferiana', 'Borghesiana'. 1972.

3. Translatio Roberti Grosseteste Lincolniensis sive 'Liber Ethicorum'. A. Recensio pura. 1972.
4. —— B. Recensio recognita. 1973.
5. Indices verborum: R. A. Gauthier. 1973.
XXXI.1-2. Rhetorica. Translatio anonyma sive vetus et translatio Guillelmi de Moerbeka. 1978.

Corpus Scriptorum Christianorum Orientalium. 8vo. PARIS, *etc.*
1903+ [T=Textus; V=Versio.]
—— SCRIPTORES AETHIOPICI.

61. Vita di Walatta Pietros. 1970.
62-63. Actes de Marha Krestos. T.V. 1972.
64-65. Actes de Za-Yohannes de Kebran. T.V. 1972.
66-69. De transitu Mariae Apocrypha Aethiopice. I-II. T.V. 1973-74.

70-71. Abba Nabyud de Dabra Sihat: Visions et conseils ascétiques. T.V. 1976.
72. Miracoli di Zar'a Buruk. 1979.
73-74. Commentaire éthiopien sur les Bénédictions de Moïse et de Jacob. T.V. 1979.

Corpus Scriptorum Christianorum Orientalium—*continued*

Corpus Scriptorum Christianorum Orientalium—*continued*

—— SUBSIDIA.

36. Jalons pour une histoire de l'église en Iraq: J. M. Fiey.   1970.
37. Der altsyrische Paulustext: J. Kerschensteiner.   1970.
38. Syrische Kanonessammlungen: ein Beitrag zur Quellenkunde. I. Westsyrischer Originalurkunden. 1, B: A. Vööbus.   1970.
39-40. Handschriftliche Überlieferung der Memre-Dichtung des Ja'qob von Serug: A. Vööbus. I-II. 1973.
41. Byzantine iconoclasm during the reign of Leo III, with particular attention to the oriental sources: S. Gero.   1973.
42-43. Paterica armeniaca a P.P. Mechitaristis edita (1855) nunc latine reddita: L. Leloir. I-II.   1974-75.
44. Chrétiens syriaques sous les Mongols (Il-Khanat de Perse, XIIIe-XIVe s.): J. M. Fiey.   1975.
45. The Pentateuch in the version of the Syro-Hexapla: a fac-simile edition of a Midyat MS. discovered 1964: A. Vööbus.   1975.
46. Christlich-arabische Chrestomathie aus historischen Schriftstellern des Mittelalters: P. Kawerau. 1, 1: Texte.   1976.
47. Paterica armeniaca a P.P. Mechitaristis edita (1855) nunc latine reddita: L. Leloir. III.   1976.
48. Materials for the study of Georgian monasteries in the western environs of Antioch on the Orontes: W. Z. Djobadze.   1976.

50. Christlich-arabische Chrestomathie aus historischen Schriftstellern des Mittelalters: P. Kawerau. 1, 2: Glossar.   1976.
51. Paterica armeniaca a P.P. Mechitaristis edita (1855) nunc latine reddita: L. Leloir. IV.   1976.
52. Byzantine iconoclasm during the reign of Constantine V, with particular attention to the oriental sources: S. Gero.   1977.
53. Christlich-arabische Chrestomathie aus historischen Schriftstellern des Mittelalters: P. Kawerau. 2: Übersetzung mit philologischem Kommentar.   1977.
54. Nisibe, métropole syriaque orientale, et ses suffragants, des origines à nos jours: J.-M. Fiey.   1977.
55. Ephräms Polemik gegen Mani und di Manichäer im Rahmen der zeitgenössischen greichischen Polemik der des Augustinus: E. Beck.   1978.
56. The Apocalypse in the Harklean version: a facsimile edition of Ms. Mardin Orth. 35: intro. A. Vööbus.   1978.
57. Studien zur Quellen- und Traditionsgeschichte des Evangelienkommentars der Gannat Bussame: G. J. Reinink.   1979.

Corpus Scriptorum Ecclesiasticorum Latinorum. 8vo. VIENNA.

1+   1866+

77. Augustine: Opera. VI. iv. De magistro. Liber unus.   1961.
81. Ambrosiaster: Commentarius in epistulas Paulinas. 1. In epistulam ad Romanos.   1966.
82. Ambrose: Opera. X. Epistolae et acta. I.   1968.
83. Victorinus: Opera. I. Opera theologica.   1971.

84. Augustine: Opera. IV. i. Expositio quarundam propositionum ex epistola ad Romanos, *etc.*   1971.
85/1. Augustine: Opera. VIII. iv. Contra Iulianum (opus imperfectum). I.   1974.
87. Eugyppius: Regula.   1976.

Cymdeithas Hanes Annibynwyr Cymru. *See* Cofiadur.

Cymdeithas Hanes Bedyddwyr Cymru. *See* Trafodion Cymdeithas Hanes Bedyddwyr Cymru.

Danish Yearbook of Philosophy. 8vo. COPENHAGEN. 1+   1964+

Dr. Williams's Library, Friends of. *See* Friends of Dr. Williams's Library.

Dölger-Institut. *See* Jahrbuch für Antike und Christentum.

Dublin Review. *See* Month.

Duckworth Studies in Theology. 8vo. LOND. 1908+
Christian theology since 1600: H. Cunliffe-Jones. 1970.

Dumbarton Oaks (Center for Byzantine Studies). PAPERS. 4to.
CAMBRIDGE (Mass.) 3, 4, 6. 1946, 1948, 1951.
WASHINGTON (D.C.) 13+ 1959+
—— STUDIES. 4to & 8vo. CAMBRIDGE (Mass.) [2-5]; WASHINGTON (D.C.) [6+]. 2+ 1951+
14. The Church of the Panagiá Kanakaria at Lythrankomi in Cyprus: its mosaics and frescoes: A. H. S. Megaw and E. J. H. Hawkins. 1977.

Early English Text Society. PUBLICATIONS. ORIGINAL SERIES. 8vo. LOND. 1+ 1864+

265. The Cyrurgie of Guy de Chauliac: ed. M. S. Ogden. 1. Text. 1971.
266. Wulfstan's Canons of Edgar: ed. R. Fowler. 1972.
267. The English text of the Ancrene Riwle: B. M. Cotton MS. Cleopatra C.vi: ed. E. J. Dobson. 1972.
268. Of Arthour and of Merlin: ed. O. D. Macrae-Gibson. 1. Text. 1973.
269. The metrical version of Mandeville's travels, from the unique MS. in the Coventry Corporation Record Office: ed. M. C. Seymour. 1973.
270. Fifteenth-century English translations of Alain Chartier's Le Traité de l'esperance and Le Quadrilogue invectif: ed. M. S. Blayney. [1. Text.] 1974.
271. Stephen Hawes: the minor poems: ed. F. W. Gluck and A. B. Morgan. 1974.
272. Thomas Norton's Ordinal of Alchemy: ed. J. Reidy. 1975.
273. The Cely letters, 1472-1488: ed. A. Hanham. 1975.

274. The English text of the Ancrene Riwle: Magd. Coll. Camb. MS. Pepys 2498: ed. A. Zettersten. 1976.
275. Dives and Pauper: ed. P. H. Barnum. [1, 1.] 1976.
276. Secretum secretorum: nine English versions: ed. M. A. Manzalaoui. 1. Text. 1977.
277. Layamon: Brut: ed. G. L. Brooke and R. F. Leslie. 11. Text, ii. 1978.
278. Dan Michel's Ayenbite of Inwyt. 11. Introd., notes and glossary: P. Gradon. 1979.
279. Of Arthour and of Merlin: ed. O. D. Macrae-Gibson. 11. Introd., notes and glossary. 1979.
280. Dives and Pauper: ed. P. H. Barnum. 1, 2. 1980.
281. Fifteenth-century English translations of Alain Chartier's Le Traité de l'esperance, and Le Quadrilogue invectif: ed. M. S. Blayney. [11. Introd., notes and glossary.] 1980.

—— —— SUPPLEMENTARY TEXTS. 8vo. LOND. 1+ 1970+

2. The Book of the Knight of the Tower, trans. W. Caxton: ed. M. Y. Offord. 1971.
3. The Chester Mystery Cycle: ed. R. M. Lumiansky and D. Mills. [1. Text.] 1974.

Eastern Churches Review. *See* Sobornost.

Ecclesiastical History Society. STUDIES IN CHURCH HISTORY. EDITORS: C. W. DUGMORE AND C. DUGGAN [1]; G. J. CUMMING [2-8]; DEREK BAKER [7+]. 8vo. LOND., *etc.* 1+ 1964+

7. Councils and Assemblies 1971.
8. Popular belief and practice. 1972.
9. Schism, heresy and religious protest. 1972.
10. Sanctity and secularity: the Church and the world. 1973.
11. The materials, sources and methods of ecclesiastical history. 1975.
12. Church, society and politics. 1975.

13. The Orthodox Churches and the West. 1976.
14. Renaissance and renewal in Christian history. 1977.
15. Religious motivation: biographical and sociological problems for the Church historian. 1978.
16. The Church in town and country-side. 1979.

—— —— SUBSIDIA. ED. DEREK BAKER. 8vo. OXF. 1+ 1978+

1. Medieval women. Dedicated and presented to Prof. Rosalind M. T. Hill. 1978.

2. Reform and Reformation: England and the Continent, c.1500-c.1750. Dedicated and presented to Prof. C. W. Dugmore. 1979.

Ecumenical Review. (World Council of Churches.) 8vo. GENEVA. 1+ 1948/49+

Egypt Exploration Society (*formerly* Fund). JOURNAL OF EGYPTIAN ARCHAEOLOGY. 4to. LOND. 1+ 1914+
[*Formerly* Egypt Exploration Fund. Archaeological Reports.]

—— ARCHAEOLOGICAL SURVEY. 4to. LOND. 1+ 1893+

32. The shrines and rock-inscriptions of Ibrim: R. A. Caminos. 1968.
33-34. *Not yet in Library*, 1980.

35. The royal tomb at El-Amarna: the rock tombs, vii: G. T. Martin. I. The objects. 1974.

—— GRAECO-ROMAN MEMOIRS (*formerly* BRANCH). 4to. LOND. [1]+ 1898+

52. The Tebtunis papyri. II. [Univ. of California Publs., Graeco-Rom. Archaeol., 2, 1907.] repr. 1970.
53-58. The Oxyrhynchus papyri. XXXVII-XLII. 1971-74.
59. Location-list of the Oxyrhynchus papyri and of other Greek papyri publ. by the Egypt Exploration Society: comp. R. A. Coles. 1974.
60. The Oxyrhynchus papyri. XLIII. 1975.

61. Proceedings of the XIV International Congress of Papyrologists, Oxford, 24-31 July 1974. 1975.
62-63: The Oxyrhynchus papyri. XLIV-XLV. 1976-77.
64. The Tebtunis papyri. IV. 1976.
65-66. The Oxyrhynchus papyri. XLVI-XLVII. 1978-80.

—— MEMOIRS. 4to. LOND. 1+ 1885+

48. The Fortress of Buhen: the inscriptions: H. S. Smith, *etc.* 1976.

Elenchus Bibliographicus Biblicus. *See* Biblica.

Elim Foursquare Gospel Alliance. ELIM YEAR BOOK. 8vo. LOND. 1950, 1958, 1959.

Elim Pentecostal Church. YEAR BOOK. 8vo. CHELTENHAM. 1974/75 ...

English Association, ESSAYS AND STUDIES. 8vo. OXF. 1-29, 31, 32. 1910-47.

—— PAMPHLETS. 8vo. OXF. 4 . . . 47, 57, 73, 83, 88. 1908 . . . 1934.

English Historical Review. 8vo. LOND. 1+ 1886+

English Place-Name Society. JOURNAL. 8vo. LOND. [1-4], NOT-TINGHAM [5+]. 1+ 1969+

—— PUBLICATIONS. GENERAL EDITORS: A. MAWER AND F. M. STENTON [1-19]; B. DICKINS [20-22]; A. H. SMITH [23-43]; K. CAMERON [44+]. 8vo. CAMB. 1+ 1924+

45-47. Cheshire. II-IV.   1970-72.   49-51. Berkshire. I-III.   1973-76.
48. *Not yet published*, 1980.   52-53. Dorset. I-II.   1977-80.

Epiphany Philosophers. *See* Theoria to Theory.

Epworth Review. 8vo. LOND. 1+ 1974+

Essex Hall Lectures. 8vo. LOND. 1893+

1971. Mellanby (K.): The threat of world pollution. 1971.
1972. Wrigley (E. A.): Population: private choice and public policy. 1972.
1973. Gunter-Jones (R.): Buddhism and the West. 1973.
1974. Findlow (B.): I believe. 1974.
1975. Mays (J. B.): Urban problems and moral issues. 1975.
1976. Downing (A. B.): Beyond the horizon: Dissent, independence, and the future of the free religious tradition. 1976.

1977. Curle (A.): Peace and love: the violin and the oboe. 1977.
1978. Long (A. J.): Fifty years of theology, 1928-1978: the vindication of liberalism. 1978.
1979. Toynbee (P.): Christians, then and now. 1979.
1980. Doel (D. C.): I and my Father are one: the struggle for freedom from 'Mother'. 1980.

Essex Hall Year Book. *See* General Assembly of Unitarian and Free Christian Churches.

Ethics. 8vo. CHICAGO. 50+ 1939/40+
[51 imperfect.]
[*Formerly* International Journal of Ethics.]

Études Bergsoniennes. 8vo. PARIS. I-IO. 1948-73.

Everyman: AN ANNUAL RELIGIO-CULTURAL REVIEW. (Servite Priory, Benburb, Co. Tyrone.) 4to. BENBURB. nos. 1-3. 1968-70. [*Contd. as* Aquarius.]

Expository Times. 8vo. EDIN. 4+ 1892/93+
[*Wanting* 74.]

Faith and Freedom: A JOURNAL OF PROGRESSIVE RELIGION. 8vo. LEEDS [1-3], OXF. [4+]. 1+ 1947/48+

Fellowship of St. Alban and St. Sergius. *See* Sobornost.

Fernley (-Hartley) Lectures. 8vo. LOND. 1870+

1973. Wilson (K. B.): Making sense of it: an essay in philosophical theology. 1973.
1974. Rowe (T. T.): St. Augustine, pastoral theologian. 1974.

1975. Bowmer (J. C.): Pastor and people: a study of Church and ministry in Wesleyan Methodism from the death of John Wesley (1791) to the death of Jabez Bunting (1858). 1975.

Ford Lectures. 8vo. CAMB., *etc.*

1967. Smalley (B.): The Becket conflict and the schools: a study of intellectuals in politics. 1973.

1975-76. Kenyon (J. P.): Revolution principles: the politics of party, 1689-1720. 1977.

Forschungen zur Religion und Literatur des Alten und Neuen Testaments. HRSG. W. BOUSSET UND W. GUNKEL; R. BULTMANN [1933-61]; E. KÄSEMANN UND E. WURTHWEIN [1962+]. 8vo. GÖTTINGEN. 1+ 1903+

103. Der dreizehnte Zeuge: traditions- und kompositions- geschichtliche Untersuchungen zu Lukas' Darstellung der Frühzeit des Paulus: C. Burchard. 1970.
104. Studien zum dritten Esra: ein Beitrag zur Frage nach dem ursprünglichen Schluss des chronistischen Geschichtswerkes: K. F. Pohlmann. 1970.
105. "Einst" und "Jetzt" im Neuen Testament: Beobachtungen zu einem urchristlichen Predigtschema in der neutestamenlichen Briefliteratur und zu seiner Vorgeschichte: P. Tachau. 1972.
106. Die Chronik als Auslegung: Untersuchungen zur literarischen Gestaltung der historischen Uberlieferung Israels: T. Willi. 1972.
107. Das davidische Königtum im Zeugnis der Propheten: K. Seybold. 1972.
108. Prophetie und Geschichte: eine redaktionsgeschichtliche Untersuchung zum deuteronomistischen Geschichtswerk: W. Dietrich. 1972.
109. The origin and intention of the Colossian Haustafel: J. E. Crouch. 1972.
110. Eschatologische Existenz: ein exegetischer Beitrag zum Sachanliegen von 1. Thess. 4,13 - 5,11: W. Harnisch. 1973.
111. Tendenz und Ansicht des Epheserbriefes: K. M. Fischer. 1973.
112. Römer 8 als Beispiel paulinischer Soteriologie: P. von der Osten-Sacken. 1975.
113. Askese und Mysterium: über Ehe, Ehescheidung und Eheverzicht in den Anfängen des christlichen Glaubens: K. Niederwimmer. 1975.

114. Das Privilegrecht Jahwes, Ex 34, 10-26, Gestalt und Wesen, Herkunft und Wirken in vordeuteronomischer Zeit: J. Halbe. 1975.
115. Der Schöpfungsbericht der Priesterschrift: Studien zur literarkritischen und überlieferungsgeschichtlichen Problematik von Genesis 1, 1 -2, 4a: O. H. Steck. 1975.
116. Die Verheissungen an die Väter: Studien zur Vätergeschichte: C. Westermann. 1976.
117. Die Nachtgeschichte des Sacharja: Untersuchungen zu ihrer Stellung im Zusammenhang der Visionsberichte und zu ihrem Bildmaterial: C. Jeremias: 1977.
118. Studien zum Jeremiabuch: ein Beitrag zur Frage nach der Entstehung des Jeremiabuches: K. F. Pohlmann. 1978.
119. Das Gesetz bei Paulus: ein Beitrag zum Werden der paulinischen Theologie: H. Hübner. 1978.
120. Die Gleichnisse Jesu als Metaphern: traditions- und redaktionsgeschichtliche Analysen und Interpretationen: H. Weder. 1978.
121. Jahwes Entgegnung an Ijob: eine Deutung von Ijob 38-41 vor dem Hintergrund der zeitgenössischen Bildkunst: O. Keel. 1978.
122. Glaube, Gemeinde, Amt: zum Verständnis der Ordination in den Pastoralbriefen: H. von Lips. 1979.
123. Paulus, der Heidenapostel: G. Lüdemann. I. Studien zur Chronologie. 1980.

Franz Joseph Dölger-Institut. *See* Jahrbuch für Antike und Christentum.

Freiburger Rundbrief: BEITRÄGE ZUR CHRISTLICH-JÜDISCHEN BEGEGNUNG. fol. FREIBURG IM B. 22+ 1970+

Friends' Historical Society. JOURNAL. 8vo. LOND. 1+ 1903/04+

—— JOURNAL SUPPLEMENT. 8vo. LOND. 1+ 1904+

32. John Woolman in England: a documentary supplement: H. J. Cadbury. 1971.
33. John Perrot, early Quaker schismatic: K. L. Carroll. 1971.

34. "The other branch": London Yearly Meeting and the Hicksites, 1897-1912: E. B. Bronner. 1975.

Friends of Dr. Williams's Library. **Lectures.** 8vo. CAMB. [1947-48], LOND. [1949+]. 1+ 1947+

25. 1971. Hall (B.): John à Lasco, 1499-1560: a Pole in Reformation England. 1971.
26. 1972. Holt (P. M.): A seventeenth-century defender of Islam: Henry Stubbe (1632-76) and his book. 1972.
27. 1973. Longford (Elizabeth): Piety in Queen Victoria's reign. 1973.
28. 1974. Zaehner (R. C.): Which God is dead? 1974.
29. 1975. Williams (N. J.): John Foxe the martyrologist: his life and times. 1975.

30. 1976. Stell (C. F.): Architects of Dissent: some Nonconformist patrons and their architects. 1976.
31. 1977. White (B. R.): Hanserd Knollys and Radical Dissent in the 17th century. 1977.
32. 1978. Sharrock (R. I.): Life and story in The Pilgrim's Progress. 1978.
33. 1979. Payne (E. A.): A venerable Dissenting institution: Dr. Williams's Library, 1729-1979. 1979.

General Assembly of Unitarian and Free Christian Churches. DIRECTORY. 8vo. LOND. 1968/69+ [Annual.] HANDBOOK. 8vo. LOND. 1967/70+ [Publ. every three (then five) years.]

[*Formerly* Essex Hall Year Book (1890-1928): Yearbook of the General Assembly of Unitarian and Free Christian Churches (1929-33); Unitarian and Free Christian Churches: Year Book of the General Assembly (1934-66).]

Gifford Lectures. 8vo. EDIN., *etc.* 1890+

1965-66. MacKinnon (D. M.): The problem of metaphysics. 1974.
1967-69. Zaehner (R. C.): Concordant discord: the interdependence of faiths. 1970.
1969-71. Thorpe (W. H.): Animal nature and human nature. 1974.
1970-71. Mascall (E. L.): The openness of being: natural theology today. 1971.
1970. Leeuwen (A. T. van): Critique of heaven. 1972.

1972. —— Critique of earth. 1974.
1971-72. Kenny (A. J. P.) *and others*: The nature of mind. 1972.
1972-73. —— The development of mind. 1973.
1972-73. Ayer (A. J.): The central questions of philosophy. 1973.
1973-74. Chadwick (W. O.): The secularization of the European mind in the nineteenth century. 1975.
1977-78. Eccles (J. C.): The human mystery. 1979.

Gottfried-Wilhelm-Leibniz-Gesellschaft. *See* Mitteilungen der Gottfried-Wilhelm-Leibniz-Gessellschaft.

Greater London Council (*formerly* London County Council). SURVEY OF LONDON. 4to. LOND. 1+ 1900+

37. Northern Kensington. 1972.
38. The museums area of South Kensington and Westminster. 1975.

39. The Grosvenor Estate in Mayfair. Pt. 1. General history. 1977.

Harleian Society. PUBLICATIONS. 4to. LOND. 1-117. 1869-1977.

111-112. The life of William Bruges, the first Garter King of Arms, by the late Hugh Stanford London. With a biog. notice of the author and a bibliog. of his publ. writings: Sir Anthony Wagner. 1970.

117. The visitation of Dorset, 1677, made by Sir Edward Bysshe: ed. G. D. Squibb. 1977

—— REGISTER SECTION. 4to. LOND. 1-89. 1877-1977.

89. The registers of St. Margaret's, Westminster. III. Burials, 1666-73; christenings, 1681-88; weddings, 1681-99. 1977.

—— PUBLICATIONS. N.S. 4to. LOND. 1+ 1979+

1. The register of the Temple Church, London: baptisms, 1629-1853; marriages, 1628-1760. 1979.

Harvard Theological Review. 8vo. CAMBRIDGE (Mass.) 10, no. 4 . . . 18, no. 3. 1917-25. 19+ 1926+

Hebraica. *See* Journal of Near Eastern Studies.

Henry Bradshaw Society. 8vo. LOND. 1+ 1891+

88. The Benedictionals of Freising: ed. R. Amiet, *etc.* 1974.
97. The Claudius Pontificals: ed. D. H. Turner. 1971.
98. Expositio antiquae liturgiae Gallicanae: ed. E. C. Ratcliff. 1971.

99. The Customary of the Benedictine Abbey of Bury St. Edmunds in Suffolk: ed. A. Gransden. 1973.
100. The Cracow Pontifical: ed. Z. Obertyński. 1977.

Heythrop Journal: A QUARTERLY REVIEW OF PHILOSOPHY AND THEOLOGY. 8vo. LOND. 1+ 1960+

Historical Association. ANNUAL BULLETIN OF HISTORICAL LITERATURE. 8vo. LOND. 1-55. 1911-72.
[*Wanting* 26, 30.]

—— HISTORY. *See* History.

—— LEAFLETS. 8vo. LOND. 32 . . . 97. 1913 . . . 1934.

79. The philosophy of history: R. G. Collingwood. 1930.

—— GENERAL SERIES. 8vo. LOND. 1 . . . 1945 . . .

76. Elementary education in the late nineteenth century: Gillian Sutherland. 1971.
77. The Kingdom of Germany in the High Middle Ages (900-1200): J. B. Gillingham. 1971.
85. The Albigensian Crusade: Bernard Hamilton. 1974.

86. Religion and party in late Stuart England: G. S. Holmes. 1975.
87. The War of American Independence: Esmond Wright. 1976.
89. Ulrich Zwingli: G. R. Potter. 1977.
92. Regional aspects of the Scottish Reformation: I. B. Cowan. 1978.
94. William the Silent and the Revolt of

Historical Association—*continued*

the Netherlands: K. W. Swart. 1978.
95. Peter Abelard: D. E. Luscombe. 1979.

98. The Church of England in the mid-nineteenth century: a social geography: B. I. Coleman. 1980.

—— SPECIAL SERIES. 8vo. LOND.

2. Local history handlist: a short bibliography and list of sources for the study of local history and antiquities in England and Wales. (1947.) repr. 1950.

—— APPRECIATIONS IN HISTORY. 8vo. LOND.

7. The English town, 1660-1760: Angus McInnes. 1980.

Historical Manuscripts Commission. REPORTS. fol. & 8vo. LOND. 1870-1962.

—— JOINT PUBLICATIONS. 8vo. LOND.

23. Manorial records of Cuxham, Oxfordshire, c.1200-1359: ed. P. D. A. Harvey. 1976.

26. Calendar of the correspondence of Philip Doddridge, D.D. (1702-1751): G. F. Nuttall. 1979.

Historical Monuments Commission. ENGLAND. 4to. LOND. 1910+

Cambridgeshire. 2. North-East. 1972.
Dorset. 2. South-East.I-III. 1970.
—— 3. Central. I-II. 1970.
—— 4. North. 1972.
—— 5. East. 1975.

City of York. 2. The defences. 1972.
—— 3. South-West of the Ouse. 1972.

—— SCOTLAND. 8vo. & 4to. EDIN., *etc.* 1909+

18. Argyll. 1. Kintyre. 1971.

History: THE (QUARTERLY) JOURNAL OF THE HISTORICAL ASSOCIATION. 8vo. LOND. N.S. 1+ 1916/17+
[*Subtitle shortened* 1947.]
[*Formerly* History: a Quarterly Magazine for the Student and the Expert.]
—— Index, 1-50 (1916-65). 1972.

Huguenot Society of London. PROCEEDINGS. 8vo. [LOND.] 1+ 1885/86+

—— PUBLICATIONS. 4to. [LOND.] 1+ 1887/88+
[Vols. 48+ *called* Quarto Series.]

49. French Protestant refugees relieved through the Threadneedle Street Church, London, 1681-1687. 1971.
50. The archives of the French Protestant Church of London. 1972.
51. Records of the Royal Bounty and connected funds, the Burn donation, and the Savoy Church, in the Huguenot Library, University College, London. 1974.

52-53. The French Protestant Hospital: extracts from the archives of "La Providence" relating to inmates and applicants for admission 1718-1957, and to recipients of and applicants for the Coqueau Charity 1745-1901. 2 vols. 1977.
54. A calendar of the letter books of the French Church of London from the Civil War to the Restoration, 1643-1659. 1979.

Hulsean Lectures. 8vo. LOND., CAMB., *etc.* 1820 . . .

1970. Ramsey (A. M): Freedom, faith and the future.   1970.
1973. Wiles (M. F.): The remaking of Christian doctrine.   1974.

1978. Davis (Charles): Theology and political society.   1980.

Hymn. (Hymn Society of America.) 8vo. NEW YORK.   8, no. 1. 18, no. 4-30, no. 3.   Jan. 1957.   Oct. 1967-Jul. 1979.
   [*Wanting* 24, no. 3, 27, no. 2.]

Hymn Society of America. PAPERS.   8vo.   NEW YORK.

20. The Olney hymns: J. H. Johansen.   1956.
25. A short bibliography for the study of hymns.   1964.
26. Henry Wilder Foote, hymnologist: Arthur Foote.   1968.

28. Born to music: the ministry of Robert Guy McCutchan: Helen Cowles McCutchan.   1972.
30. Two early American tunes: fraternal twins? (A study of a hymn family): Ellen Jane Porter.   1975.

—— MISCELLANEOUS PUBLICATIONS.

1970. The hymns of Frank Mason North.
[1973.] 16 new hymns on the steward-ship of the environment (ecology).

[1974.] New hymns, songs and prayers for Church and home.
[1975.] New hymns for America, 1976.

Hymn Society of Great Britain and Ireland. BULLETIN. 8vo. [n.p.]   2, no. 1 (42)—9, no. 6 (146).   Jan. 1948-Sep. 1979.
   [*Wanting* nos. 44, 73.]

Inquirer. fol. LOND. 1+ 1842+

Institut International de Philosophie. *See* Bibliographie de la Philosophie.

Institute of Historical Research. *See* London University.   Institute of Historical Research.   Bulletin.

Intellectual Repository and New Jerusalem Magazine. 8vo. LOND. nos. 321 . . . 335.   Sep. 1880 . . . Nov. 1881.
   [*Wanting* no. 332, Aug. 1881.]
   [*Contd. as* New-Church Magazine.]

International Association for the History of Religions. *See* Numen.

International Bibliography of the History of Religions. *See* Numen.

International Journal of Ethics. *See* Ethics.

International Library of Philosophy and Scientific Method. 8vo. LOND. 1961 . . .

Truth, knowledge and causation: C. J. Ducasse.   1969.
Plato's 'Euthyphro' and the earlier theory of forms: R. E. Allen. 1970.

Responsibility: Jonathan Glover. 1970.
Explanation and understanding: G. H. von Wright.   1971.

International Organization for the Study of the Old Testament. *See* Vetus Testamentum.

International Review of Biblical Studies. *See* Internationale Zeit-schriftenschau für Bibelwissenschaft und Grenzgebiete.

International Review of Missions. 8vo. EDIN., LOND., *etc.* [1912-62], GENEVA, *etc.* [1963+]. 1+ 1912+

Internationale Zeitschriftenschau für Bibelwissenschaft und Grenzgebiete: International Review of Biblical Studies: Review Internationale des Études Bibliques. 8vo. DÜSSELDORF. 6+ 1958/59+

Interpretation: A JOURNAL OF BIBLE AND THEOLOGY. 8vo. RICHMOND (Va.). 13, no. 1+ Jan. 1959+

—— Index, 1-10 (1947-56). n.d.
—— —— 11-25 (1957-71). [1974.]

Irish Mission. *See* Christian Irishman.

Jahrbuch für Antike und Christentum. (Franz Joseph Dölger - Institut.) 4to. MÜNSTER. 1+ 1958+

—— ERGANZUNGSBÄNDE. 4to. MÜNSTER. 1+ 1964+

2. Untersuchungen zur Sepulkrasymbolik der späteren römischen Kaiserzeit: J. Engemann. 1973.
3. Gesammelte Arbeiten zur Liturgiegeschichte, Kirchengeschichte und christlichen Archäologie: T. Klauser. Hrsg. E. Dassmann. 1974.
4. Die neue Katakombe an der Via Latina in Rom: Untersuchungen zur Ikonographie der alttestamentlichen Wandmalereien: L. Kötzsche-Breitenbruch. 1976.

5. Henri Leclerq, 1869-1945: vom Autodidakten zum Kompilator grossen Stils: T. Klauser. 1977.
6. *Not yet published*, 1980.
7. Franz Joseph Dölger, 1879-1940: sein Leben und sein Forschungsprogramm "Antike und Christentum": T. Klauser. 1980.
8. Pietas: Festschrift für Bernhard Kötting. Hrsg. E. Dassmann und K. Suso Frank. 1980.

Jewish Annual. ED. S. LEVY. 8vo. LOND. [2-3], 14-16. 1939/40-40/ 41, 1951/52-53/54.

Jewish Historical Society of England. TRANSACTIONS. 4to. LOND. 1+ 1895+
[22+ *incl.* Miscellanies 7+]

—— MISCELLANIES. 4to. LOND. 1-6. 1925-62.
[*Further pts. incl. in* Transactions.]

—— PUBLICATIONS. 4to. & 8vo. LOND., *etc.* 1901+

1970. The Treaty of Utrecht 1713 and the Jews of Gibraltar. Lecture, 1963: J. A. Hassan.
1971. Migration and settlement. Proceedings of the Anglo-American Jewish Historical Conference, London, 1970. Rapporteur: Aubrey Newman.
1972. Calendar of the Plea Rolls of the Exchequer of the Jews, vol. 4: ed. H. G. Richardson.

1972. The Jews of Ireland from earliest times to the year 1910: Louis Hyman.
1973. Bevis Marks records, pt. 3: ed. G. H. Whitehill. [Publ. jointly with the Spanish and Portuguese Jews' Congregation, London.]
1974. Sir Solomon de Medina: O. K. Rabinowicz. With a biog. of the author: J. K. Tapiero and T. K. Rabb.

Jewish Quarterly Review. 8vo. LOND., *etc.* 1-20. 1888/89-1907/08.
—— N.S. 8vo. PHILADELPHIA. 1+ 1910/11+ [31, 33 imperfect.]

John Rylands Library. *See* Bulletin of the John Rylands Library.

Journal of Biblical Literature. (Society of Biblical Literature [and Exegesis].) 8vo. PHILADELPHIA. *etc.* 46+ 1927+
[*Name shortened* 1963.] [81 imperfect.]

Journal of Ecclesiastical History. 8vo. LOND., *etc.* [1-16], CAMB. [17+] 1+ 1950+

Journal of Egyptian Archaeology. *See* Egypt Exploration Society.

Journal of Hellenic Studies. (Society for the Promotion of Hellenic Studies.) 8vo. LOND. 1-95. 1880-1975.

Journal of Near Eastern Studies. 8vo. CHICAGO. 1+ 1942.
[*Formerly* Hebraica, *then* American Journal of Semitic Languages and Literature.]

Journal of Philosophical Studies. *See* Philosophy.

Journal of Religion. 8vo. CHICAGO. 1+ 1921+
[21 imperfect.]
[*Formerly* American Journal of Theology.]

Journal of Semitic Studies. 8vo. MANCHESTER. 1+ 1956+

Journal of the Christian Brethren Research Fellowship. *See* Christian Brethen Research Fellowship.

Journal of the English Place-Name Society. *See* English Place-Name Society.

Journal of the Fellowship of St. Alban and St. Sergius. *See* Sobornost.

Journal of the Friends' Historical Society. *See* Friends' Historical Society.

Journal of the Presbyterian Historical Society of England. *See* Presbyterian Historical Society.

Journal of the Society for Psychical Research. *See* Society for Psychical Research.

Journal of the United Reformed Church History Society. *See* United Reformed Church History Society.

Journal of the Universalist Historical Society. *See* Universalist Historical Society.

Journal of Theological Studies. 8vo. OXF. 1-50. 18991/900-1949.
[*Wanting* 11.] [5, 48 imperfect.]
—— N.S. 1+ 1950+

King's Weigh House Monthly. 8vo. LOND. Jan. 1927-Dec. 1932.
[1929 imperfect.]
—— N.S., nos. 1-9. Jan.-Sep. 1933. [*Wanting* no. 8, Jul.]
—— 3rd Ser., nos. 1-12. Jan.-Dec. 1934.
[*Contd. as*] **Weigh House Quarterly.** N.S., no. 1. Mar. 1939.
[*No more published.*]

Lancashire. *See* Record Society of Lancashire and Cheshire.

Leaders of Religion. 8vo. LOND.

Thomas Becket: David Knowles. 1970.

Lexington Theological Quarterly. 8vo. LEXINGTON (Ken.). 1+
1966+
[*Formerly* College of the Bible Quarterly.]

Library: TRANSACTIONS OF THE BIBLIOGRAPHICAL SOCIETY. 8vo. LOND.
5th Ser. 1-33. 1946-78.
—— 6th Ser. 1+ 1979+

Library of Constructive Theology. 8vo. LOND.

The Spirit and the forms of love: D. D.
Williams. 1968.

Library of Living Philosophers. ED. P.A. SCHILPP. 8vo. EVANSTON
& CHICAGO, *etc.* 1+ 1939+

11. Rudolf Carnap. 1963.   14. Karl Popper. 1974.
13. C. I. Lewis. 1968.

Library of Philosophy. ED. J. H. MUIRHEAD [1890-1939]; H. D. LEWIS
[1953+]. 8vo. LOND. 1890 . . .

Meaning in the arts: L. A. Reid. 1969.
Hypothesis and perception: the roots of
scientific method: E. E. Harris.
1970.
Ethical knowledge: J. J. Kupperman.
1970.
Broad's critical essays in moral philo-
sophy: ed. D. R. Cheney. 1971.
Mental images a defence: A. Hannay.
1971.
Our knowledge of right and wrong: J.
Harrison. 1971.

Ludwig Wittgenstein: philosophy and
language: ed. A. Ambrose and M.
Lazerowitz. 1972.
Value and reality: the philosophical
case for theism: A. C. Ewing. 1973.
The varieties of belief: P. Helm. 1973.
Contemporary British philosophy: per-
sonal statements. Fourth ser.: ed.
H. D. Lewis. 1976.
Bertrand Russell memorial volume: ed.
G. W. Roberts. 1979.

Library of Philosophy and Religion. 8vo. LOND. 1975 . . .

Freedom, responsibility and God: R.
Young. 1975.
Christian beliefs about life after death:
P. Badham. 1976.
Hegel's philosophy of religion: B. M. G.
Reardon. 1977.

Hume's philosophy of religion: J. C. A.
Gaskin. 1978.
Persons and life after death: H. D.
Lewis, *etc.* 1978.

Library of Philosophy and Theology. 8vo. LOND. 1955 . . .

Do religious claims make sense? S. C.
Brown. 1969.

Library of Protestant Thought. 8vo. NEW YORK. 1964 . . .

Elizabethan Puritanism: ed. L. J.
Trinterud. 1971.

Lincoln Record Society. PUBLICATIONS. 8vo. HEREFORD. 8 . . . 58. 1917 . . . 1963.

38, 40, 44. The first Minute Book of the Gainsborough Monthly Meeting of the Society of Friends, 1669-1719. 3 vols. 1948-51.

Locke Newsletter. ED. ROLAND HALL. 8vo. YORK. 1-11. 1970-80.

Loeb Classical Library. [GREEK AND LATIN TEXTS WITH PARALLEL ENGLISH TRANSLATIONS.] [A complete list of this series may be borrowed.]

London Bible College. See Vox Evangelica.

London County Council. See Greater London Council.

London Quarterly and Holborn Review. See Church Quarterly.

London University. Institute of Historical Research. BULLETIN. 4to & 8vo. LOND. 1+ 1923/4+ [18 imperfect.]

——— ——— ——— SPECIAL SUPPLEMENTS. 8vo. LOND.

9. Guy Fawkes in Spain: the 'Spanish Treason' in Spanish documents: A. J. Loomie. 1971.
10. The Cabinet journal of Dudley Ryder, Viscount Sandon (later third Earl of Harrowby), 11 May - 10 August 1878. 1974.
11. Elizabethan Popish recusancy in the Inns of Court: G. de C. Parmiter. 1976.

Medieval Classics [also **Medieval Texts**]. See Oxford Medieval Texts.

Mennonite Quarterly Review. (Mennonite Historical Society.) 8vo. GOSHEN (Indiana). 32+ 1958+

Methodist Sacramental Fellowship. M.S.F. BOOKLETS. Wesley Reprints. 8vo. n.p., 1936. [Pamphs.]

1. A selection of hymns on the Lord's Supper, by John and Charles Wesley.
2. The means of grace. A sermon by John Wesley.
3. The new birth. A sermon by John Wesley.
4. A companion for the altar. Extracted from Thomas à Kempis by John Wesley.
5. The duty of constant communion. A sermon by John Wesley.

——— M.S.F. BOOKLETS. N.S. 8vo. n.p., 1937. [Pamphs.]

1. Called to be saints: Mabel A. Rayner.
2. The Methodist office of the Holy Communion: its use as a complete service: Duncan Coomer.
3. The power of his resurrection: D. M. Jones.
4. The nature of the church: J. D. C. Pellow.
5. The Old Testament as a standard and rule of the Christian faith: H. Cunliffe-Jones.

Mind: A QUARTERLY REVIEW OF (PSYCHOLOGY AND) PHILOSOPHY. 8vo.
LOND. & EDIN. 1-16. 1876-91.
—— N.S. 8vo. LOND. & EDIN. [1892-1965], OXF. [1966+]. 1+
1892+
[50, 53 imperfect.] [*Subtitle shortened* 1974.]

Mind Association. *See* Aristotelian Society. Supplementary volumes.

Mitteilungen der Gottfried-Wilhelm-Leibniz-Gesellschaft. fol.
HANOVER. 10+ 1976+

Mitteilungen und Neuerwerbungen. (Universitätsbibliothek Tübingen
Theologische Abteilung.) fol. TÜBINGEN. 5-8. 1977-80.

Modern Churchman. 8vo. OXF. 11-46. 1921/22-1936.
—— N.S. 8vo. LOND. [1-3], CAYNHAM (Salop.) [4-20], LEOMINSTER
[21+]. 1+ 1957/58+

Modern Free Churchman. 8vo. CRAWLEY DOWN (Sussex), *etc.* nos.
69-98. Spring 1958-Winter 1973/74.
[*Wanting* nos. 70, 77, 81, 90.]

Month. 8vo & 4to. N.S. 42+ Jul./Aug. 1969+
[*Incorporating* Dublin Review.]

Moravian Almanack: YEAR BOOK OF THE BRETHREN'S CHURCH IN THE
UNITED KINGDOM. 12mo. LOND. 34-50. 1903-18.

Muirhead's Library of Philosophy. *See* Library of Philosophy.

Nelson's Medieval Classics/Texts. *See* Oxford Medieval Texts.

New-Church Magazine. 8vo. LOND. [1,] no. 1 . . . 95, no. 675. Jan.
1882 . . . Jan./Apr. 1976.
[*Formerly* Intellectual Repository and New Jerusalem Magazine.]

New Studies in the Philosophy of Religion. 8vo. LOND. 1970 . . .
Death and immortality: D. Z. Phillips. 1970.
The logical status of 'God' and the
function of theological sentences:
M. Durrant. 1973.
Scepticism: K. Nielsen. 1973.
Analogy: a study of qualification and
argument in theology: H. Palmer. 1973.
Wittgenstein and religious belief: W. D.
Hudson. 1975.

New Testament Abstracts. (Weston School of Theology, *formerly*
Weston College.) 8vo. WESTON (Mass.) [-1968], CAMBRIDGE
(Mass.) [1968+]. 3, no. 2+ 1959+
—— Cumulative indexes, 1-15 (1955-
71). 1974.

New Testament Library. 8vo. LOND. 1963 . . .

New Testament theology: J. Jeremias.
Pt. I. The proclamation of Jesus.
1971.
Perspectives on Paul: E. Käsemann.
1971.
Jesus: E. Schweizer. 1971.
The New Testament: the history of the investigation of its problems: W. G. Kümmel. 1973.
The theology of the New Testament according to its major witnesses: Jesus-Paul-John: W. G. Kümmel. 1974.

Jesus and the Spirit: J. D. G. Dunn. 1975.
The Johannine circle: O. Cullmann. 1976.
Jesus and the language of the kingdom: N. Perrin. 1976.
Unity and diversity in the New Testament: J. D. G. Dunn. 1977.
Community of the new age: studies in Mark's Gospel: H. C. Kee. 1977.

New Testament Studies: AN INTERNATIONAL JOURNAL. (Studiorum Novi Testamenti Societas.) 8vo. CAMB. 1+ 1954+

Northamptonshire Past & Present. (Northamptonshire Record Society.) 8vo. NORTHAMPTON. 1, no. 1—5, no. 2. 1948-74. [*Wanting* 2, nos. 1 & 2, 1954 & 1955.]

Novum Testamentum: AN INTERNATIONAL QUARTERLY FOR NEW TESTAMENT AND RELATED STUDIES. 8vo. LEIDEN. 1+ 1956+

—— SUPPLEMENTS. 8vo. LEIDEN. 1+ 1958+

26. Creation and redemption: a study in Pauline theology: J. G. Gibbs. 1971.
27. The morphology of Koine Greek as used in the Apocalypse of St. John: a study in bilingualism: G. Mussies. 1971.
28. The cultic setting of realized eschatology in early Christianity: D. E. Aune. 1972.
29. Sparsa collecta: the collected essays of W. C. van Unnik. I. Evangelia, Paulina, Acta. 1973.
30, 31. *Not yet in Library*, 1980.
32. The Semeia in the Fourth Gospel: tradition and reaction: W. Nicol. 1972.
33. Studies in New Testament and early Christian literature. Essays in honor of Allen P. Wikgren: ed. D. E. Aune. 1972.
34. The use of the Old and New Testaments in Clement of Rome: D. A. Hagner. 1973.
35. St. Paul's opponents and their background: a study of apocalyptic and Jewish sectarian teachings: J. J. Gunther. 1973.
36. Patristic evidence for Jewish-Christian sects: A. F. J. Klijn and G. J. Reinink. 1973.
37. Hermas and Christian prophecy: a study of the eleventh Mandate: J. Reiling. 1973.

38. The setting of Second Clement in early Christianity: K. P. Donfried. 1974.
39. The authenticity of Ephesians: A. van Roon. 1974.
40. Faith and human reason: a study of Paul's method of preaching as illustrated by 1-2 Thessalonians and Acts 17, 2-4: D. W. Kemmler. 1975.
41. The roots of pagan anti-Semitism in the ancient world: J. N. Sevenster. 1975.
42. The Law in the fourth Gospel: the Torah and the Gospel, Moses and Jesus, Judaism and Christianity, according to John: S. Pancaro. 1975.
43. Les variétés de la pensée biblique et le problème de son unité: esquisse d'une théologie de la Bible sur les textes originaux et dans leur contexte historique: H. Clavier. 1976.
44. Studies in New Testament language and text. Essays in honour of George D. Kilpatrick: ed. J. K. Elliott. 1976.
45. Prophetic vocation in the New Testament and today: ed. J. Panagopoulos. 1977.
46. Seth in Jewish, Christian and Gnostic literature: A. F. J. Klijn. 1977.
47-48. Miscellanea Neotestamentica: Studia a sociis sodalicii Batavi c.n. Studiosorum Novi Testamenti Con-

Novum Testamentum—*continued*

ventus: ed. T. Baarda, A. F. J.
Klijn, W. C. van Unnik. I-II. 1978.
49. Introductory thanksgivings in the
letters of Paul: P. T. O'Brien. 1977.
50. Religionsgeschichtliche Studien:
Aufsätze zur Religionsgeschichte
des Hellenistischen Zeitalters:
Wilhelm Bousset. Hrsg. A. F.
Verheule. 1979.

51. Mark's treatment of the Jewish
leaders: M. J. Cook. 1978.
52. The intention of Matthew 23: D. E.
Garland. 1979.

Numen: INTERNATIONAL REVIEW FOR THE HISTORY OF RELIGIONS. (International Association for the History of Religions.) 8vo. LEIDEN.
1+ 1954+

—— INTERNATIONAL BIBLIOGRAPHY OF THE HISTORY OF RELIGIONS. (Publ.
in connection with Numen, by the International Association for
[the Study of] the History of Religions.) 8vo. LEIDEN. Year
1952-73. 1954-79.
[*No more published.*]

Old Testament Library. 8vo. LOND. 1960 . . .

A history of Israel: John Bright.
(1960.) 2nd ed.: John Bright. 1972.
Isaiah 1-12: a commentary: O. Kaiser.
1972.
Joshua: a commentary. J. A. Soggin.
1972.
Isaiah 13-39: a commentary: O. Kaiser.
1974.

Exodus: a commentary: B. S. Childs.
1974.
Micah: a commentary: J. L. Mays. 1976.
Israelite and Judaean history: ed. J. H.
Hays and J. M. Miller. 1977.

Oxford Historical Monographs. 8vo. LOND., OXF. 1971 . . .

Charles James Fox and the disintegra-
tion of the Whig party, 1782-1794:
L. G. Mitchell. 1971.
Cheshire, 1630-1660: county govern-
ment and society during the English
Revolution: J. S. Morrill 1974.
A Byzantine government in exile:
government and society under the
Laskarids of Nicaea (1204-1261):
M. Angold. 1975.
Cromwellian Ireland: English govern-
ment and reform in Ireland, 1649-
1660: T. C. Barnard. 1975.
The English Church under Henry I:
M. Brett. 1975.

The re-establishment of the Church of
England, 1660-1663: I. M. Green.
1978.
Ascetics, authority, and the Church in
the age of Jerome and Cassian:
P. Rousseau. 1978.
The social and political thought of
Herbert Spencer: D. Wiltshire.
1978.
The apocalyptic tradition in Reforma-
tion Britain, 1530-1645: K. R.
Firth. 1979.
Church courts and the people during
the English Reformation, 1520-
1570: R. A. Houlbrooke. 1979.

Oxford Historical Society. PUBLICATIONS. 8vo. OXF. I-IOI. 1885-
1936.
—— —— N.S. 1+ 1939+

22. The register of Congregation, 1448-
1463. 1972.
23. Registrum annalium Collegii Mer-
tonensis, 1521-1567. 1974.
24. —— 1567-1603. 1976.

25. A bibliography of printed works
relating to the City of Oxford:
E. H. Cordeaux and D. H. Merry.
1976.
26. Epistolae academicae, 1508-1596.
1980.

Oxford Medieval Texts. ED. V. H. GALBRAITH, R. A. B. MYNORS, C. N. L.
BROOKE, *etc.* 8vo. OXF. 1967-80.
[Latin texts with parallel translations.] [*Formerly* (Nelson's) Medieval
Classics *and* Medieval Texts.]

Peter Abelard's Ethics. Ed. and trans.
D. E. Luscombe. 1971.
Eadmer: The life of St. Anselm. Ed. and
trans. R. W. Southern. (1962.)
repr. 1972.
The Carmen de Hastingae Proelio of
Guy, Bishop of Amiens. Ed. C.
Morton and H. Muntz. 1972.
The Epistolae Vagantes of Pope Gregory
VII. Ed. and trans. H. E. J. Cowdrey.
1972.
Libellus de diversis ordinibus et profes-
sionibus qui sunt in aecclesia. Ed.
and trans. G. Constable and B.
Smith. 1972.

Ordericus Vitalis: The ecclesiastical
history. Ed. and trans. M. Chibnall.
Vols. 3-6, 1. 1972-80.
Documents of the baronial movement
of reform and rebellion, 1258-1267.
Selected by R. F. Treharne. Ed.
I. J. Sanders. 1973.
The letters of Lanfranc, Archbishop of
Canterbury. Ed. and trans. H.
Clover and M. Gibson. 1979.
The letters of John of Salisbury. Vol. 2.
Ed. W. J. Millor and C. N. L.
Brooke. 1979.

Oxford Theological Monographs. 8vo. LOND., OXF. 1958 . . .

The canons of the Council of Sardicia,
A.D. 343: H. Hess. 1958.
The new temple: the Church in the
New Testament: R. J. McKelvey.
1969.
Clement of Alexandria's treatment of
the problem of evil: W. E. G.
Floyd. 1971.
Clement of Alexandria: a study in
Christian Platonism and Gnosti-
cism: S. R. C. Lilla. 1971.
The English Separatist tradition: B. R.
White. 1971.

Three Monophysite Christologies:
Severus of Antioch, Philoxenus of
Mabbug, and Jacob of Sarug: R. C.
Chesnut. 1976.
Ritualism and politics in Victorian
Britain: J. Bentley. 1978.
Becoming and being: the doctrine of
God in Charles Hartshorne and
Karl Barth: C. E. Gunton. 1978.
The ontology of Paul Tillich: A.
Thatcher. 1978.
Calvin and English Calvinism to 1649:
R. T. Kendall. 1979.

Oxfordshire Record Society. 8vo. OXF. 1+ 1919+

48. Agricultural trade unionism in
Oxfordshire, 1872-81: ed. Pamela
Horn. 1974.
49. The Royalist Ordnance Papers,
1642-1646. II. 1975.
50. Manorial records of Cuxham,
Oxfordshire, c. 1200-1359: ed. P.
D. A. Harvey. 1976.

51. Village education in nineteenth-
century Oxfordshire: the Whitchurch School log book (1868-93)
and other documents. 1979.
52. Bishop Fell and Nonconformity:
visitation documents from the
Oxford diocese, 1682-83. 1980.

Palestine Exploration Quarterly. 8vo. LOND. 1937+
[*Incorporating* Palestine Exploration Fund Quarterly Statement, *and*
Bulletin of the British School of Archaeology in Jerusalem.]

Patrologia Orientalis. (Association de l'Orient Chrétien.) ED. F.
GRAFFIN [R. GRAFFIN ET F. NAU, FONDATEURS]. 8vo. PARIS
[-1966], TURNHOUT [1968+]. 1+ 1907+

XXXV.4 Textes coptes relatifs à Saint
Claude d'Antioche. 1970.
XXXVI.1. Les Homiliae cathedrales de
Sévère d'Antioche. Homélies 40-45.
Syriaque et français. 1971.

2. Le codex arménien Jérusalem 121.
II. 1971.
3. Les Homiliae cathedrales de Sévère
d'Antioche. Homélies 32-39.
Syriaque et français. 1972.

Patrologia Orientalis—*continued*

XXXVII.1. —— —— Homélies 18-25.
1975.
2-3. Éphrem de Nisibe: Memre sur
Nicomédie. Syriaque, arménien et
français. 1975.
XXXVIII.1. Jacques de Saroug: Homélies contre les Juifs. Syriaque et
français. 1976.
2. Les Homiliae cathedrales de Sévère
d'Antioche. Homélies 1-17.
Syriaque et français. 1976.
3. Sancti Philoxeni episcopi Mab-
bugensis dissertationes decem de
Uno e Sancta Trinitate incorporato
et passo. II. Dissertationes 3a, 4a,
5a. Syriacum Latineque. 1977.
4. Trois homélies syriaques anonymes
et inédites sur l'Épiphanie.
Syriaque et français. 1977.

XXXIX.1. Irénée de Lyon: Nouveaux
fragments arméniens de l'Adversus
haereses et de l'Epideixis. Arménien
et latin. 1978.
2. Lettre de Sophrone de Jérusalem à
Arcadius de Chypre. Syriaque et
français. 1978.
3. La collection des lettres de Jean de
Dalyatha. Syriaque et français.
1978.
4. Sancti Philoxeni episcopi Mab-
bugensis dissertationes decem de
Uno e Sancta Trinitate incorporato
et passo (Memre contre Habib).
III. Dissertationes 6a, 7a, 8a.
Syriaque et français. 1979.
XL.1. Narsai's metrical homilies on the
Nativity, Epiphany, Passion, Resurrection and Ascension. Syriac and
English. 1979.

Pentecostal. (Students' Pentecostal Fellowship.) 8vo. DUBLIN. 1, nos.
1-4. [1963]-1965.
[*No more published.*]

Philosophical Books. ED. M. A. STEWART. 8vo. LEICESTER [16-20],
OXFORD [21+]. 16, no. 1+ Jan. 1975+

Philosophical Quarterly. (Scots Philosophical Club.) 8vo. ST.
ANDREWS. 1+ 1950/51+

Philosophy: THE JOURNAL OF THE ROYAL (*formerly* BRITISH) INSTITUTE OF
PHILOSOPHY. 8vo. LOND. 6+ 1931+
[*Formerly* Journal of Philosophical Studies.]

Philosophy of Religion. 8vo. LOND. 1970 . . .

Arguments for the existence of God:
J. H. Hick. 1970.
Contemporary critiques of religion:
K. Nielsen. 1971.
Concepts of deity: H. P. Owen. 1971.
Problems of religious knowledge: T.
Penelhum. 1971.

The self and immortality: H. D. Lewis.
1973.
The justification of religious belief: B.
Mitchell. 1973.
The phenomenon of religion: R. N.
Smart. 1973.

Praxis: REVUE PHILOSOPHIQUE. Édition internationale. 8vo. ZAGREB.
1, no. 1 - 10, no. 1/2. 1965-74.
[*No more published.*]

Presbyterian Church in Ireland. *See* Christian Irishman.

Presbyterian Church of England. OFFICIAL HANDBOOK. 8vo. LOND.
1894/95-1910/11, 1914/15 . . . 1966/67.
[*Contd. in* United Reformed Church Year Book.]

Presbyterian Historical Society of England. JOURNAL. 8vo. MAN-
CHESTER. [1-8], LOND. [9-14]. 1-14, no. 5. 1914/19-1972.
[*Contd. in* United Reformed Church History Society Journal.]
—— ANNUAL LECTURES. 8vo. LOND. & MANCHESTER.

5. 1927 Presbyterianism and nationality: J. D. Mackie.   1927.

14. 1937. Robert Crowley: Puritan,
printer, poet: A. Peel.   [1937.]

Price-Priestley Newsletter. ED. M. H. FITZPATRICK & D. O. THOMAS.
fol. ABERYSTWYTH. 1-4. 1977-80.

Proceedings of the Aristotelian Society. *See* Aristotelian Society.

Proceedings of the British Academy. *See* British Academy.

Proceedings of the Society for Psychical Research. *See* Society for
Psychical Research.

Proceedings of the Unitarian Historical Society [of America]. *See*
Unitarian Historical Society [of America].

Proceedings of the Wesley Historical Society. *See* Wesley Historical
Society.

Record Society of Lancashire and Cheshire. 8vo. [CHESTER, *etc.*]
1+ 1879+

113. Index to wills and administrations
formerly preserved in the Probate
Registry, Chester, 1826-1830. 1972.
114. The Great Diurnal of Nicholas
Blundell of Little Crosby, Lancashire. III. 1720-1728.   [1972.]
115. Marriage bonds for the deaneries
of Lonsdale, Kendal, Furness,
Copeland & Amounderness in the
Archdeaconry of Richmond. VII.
1746-1755.   1975.
116. Letters and accounts of William
Brereton of Malpas.   1976.

117. The registers of estates of Lancashire Papists, 1717-1788. III. 1717.
With list of persons registered,
1718-1785.   1977.
118. Index to wills and administrations
formerly preserved in the Probate
Registry, Chester, 1831-1833. Pre-
faced by a history of the Society &
guide to publications, vols. 1-117,
1878-1977: B. E. Harris.   1978.
119. Northwich hundred poll tax 1660
and hearth tax 1664.   1979.

Recusant History: A JOURNAL OF RESEARCH IN POST-REFORMATION CATHOLIC
HISTORY IN THE BRITISH ISLES. (Catholic Record Society.) 4to
& 8vo. BOGNOR REGIS, *etc.* 4+ 1957+
[*Formerly* Biographical Studies.]

Religion och Kultur: TIDSKRIFT FÖR RELIGIÖS IDÉDEBATT OCH KYRKLIGA
REFORMER. 8vo. STOCKHOLM, *etc.* 37-49, no. 2. 1966-78.
[42, 43 imperfect.]

Religious Studies. 8vo. CAMB. 1+ 1965.

Renaissance and Modern Studies. 8vo. NOTTINGHAM. 2-16. 1958-72.

Revue Bénédictine. 8vo. MAREDSOUS. 24+ 1907+

Revue Biblique. 8vo. PARIS. 31-48, 53+ 1922-39, 1946+

Revue de l'Histoire des Religions. 8vo. PARIS. 1+ 1880+
[123-4 imperfect.]

Revue d'Histoire Ecclésiastique. 8vo. LOUVAIN. 4 . . . 9, 16+
1903 . . . 1908, 1915+

Revue Internationale de Philosophie. 8vo. BRUXELLES. 1-28. 1938/
39-1974.

Revue Internationale des Études Bibliques. *See* Internationale Zeitschriftenschau für Bibelwissenschaft und Grenzgebiete.

Revue Mabillon. (Archives de la France Monastique.) 8vo. PARIS,
LIGUGÉ. 1, no. 1 - 57, no. 229/230. 1905 . . . 1967.

Royal Commission on Historical Manuscripts. *See* Historical Manuscripts Commission.

Royal Commission on Historical Monuments. *See* Historical Monuments Commission.

Royal Historical Society. CAMDEN FOURTH SERIES. 8vo. LOND.
1+ 1964+

8. Documents illustrating the British
conquest of Manila. 1762-1763.
1971.
9. Camden miscellany. XXIV. 1972.
10. Herefordshire militia assessments
of 1663. 1972.
11. The early correspondence of Jabez
Bunting, 1820-1829. 1972.
12. Wentworth papers, 1597-1628.
1973.
13. Camden miscellany XXV. 1974.
14. —— XXVI. 1975.
15. Sidney ironworks accounts, 1541-
1573. 1975.
16. The account-book of Beaulieu
Abbey. 1975.
17. Western Circuit assize orders, 1629-
1648: a calendar. 1976.

18. Four English political tracts of the
later Middle Ages. 1977.
19. Proceedings of the Short Parliament
of 1640. 1977.
20. Heresy trials in the Diocese of
Norwich, 1428-31. 1977.
21. Edmund Ludlow: A voyce from
the watch tower, part five, 1660-
1662. 1978.
22. Camden miscellany. XXVII. 1979.
23. The letters of the third viscount
Palmerston to Laurence and Elizabeth Sulivan, 1804-1863. 1979.
24. Documents illustrating the crisis of
1297-98 in England. 1980.

—— GUIDES AND HANDBOOKS. 8vo. & 4to. LOND. 1+ 1938+

10. Guide to the local administrative
units of England. 1. Southern
England: F. A. Youngs. 1979.

—— —— SUPPLEMENTARY SERIES. 4to. LOND. 1+ 1974+

1. A guide to the papers of British
Cabinet ministers, 1900-1951: C.
Hazlehurst and C. Woodland. 1974.

Royal Institute of Philosophy Lectures. 8vo. LOND., *etc.* 1+ 1968+

4. 1969-70. The proper study. 1971.
5. 1970-71. Reason and reality. 1972.
6. 1971-72. Philosophy and the arts.
1973.
7. 1972-73. Understanding Wittgenstein. 1974.

8. 1973-74. Nature and conduct: ed.
R. S. Peters. 1975.
9. 1974-75. Impressions of empiri-
cism: ed. G. Vesey. 1976.
10. 1975-76. Communication and
understanding: ed. G. Vesey. 1977.

Royal Institute of Philosophy Lectures—*continued*

11. 1976-77. Human values: ed. G. Vesey. 1978.

12. 1977-78. Philosophers of the Enlightenment: ed. S. C. Brown. 1979.

—— JOURNAL. *See* Philosophy.

St. Mark's Review: AN ANGLICAN QUARTERLY [-58]; A NATIONAL PERIODICAL [59-67]. 8vo. CANBERRA. no. 28+ 1962+
[*No subtitle from* no. 68, May 1972.]

Schweich Lectures. 8vo. LOND. 1908+

1959. Vaux (R. de): Archaeology and the Dead Sea Scrolls. (1961.) [Rev. ed., tr. from French.] 1973.
1970. Yadin (Y.): Hazor. 1972.
1976. Gurney (O. R.): Some aspects of Hittite religion. 1977.

1977. Roberts (C. H.): Manuscript, society and belief in early Christian Egypt. 1979

Scots Philosophical Club. *See* Philosophical Quarterly.

Scottish Baptist Yearbook. (Baptist Union of Scotland.) 8vo. GLASGOW. 1916 . . .

Scottish Journal of Theology. 8vo. EDIN. 1+ 1948+

Seventeenth-Century News. fol. NEW YORK, *etc.* 17+ 1959+

Sixteenth Century Essays and Studies. ED. C. S. MEYER. 8vo. SAINT LOUIS (Mo.). 1-2. 1970-71.
[*No more in Library.*]

Sobornost. (Fellowship of St. Alban and St. Sergius.) 8vo. LOND. N.S., no. 1 - Ser. 6, no. 10. 1935-74.
[*Wanting* N.S. nos. 19, 27-29.]
[*Formerly* Journal of the Fellowship of St. Alban and St. Sergius.]

—— INCORPORATING EASTERN CHURCHES REVIEW. 8vo. LOND. N.S. 1, no. 2+ 1979+

Société des Bollandistes. *See* Analecta Bollandiana.

Société Mabillon. *See* Revue Mabillon.

Society for New Testament Studies. MONOGRAPH SERIES. GENERAL EDITOR: MATTHEW BLACK. 8vo. CAMB. 1+ 1965+

14. Der Markus-Stoff bei Lukas: eine literarkritische und redaktionsgeschichtliche Untersuchung: T. Schramm. 1971.
15. The New Testament Christological hymns: their historical religious background: J. T. Sanders. 1971.
16. 'And the two shall become one flesh': a study of traditions in Ephesians 5: 21-23: J. P. Sampley. 1971.
17. Herod Antipas: H. W. Hoehner. 1972.

18. Enigmes de la deuxième épître de Paul aux Corinthiens: étude exégétique de 2 Cor. 2:14 - 7:4: J.-F. Collange. 1972.
19. The Passion narrative of St. Luke: a critical and historical investigation: V. Taylor, ed. O. E. Evans. 1972.
20. The meaning of righteousness in Paul: a linguistic and theological enquiry: J. A. Ziesler. 1972.
21. Pre-existence, Wisdom, and the Son of Man: a study of the idea of

xxxii

Society for New Testament Studies—*continued*

pre-existence in the New Testament: R. G. Hamerton-Kelly. 1973.
22. Studien zum alttestamentlichen Hintergrund des Johannesevangeliums: G. Reim. 1974.
23. The Gentiles and the Gentile mission in Luke-Acts: S. G. Wilson. 1973.
24. Paul's intercessory prayers: the significance of the intercessory prayer passages in the letters of St. Paul: G. P. Wiles. 1974.
25. The last twelve verses of Mark: W. R. Farmer. 1974.
26. Paul and the anatomy of apostolic authority: J. H. Schütz. 1975.
27. Jesus of Nazareth in New Testament preaching: G. N. Stanton. 1974.
28. Jesus and the Law in the Synoptic tradition: R. Banks. 1975.
29. Sōma in biblical theology, with emphasis on Pauline anthropology: R. H. Gundry. 1976.
30. The Melchizedek tradition: a critical examination of the sources to the fifth century A.D. and in the Epistle to the Hebrews: F. L. Horton. 1976.

31. The New Testament concept of witness: A. A. Trites. 1977.
32. On the independence of Matthew and Mark: J. M. Rist. 1978.
33. Redactional style in the Marcan Gospel: a study of syntax and vocabulary as guides to redaction in Mark: E. J. Pryke. 1978.
34. J. J. Griesbach: synoptic and text-critical studies, 1776-1976: ed. J. B. Orchard and T. R. W. Longstaff. 1978.
35. Paul: crisis in Galatia. A study in early Christian theology: G. Howard. 1979.
36. Hebrews and hermeneutics: the Epistle to the Hebrews as a New Testament example of biblical interpretation: G. Hughes. 1979.
37. Kerygma and didache: the articulation and structure of the earliest Christian message: J. I. H. McDonald. 1980.
38. 'Love your enemies': Jesus' love command in the Synoptic Gospels and in the early Christian paraenesis: J. Piper. 1979.

Society for Old Testament Study. BOOK LIST. 8vo. [MANCHESTER, *etc.*] 1946-69, 1972-76.

—— MONOGRAPH SERIES. GENERAL EDITOR: J. A. EMERTON [1-3]; R. E. CLEMENTS [4+]. 8vo. CAMB. 1+ 1971+

1. The heavenly counsellor in Isaiah XL. 13-14: a study of the sources of the theology of Deutero-Isaiah R. N. Whybray. 1971.
2. Gibeon and Israel: the role of Gibeon and the Gibeonites in the political and religious history of early Israel: J. Blenkinsopp. 1972.
3. The meaning of 'bāmâ' in the Old Testament: a study of etymological, textual and archaeological evidence: P. H. Vaughan. 1974.

4. Relics of ancient exegesis: a study of the miscellanies in 3 Reigns 2: D. W. Gooding. 1976.
5. The way of the wilderness: a geographical study of the wilderness itineraries in the Old Testament: G. I. Davies. 1979.

Society for Promoting Christian Knowledge. THEOLOGICAL COLLECTIONS. 8vo. LOND. 1-15. 1960-72. [*No more published.*]

15. Christ and the younger Churches: theological contributions from Asia, Africa, and Latin America: ed. G. F. Vicedom. 1972.

Society for Psychical Research. PROCEEDINGS. 8vo. LOND, *etc.* 1+ 1882/83+

—— JOURNAL. 8vo. LOND. 1+ 1884/85+

Society for the Promotion of Hellenic Studies. *See* Journal of Hellenic Studies.

Society of Biblical Literature. *See* Journal of Biblical Literature.

Sociological Yearbook of Religion in Britain. ED. DAVID MARTIN [1-3], MICHAEL HILL [3-4]. 8vo. LOND. 1-4. 1968-71. [*No more in Library.*]

Strict Baptist Historical Society. ANNUAL REPORT AND BULLETIN. 8vo. LOND. 1 ... 13. 1961 ... 1976.

Studia Evangelica. *See* Texte und Untersuchungen zur Geschichte der altchristlichen Literatur.

Studia Patristica. *See* Texte und Untersuchungen zur Geschichte der altchristlichen Literatur.

Studies in Biblical Theology. 8vo. LOND.

33*. Biblical words for time: James Barr. (1962.) 2nd ed. 1969.

—— SECOND SERIES. 8vo. LOND. 1-32. 1967-76. [*No more published.*]

18. The sign of Jonah in the theology of the Evangelists and Q: R. A. Edwards. 1971.
19. The obedience of faith: the purposes of Paul in the Epistle to the Romans: P. S. Minear. 1971.
20. Man and his hope in the Old Testament: W. Zimmerli. 1971.
21. The settlement of the Israelite tribes in Palestine: a critical survey of recent scholarly debate: M. Weippert. 1971.
22. The rediscovery of apocalyptic: a polemical work on a neglected area of biblical studies and its damaging effects on theology and philosophy: K. Koch. 1972.
23. The future of the world: an exegetical study of Revelation 19.11-22.15: M. Rissi. 1972.
24. Semantics in biblical research: new methods of defining Hebrew words for salvation: J. F. A. Sawyer. 1972.

25. The nature of New Testament theology: the contribution of William Wrede and Adolf Schlatter: ed. R. Morgan. 1973.
26. Religion in Judah under the Assyrians, 732-609 B.C.: J. W. McKay. 1973.
27. Israel in Egypt: S. Herrmann. 1973.
28. Hellenistic magic and the Synoptic tradition: J. M. Hull. 1974.
29. Israel in the period of the Judges: A. D. H. Mayes. 1974.
30. Two Old Testament theologies: a comparative evaluation of the contributions of Eichrodt and von Rad to our understanding of the nature of Old Testament theology: D. G. Spriggs. 1974.
31. Ezekiel among the prophets: a study of Ezekiel's place in prophetic tradition: K. W. Carley. 1975.
32. Kingship and the Psalms: J. H. Eaton. 1976.

Studies in Church History. *See* Ecclesiastical History Society.

Studies in Theology. *See* Duckworth Studies in Theology.

Studiorum Novi Testamenti Societas. *See* New Testament Studies.

Subsidia Hagiographica. *See* Analecta Bollandiana.

Surtees Society. PUBLICATIONS. 8vo. LOND., DURHAM, *etc.* 1+
1835+

183. Parliamentary surveys of the Bishopric of Durham. I. 1971.
184. The records of the Company of Shipwrights of Newcastle upon Tyne, 1622-1967. II. 1971.
185. Parliamentary surveys of the Bishopric of Durham. II. 1972.
186. York Memorandum Book BY [*sic, i.e.* B/Y]. 1973.
187. The royal visitation of 1559: Act Book for the northern province. 1975.

188. Lonsdale documents. 1976.
189. Commercial papers of Sir Christopher Lowther, 1611-1644. 1977.
190. The meditations of Lady Elizabeth Delaval written between 1662 and 1671. 1978.
191. Lowther family estate books, 1617-1675. 1979.

Survey of London. *See* Greater London Council.

Swarthmore Lectures. 8vo. LOND. 1908+

1971. Carter (C. F.): On having a sense of all conditions. 1971.
1972. Peters (R. S.): Reason, morality and religion. 1972.
1973. Gorman (G. H.): The amazing fact of Quaker worship. 1973.
1974. Mendl (W.): Prophets and reconcilers: reflections on the Quaker Peace Testimony. 1974.
1975. Hetherington (R.): The sense of glory: a psychological study of peak experiences. 1975.
1976. McClelland (W. G.): And a new earth: making tomorrow's society better than today's. 1976.

1977. Parker-Rhodes (D.): Truth: a path and not a possession: a Quaker woman's journey. 1977.
1978. Greenwood (J. O.): Signs of life: art and religious experience. 1978.
1979. Reader (J.): Of schools and schoolmasters: some thoughts on the Quaker contribution to education. 1979.
1980. Scott (J.): What canst thou say? towards a Quaker theology. 1980.

Texte und Untersuchungen zur Geschichte der altchristlichen Literatur. BEGRÜNDET VON O. VON GEBHARDT UND A. VON HARNACK. 8vo. LEIPZIG, BERLIN. 1-50. 1882-1936.

—— FÜNFTE REIHE. 8vo. BERLIN. 56 ... 1951 ...

103. Studia Evangelica, 5. Papers presented to the Third International Congress on New Testament Studies, 1965. II. Ed. F. L. Cross. 1968.
108. Studia Patristica, 11. Papers presented to the Fifth International Conference on Patristic Studies, 1967. II. Ed. F. L. Cross. With a cumulative index of contributors to Studia Patristica, vols. 1-11. 1972.
112. Studia Evangelica, 6. Papers presented to the Fourth International Congress on New Testament

Studies, 1969. Ed. E. A. Livingstone. With a cumulative index of contributors to Studia Evangelica, vols. 1-6. 1973.
115-117. Studia Patristica, 12-14. Papers presented to the Sixth International Conference on Patristic Studies, 1971. Ed. E. A. Livingstone. 3 vols. 1975-76.
123. Basile de Césarée: la tradition manuscrite directe des neuf homélies sur l'Hexaéméron. Étude philologique: E. Amand de Mendieta et S. Y. Rudberg. 1980.

Theological Collections. *See* Society for Promoting Christian Knowledge.

Theologische Literaturzeitung. MONATSCHRIFT. 8vo. LEIPZIG. 1-64,
nr. 8/9, 67+ 1876-1939, 1942+
[*Wanting* 12 (1887); 70-71 (1945-46) *never publ.*]

Theologische Rundschau. 8vo. TÜBINGEN. N.F. 1-15, 17+ 1929-
43, 1948+
[11, 15 imperfect.]

Theology: A MONTHLY JOURNAL OF HISTORIC CHRISTIANITY [1-37]; A
MONTHLY REVIEW [38-78]. 8vo. LOND. 1+ 1920+
[*Bi-monthly, with no subtitle, from* 79 (1976).]

Theology Today. 8vo. PRINCETON. 16+ 1959+

Theoria to Theory. (Epiphany Philosophers.) 8vo. CAMB. 1, no. 1-
2, no. 1, 3, nos. 2-4. Oct. 1966-Oct. 1967, Jan.-Sep. 1969.
[*No more in Library.*]

Trafodion Cymdeithas Hanes Bedyddwyr Cymru. 8vo. LOND.
1977+

Transactions of the Baptist Historical Society. *See* Baptist Quarterly.

Transactions of the Bibliographical Society. *See* Library.

Transactions of the Unitarian Historical Society. *See* Unitarian
Historical Society.

Tübingen. Universitätsbibliothek. Theologische Abteilung. *See*
Mitteilungen und Neuerwerbungen; Zeitschrifteninhaltsdienst
Theologie.

Unitarian and Free Christian Churches: YEARBOOK OF THE GENERAL
ASSEMBLY. *See* General Assembly of Unitarian and Free Christian
Churches.

Unitarian Historical Society. TRANSACTIONS. 8vo. LOND. 1+
1917/18+
—— Supplement to vol. 16, no. 1, Oct.
1975. The founding of the British
& Foreign Unitarian Association:
H. L. Short. 1975.

Unitarian Historical Society [of America]. PROCEEDINGS. 8vo. BOSTON
(Mass.). 8+ 1947+

Unitarian Information Department. *See* Chalice.

Unitarian Universalist Association. DIRECTORY. fol. BOSTON (Mass.).
1979.
[*No more in Library.*]

United Bible Societies. *See* Bible Translator.

United Reformed Church History Society. JOURNAL. 8vo. LOND.
1+ 1973+
[*Incorporating* Congregational Historical Society Transactions *and* Presbyterian Historical Society of England Journal.]

United Reformed Church Year Book. 8vo. LOND. 1973/74+
[*Incorporating* Congregational Year Book *and* Presbyterian Church of
England Official Handbook.]

Universalist Historical Society. ANNUAL JOURNAL [1-6], JOURNAL [7-9]. 8vo. BOSTON (Mass.). 1-9. 1959-71.

Vetus Testamentum. (International Organization for the Study of the Old Testament.) 8vo. LEIDEN. 1+ 1951+

―― SUPPLEMENTS. 8vo. LEIDEN. 1+ 1953+

21. Joel and the Temple cult of Jerusalem: G. W. Ahlström. 1971.
22. Congress volume, Uppsala, 1971. 1972.
23. Studies in the religion of Ancient Israel. 1972.
24. I am God your Saviour: a form-critical study of the main genres in Is. XL-LV: A Schoors. 1973.
25. The Greek Chronicles: the relation of the Septuagint of I and II Chronicles to the Massoretic Text: L. C. Allen. 1. The translator's craft. 1974.

26. Studies on prophecy: a collection of twelve papers. 1974.
27. The Greek Chronicles: the relation of the Septuagint of I and II Chronicles to the Massoretic text: L. C. Allen. 11. Textual criticism. 1974.
28. Congress volume, Edinburgh, 1974. 1975.
29. Congress volume, Göttingen, 1977. 1978.
30. Studies in the historical books of the Old Testament: J. A. Emerton. 1979.

Victoria History of the Counties of England. fol. LOND. 1900+

Cambridgeshire and the Isle of Ely. 5-7. 1973-78.		Oxfordshire. 4, 10.	1979-72.
Cheshire. 2.	1979.	Shropshire. 2, 8.	1973-68.
Essex. 6-7.	1973-78.	Somerset. 3-4.	1974-78.
Gloucestershire. 10-11.	1972-76.	Staffordshire. 2-3, 6, 17.	1967-79.
Middlesex. 4-6.	1971-80.	Wiltshire. 1 (pt. 2), 10.	1973-75.
		Yorkshire. East Riding. 1-4	1969-79.

Vigiliae Christianae: A REVIEW OF EARLY CHRISTIAN LIFE AND LANGUAGE. 8vo. AMSTERDAM. 1+ 1947+

Vizantijskij Vremennik. (Byzantina Chronica.) 8vo. ST. PETERSBURG [1-23], MOSCOW [N.S.]. 1-23, 26 (N.S. 1)+ 1894-1916, 1947+ [*Wanting* N.S. 13, 17-19, 21-22, 30, 32, 34-47.]

Vox Evangelica: BIBLICAL AND HISTORICAL ESSAYS BY MEMBERS OF THE FACULTY OF THE LONDON BIBLE COLLEGE. 8vo. LOND. 1+ 1962+

Weigh House Quarterly. *See* King's Weigh House Monthly.

Wesley Historical Society. PROCEEDINGS. 8vo. BURNLEY, *etc.* 1+ 1897/98+

―― PUBLICATIONS. 8vo. LOND., *etc.* 1+ 1896+

6. *Not in Library.*
7. John Jones: first after the Wesleys? A. B. Sackett. 1972.

8. James Rouquet and his part in early Methodism: A. B. Sackett. 1972.

―― OCCASIONAL PUBLICATIONS. N.S. 8vo. *Duplicated.*

1. The doctrine of infant baptism in non-Wesleyan Methodism: B. G. Holland. 1970.

Wesley Historical Society—*continved*

—— LECTURES. 8VO. LOND. 6 ... 1940 ...

13. Methodism in Scotland: the first hundred years: W. F. Swift. 1947.
32. Methodist devotion: the spiritual life in the Methodist tradition, 1791-1945: G. S. Wakefield. 1966.

[41.] Adam Clarke, controversialist: Wesleyanism and the historic faith in the age of Bunting: I. Sellers. 1976.

Weston School of Theology (*formerly* Weston College). *See* New Testament Abstracts.

William and Mary Quarterly: A MAGAZINE OF EARLY AMERICAN HISTORY. 8vo. WILLIAMSBURG (Va.) 3rd Ser. 16, no. 3+ Jul. 1959+ [*Wanting* 16, no. 4, 17, no. 3, 26, nos. 1 & 4, 30, no. 4.]

World Council of Churches. *See* Ecumenical Review.

Yale Judaica Series. 8vo. NEW HAVEN. 1 ... 1948 ... [Translations.]

19. The code of Maimonides. Book 4: the book of women. 1972.

Yearbook of the General Assembly of Unitarian and Free Christian Churches. *See* General Assembly of Unitarian and Free Christian Churches.

Yorkshire Congregational Year Book. 8vo. LEEDS. 1923 ... 1969/70.

Zeitschrift für die Alttestamentliche Wissenschaft. 8vo. GIESSEN [1-51], BERLIN [52+]. 1+ 1881+

—— BEIHEFTE. 8vo. GIESSEN [1-65], BERLIN [66+]. 1+ 1896+

117. Die Psalmen: stilistische Verfahren und Aufbau, mit besonderer Berücksichtung von Ps 1-41: N. H. Ridderbos. 1972.
119. Geschichtliche Rückblicke und Motive in der Prophetie des Amos, Hosea und Jesaja: J. Vollmer. 1971.
121. Ezechiel und Deuterojesaja: Berührungen in der Heilserwartung der beiden grossen Exilspropheten: D. Baltzer. 1971.
122. Untersuchungen zur sogenannten Baruchschrift: G. Wanke. 1971.
123. Vorformen der Schriftexegese innerhalb des Alten Testaments: Untersuchungen zum literarischen Werden der auf Amos, Hosea und Micha zurückgehenden Bücher im hebräischen Zwölfprophetenbuch: I. Willi-Plein. 1971.
124. Prophetic conflict: its effect upon Israelite religion: J. L. Crenshaw. 1971.
125. Mourning cry and woe oracle: W. Janzen. 1972.

126. Die deuteronomistische Pentateuchredaktion in Exodus 3-17: W. Fuss. 1972.
127. Rechtssätze in gebundener Sprache und Rechtssatzreihen im israelitischen Recht: ein Beitrag zur Gattungsforschung: V. Wagner. 1972.
128. Die Entstehung der Geschichtsschreibung im alten Israel: H. Schulte. 1972.
129. Das Buch Nahum: eine redaktionskritische Untersuchung: H. Schulz. 1973.
130. Kohelet und die frühhellenistische Popularphilosophie: R. Braun. 1973.
131. Verheissung und Gesetz: Untersuchungen zum sogenannten "Bund" im Alten Testament: E. Kutsch. 1973.
132. Die Prosareden des Jeremiabuches: H. Weippert. 1973.
133. The historicity of the patriarchal narratives: the quest for the histori-

Zeitschrift für die Alttestamentliche Wissenschaft—continued

cal Abraham: T. L. Thompson.
1974.
134. Myth in Old Testament interpretation: J. W. Rogerson. 1974.
135. The intellectual tradition in the Old Testament: R. N. Whybray.
1974.
136. Die Intention der Verkündigung Jesajas: H. W. Hoffmann. 1974.
137. Jahwe, Juda und die anderen Völker beim Propheten Jesaja: F. Huber. 1976.
138. Formula criticism and the poetry of the Old Testament: W. R. Watters.
1976.
139. Deuteronomium 1.1 - 6.3: literarkritisch und traditionsgeschichtlich untersucht: S. Mittmann. 1975.
140. Struktur und Bezeichnung des Scheltworts: eine gattungskritische Studie anhand des Amosbuches: L. Markert. 1977.
141. The formation of Isaiah 40-55: R. F. Melugin. 1976.
142. The royal dynasties in ancient Israel: a study on the formation and development of royal-dynastic ideology: T. Ishida. 1977.
143. "De Deo": Studien zur Literarkritik und Theologie des Buches Jona, des Gesprächs zwischen Abraham und Jahwe in Gen 18.22ff. und von Hi 1: L. Schmidt. 1976.

144. Der Tempel von Jerusalem: Gründung Salomos oder jebusitisches Erbe? K. Rupprecht. 1977.
145. Der spätbronzezeitliche Seevölkersturm: ein Forschungsüberblick mit Folgerungen zur biblischen Exodusthematik: A. Strobel. 1976.
146. Untersuchungen zur Redaktionsgeschichte des Pentateuch: P. Weimar. 1977.
147. Das überlieferungsgeschichtliche Problem des Pentateuch: R. Rendtorff. 1977.
148. Koheleth: his language and thought: C. F. Whitley. 1979.
149. Der Stamm 'ebed im Alten Testament: eine Wortuntersuchung unter Berücksichtigung neuerer sprachwissenschaftlicher Methoden: I. Riesener. 1979.
150. Prophecy. Essays presented to Georg Fohrer on his sixty-fifth birthday: ed. J. A. Emerton. 1980.
151. Wisdom as a hermeneutical construct: a study in the sapientializing of the Old Testament: G. T. Sheppard. 1980.
152. Polar structures in the Book of Qohelet: J. A. Loader. 1979.
153. Werden und Wesen des 107. Psalms: Walter Beyerlin. 1979.
154. Die nichtpriesterliche Josephs Geschichte: ein Beitrag zur neuesten Pentateuchkritik: H.-C. Schmitt.
1980.

Zeitschrift für die Neutestamentliche Wissenschaft. 8vo. GIESSEN [1-32], BERLIN [33+]. 1+ 1900+

—— BEIHEFTE. 8vo. GIESSEN [1-16], BERLIN [17+]. 1+ 1923+

40. Jesus in Nazareth: E. Grässer, A. Strobel, R. C. Tannehill, W. Eltester. 1972.
41. Sacramentum Unitatis: ein Beitrag zum Verständnis der Kirche bei Cyprian: U. Wickert. 1971.
42. Die Bedeutung der Wundererzählungen für die Christologie des Markusevangeliums: D.-A. Koch.
1975.

43. Rechtfertigung und zukünftiges Heil: Untersuchungen zu Röm 5, 1-11: M. Wolter. 1978.
44. Eschatologie und Jenseitserwartung im hellenistischen Diasporajudentum: U. Fischer. 1978.

Zeitschrifteninhaltsdienst Theologie: INDICES THEOLOGICI. (Universitätsbibliothek Tübingen Theologische Abteilung.) 8vo. TÜBINGEN. 1977, nr. 1+